Scott Foresman - Addison Wesley

MATH

Assessment Sourcebook
Grade 4

Scott Foresman - Addison Wesley

Editorial Offices: Menlo Park, California • Glenview, Illinois
Sales Offices: Reading, Massachusetts • Atlanta, Georgia • Glenview, Illinois
Carrollton, Texas • Menlo Park, California

http://www.sf.aw.com

ISBN 0–201–31296–4

Printed in the United States of America

5 6 7 8 9 10 – BW – 02 01 00

Table of Contents

Assessing Student Performance in Mathematics

> *"Instead of assuming that the purpose of assessment is to rank students on a particular trait, the new approach assumes that high public expectations can be set that every student can strive for and achieve. . ."*
>
> —*NCTM Assessment Standards for School Mathematics*

Linking Assessment and Instruction

Recommendations made by the National Council of Teachers of Mathematics stress the importance of linking assessment and instruction methods. As teachers employ more diverse methods of instruction, such as hands-on activities, open-ended investigations, and long-term projects, they also need to employ diverse methods of assessment. As we make the goal of mathematics the acquisition of dynamic processes, we strive for methods of assessment that further our goals. Authentic assessment tools require critical thinking and problem solving, not merely mastery of facts and procedures.

Because instruction and its assessment are closely linked, methods of evaluation need to change as instructional methods change. New forms of assessment provide a more authentic way of evaluating the depth of our students' knowledge of mathematics, rather than their ability to memorize facts and procedures. These alternative methods of assessment offer the opportunity for students to display how they approach problem situations, collect and organize information, formulate and test conjectures, and communicate their mathematical insights.

An authentic assessment program contains tasks that are appropriate to the topics students are learning and that provide outcomes that are valuable to the students. Such an assessment program allows for such highly individual factors as a school's curriculum objectives, a teacher's style of instruction, and a student's maturity level. Each individual teacher determines the assessment best suited to the needs of his or her students.

To help teachers select the most appropriate evaluation tools for their classrooms, the *Assessment Sourcebook* provides the following materials.

Informal Assessment Forms

- Student-completed forms, Math Logs (journals), Student Surveys, Self-Evaluations, Portfolio Guides, and more
- Teacher-completed forms for Ongoing Assessment in Problem Solving, Observation, and Cooperative Learning, as well as forms for assessing projects and portfolios

Formal Assessment Instruments

- Free-response chapter tests that cover every objective in the student text chapter and that include an Explain Your Thinking question; Parallel forms A and B of this test are provided.
- Multiple-choice tests for each chapter
- Alternative chapter assessments (Performance Assessment) comprised of several open-ended questions; Each test is accompanied by its own Evaluation Guide.
- Mixed-response chapter tests that include a short performance task
- Mixed-response cumulative chapter test that prepares students for standardized tests and includes items for current chapter objectives along with covering concepts from previous chapters
- Item Analysis management forms that teachers can use to evaluate student comprehension of each chapter objective
- Class record forms

> *"Assessment should be a means of fostering growth toward high expectations."*
>
> —*NCTM Standards for School Mathematics*

Guidelines for Developing an Authentic Assessment Program

Developing an authentic program of assessment is an ongoing process. Some assessment instruments will seem perfectly suited to the teacher and his or her students from the start. Others may be effective only after the teacher has had a chance to experiment with and refine them. Still others may be inappropriate for a given class or instructional situation. The following are some guidelines that may be helpful when choosing the types of assessment for a particular program.

Use an assessment form that serves your purposes.

- For the teacher, assessment yields feedback on the appropriateness of instructional methods and offers some clues as to how the content or pace of instruction could be modified.
- For the students, assessment should not only identify areas for improvement, but should also affirm their successes.
- Traditional forms of assessment yield a tangible score.

Make the assessment process a positive experience for students.

- Use a variety of assessment techniques.
- Provide opportunities for students to demonstrate their mathematical capabilities in an atmosphere that allows maximum performance.
- Emphasize what students *do* know and *can* do, not what they do not know and cannot do.
- Motivate students to achieve by using tasks that reflect the value of their efforts.

Use authentic assessment to focus on higher-order thinking skills.

- Authentic assessment provides a picture of the student as a critical thinker and problem solver.
- Authentic assessment helps to identify how the student does mathematics, not just what answer he or she gets.

Provide assessment activities that resemble day-to-day tasks

- Use activities similar to instructional activities to do assessment.
- Use assessment activities to further instruction.
- Give students the immediate and detailed feedback they need to further the learning process.
- Encourage students to explore how the mathematics they are learning applies to everyday life.

Include each student as a partner in the assessment process.

- Encourage students to reflect on what they have done.
- Encourage students to share their goals.

Making and Using an Assessment Portfolio

For students and teachers alike, portfolios are exciting records of progress. In mathematics, the process of making a portfolio and adding materials to it on an ongoing basis is an extremely effective method for learning and assessment. A math portfolio can contain student work, including projects, reports, drawings, reflections, and formal assessment instruments.

As students review their portfolios, they observe concrete evidence of their growth in skills and confidence. For many students, seeing progress is believing.

> *"Large pieces of work like performance tasks, projects, and portfolios provide opportunities for students to demonstrate growth in mathematical power."*
>
> —*NCTM Assessment Standards for School Mathematics*

Getting Started

There are many procedures that students and teachers can use to make and use portfolios. It might be helpful to use a two-stage approach for keeping student portfolios. In this approach, students use a work portfolio, which contains the work they have completed in a period of a few weeks. At designated times, the teacher and student can evaluate the Work Portfolio and transfer materials to the Assessment Portfolio.

At the beginning of the school year, you will want to do the following:

- Provide two file folders for each student.
- Have students label one folder *Work Portfolio* and the other *Assessment Portfolio*.

About the Work Portfolio

The *Work Portfolio* is for "work in progress" and recently completed materials. The student should have access to it on a day-to-day basis and should keep in it all class work, group work, homework, and projects for the current period, including student assessment forms such as *My Math Log*.

- You can periodically review students' *Work Portfolios* to verify that students are completing assignments on time.
- You can write notes to students, commenting on individual items in their *Work Portfolios*.
- Every two to six weeks, students should review their *Work Portfolios* to determine which materials they would like to transfer to their *Assessment Portfolios*. (See below.)
- After transferring selected items to the *Assessment Portfolio*, students complete the *About My Portfolio* and take home all items remaining in the *Work Portfolio*.

About the Assessment Portfolio

- The *Assessment Portfolio* contains materials that will help students and teachers evaluate progress over the course of an interval, such as a marking period or a school year. Some of the materials included in the *Assessment Portfolio* will be chosen by students and some may be chosen by teachers.

You may find it helpful to schedule Portfolio conferences with individual students. In that way, you can work with students to evaluate materials. The following questions may help you choose the items for the *Assessment Portfolios*:

- Does an item illustrate the student's ways of thinking about mathematical processes?
- Does an item show a baseline—a starting point for a given year?

- Does an item show progress, or growth in understanding, over time?
- Is an item an example of how mathematics connects with experiences outside the classroom?
- Does the item show positive attitudes towards mathematics?
- Does the item show problem-solving processes?

The following list includes some, but not all, of the materials you and your students may want to include in their *Assessment Portfolios*:

- Student-selected items from the *Work Portfolio*
- Letter from the student about the work included in the *Assessment Portfolio*
- Math autobiography
- Other work selected by you and the student, including math surveys, formal assessments, and informal assessments such as interviews and observations.

> *"The opportunity to share mathematical ideas through portfolios can mark a real turning point in student attitudes."*
>
> *—NCTM Mathematical Assessment*

Evaluating a Portfolio

When you need to evaluate student *Assessment Portfolios*, you may want to use the following tips:

- Keep in mind that portfolio evaluation is a matter of ongoing discussion.
- Set aside time to discuss the *Assessment Portfolio* with the student.
- Use the *Assessment Portfolio* when discussing the student's progress with his or her family.
- Use it as a basis for identifying strengths and weaknesses and for setting group and individual goals for the next period.
- Consider developing your own rubrics or other criteria for evaluating portfolios.

Table of Contents for Assessment Forms

Assessment Forms

Using Assessment Forms

Using Student-Completed Forms

This sourcebook provides eight forms that students can use as aides to self-assessment. Use one or more depending upon students' needs.

Form	Purpose	Suggested Uses
My Math Log	To write about experiences in mathematics	Keep a daily math journal that lets students reflect on how mathematics relates to daily life.
Student Survey	To check student attitudes toward various math activities	Periodically monitor the change in student attitudes toward math.
How We Worked in Our Group	To evaluate student interaction with members of groups	Complete at the conclusion of group projects.
Group Work Log	To keep records of groups assignments	Monitor and evaluate group assignments.
Checklist for Problem-Solving Guide	To organize problem-solving efforts To follow the steps given in the Student Edition	Monitor student use of the problem-solving process.
Student Self-Assessment	To encourage student awareness of independent work	Monitor student progress in working independently.
About My Portfolio	To describe the contents of student's portfolio	Update when student places materials in his or her *Assessment Portfolio*.
My Math Experiences	To summarize attitudes toward and achievement in mathematics	Complete at the end of instructional periods.

Using Teacher-Completed Forms

Eight assessment forms are provided in this sourcebook to help the teacher keep a record of authentic but informal assessments. Some forms are for use with individual students while others are for use with groups of students.

Form	Purpose	Suggested Uses
Assessing Performance in Problem Solving	To assess individual students in problem-solving situations	Describe the level of student performance. Modify instructions to meet individual needs.
Ongoing Assessment: Problem Solving	To assess groups of students in problem-solving situations	Assess the entire class. Assess small groups over time.
Ongoing Assessment: Observation	To observe and assess several students at one time	Provide a mathematical profile of the entire class. Identify common strengths and weaknesses. Modify pace or content. Determine appropriate groupings.
Ongoing Assessment: Cooperative Learning	To assess student ability to work constructively in groups	Assess one or more cooperative groups.
Individual Assessment Through Observation	To determine the student's thought processes, perform- ance, and attitudes	Record observation of a student in the classroom.
Overall Student Assessment	To summarize each student's overall performance	Evaluate student performance over an entire instructional period.
Project/Presentation Checklist	To evaluate oral presentation or extended projects	Prepare students and evaluate presentations or projects.
Portfolio Assessment	To evaluate individual portfolios	Periodically evaluate contents of portfolio. Help students assess process of creating a portfolio.

My Math Log

It's fun to do math when . . .

I discovered that math is useful for . . .

I like math because . . .

Math helps me to . . .

I could be better in math if . . .

Use this sheet to help you write about math.

You may use the phrases above to help you get started.

You may use the space at the bottom for math drawings or sample problems.

_____

_____

_____

_____

_____

_____

_____

Name _____

Date _____

Student Survey

For each statement, record a ✔ to tell how you feel.

	Most of the time	Some of the time	Hardly ever
I am good in math.			
I need help on most problems.			
I see how math is used in real life.			
I understand word problems.			
I can solve most problems.			
I like to try new strategies.			
I give up easily.			
I keep an organized notebook.			
I think math is fun.			

Describe a project you would like the class to work on.

_____

_____

What is your favorite kind of math? Explain why.

_____

_____

List some activities outside of school where you have used math.

_____

_____

Name _____

Date _____

How We Worked in Our Group

What we worked on: _____

_____

Group Members: _____

_____

Check the sentences that describe what happened.

_____ We had a new idea or made a suggestion.

_____ We asked for more information.

_____ We shared the information we found.

_____ We tried different strategies to solve the problem.

_____ We helped a group member explain his or her idea more clearly.

_____ We combined our ideas.

_____ We encouraged students who did not understand the task.

_____ Other: _____

Complete each sentence below.

We learned _____

_____

We found an answer by _____

_____

After we found an answer, we _____

_____

By working together, we _____

_____

Name _____

Date _____

Group Work Log

Group Members: _____

_____

List the date, assignment, and page numbers for each group assignment. Describe how the group worked together to arrive at a group solution for the assignment. Mention any techniques that you found helpful in completing the assignment.

Date	Assignment	Description of Group's Work

Name _____

Date _____

Checklist for Problem-Solving Guide

Put a ✔ in the box after you answer each question or complete each part.

▬ Understand ▬

☐ What do you know? _____

_____

_____

☐ What do you need to find? _____

_____

▬ Plan ▬

☐ What will you do? _____

_____

_____

☐ What operation or strategy will you use? _____

_____

▬ Solve ▬

☐ Use your plan. Show your solution.

☐ What is the answer? Give a complete sentence.

_____

▬ Look Back ▬

☐ Check your work. Is your answer reasonable?

_____

Name _____

Date _____

Student Self-Assessment

Assignment _____

Write about what you did.

What were you trying to learn? _____

_____

_____

How did you start your work? _____

_____

_____

What materials did you need? _____

What did you learn? _____

_____

_____

Check the sentences that describe your work.

_____ I made a plan before I began my work.

_____ I was able to do the work.

_____ I did not understand the directions.

_____ I followed the directions but got the wrong answer.

_____ I found a different way to do this assignment.

_____ I could explain how to do this to someone else.

_____ The work was easier than I thought it would be.

_____ The work was harder than I thought it would be.

_____ Other: _____

Name _____

Teacher _____ Date _____

About My Portfolio

Describe the assignment, giving the page number or project name.

_____

_____

Why is this assignment part of your portfolio?

_____ My teacher chose the assignment.

_____ Everyone else in the class included this assignment.

_____ I chose this assignment.

Complete each sentence.

I began my work by _____

_____

_____

I liked this assignment because _____

_____

_____

Doing this assignment helped me _____

_____

_____

This assignment was . . .   too easy.   _____

about right.   _____

                                       easy.   _____

about right.   _____

hard.   _____

too hard.   _____

Name _____

Date _____

My Math Experiences

Math that interests me: _____

_____

_____

_____

_____

My math goals: _____

_____

_____

_____

_____

Math skills I just learned and can do: _____

_____

_____

_____

_____

Math skills I need to work on: _____

_____

_____

_____

_____

Math awards I have received: _____

Assessing Performance in Problem Solving

Student _____ Date _____

Check each statement below that accurately describes the student's work.

▬ Understand ▬

_____ Reads the problem carefully

_____ Studies any tables or graphs

_____ Can restate the problem in his or her own words

_____ Can identify given information

_____ Can identify the question to be answered

▬ Plan ▬

_____ Chooses an appropriate strategy for solving the problem

_____ Estimates what the answer should be

▬ Solve ▬

_____ Works systematically

_____ Shows solution in an organized fashion

_____ Computes correctly

_____ States the answer in a complete sentence, giving correct units

▬ Look Back ▬

_____ Checks to see that the answer is reasonable

_____ Tries other ways to solve the problem

Use the following criteria to assess the student's performance:

Level 4 (11–13 items checked) The student demonstrates an in-depth understanding of the problem and communicates that understanding in a clear and concise manner. He or she is able to relate the problem to other work previously accomplished.

Level 3 (8–10 items checked) The student understands the problem and shows a correct solution in a clear and organized fashion.

Level 2 (4–7 items checked) The student displays an adequate understanding of major concepts, but may commit errors in some of the specific components.

Level 1 (0–3 items checked) The student has partial or no apparent understanding of the problem. He or she does not complete the necessary work or uses an inappropriate strategy. No answer, an inappropriate response, or an incorrect answer with no work is shown.

Ongoing Assessment: Problem Solving

Date ______________________

Rate each item with a
+ if excellent
✔ if satisfactory
− if needs improvement
NA if not applicable

	Reads problem carefully	Studies any tables or graphs	Can restate problem in own words	Can identify given information	Can identify question to be answered	Chooses appropriate strategy	Estimates what the answer should be	Works systematically	Shows solution in organized fashion	Computes correctly	States answer in sentence giving correct units	Checks that the answer is reasonable	Tries other ways to solve problem	
1.														
2.														
3.														
4.														
5.														
6.														
7.														
8.														
9.														
10.														
11.														
12.														
13.														
14.														
15.														
16.														
17.														
18.														
19.														
20.														
21.														
22.														
23.														
24.														
25.														
26.														
27.														
28.														

Ongoing Assessment: Observation

Date _____

Rate each item with a
+ if excellent
✔ if satisfactory
− if needs improvement
NA if not applicable

	Demonstrates knowledge of skills	Understands concepts	Works neatly and systematically	Works well with others	Displays a positive attitude	Considers and uses ideas of others	Shows patience and perseverance	Asks for help when needed	Uses time productively	Tries alternate approaches				
1.														
2.														
3.														
4.														
5.														
6.														
7.														
8.														
9.														
10.														
11.														
12.														
13.														
14.														
15.														
16.														
17.														
18.														
19.														
20.														
21.														
22.														
23.														
24.														
25.														
26.														
27.														
28.														

Ongoing Assessment: Cooperative Learning

Date ______________________

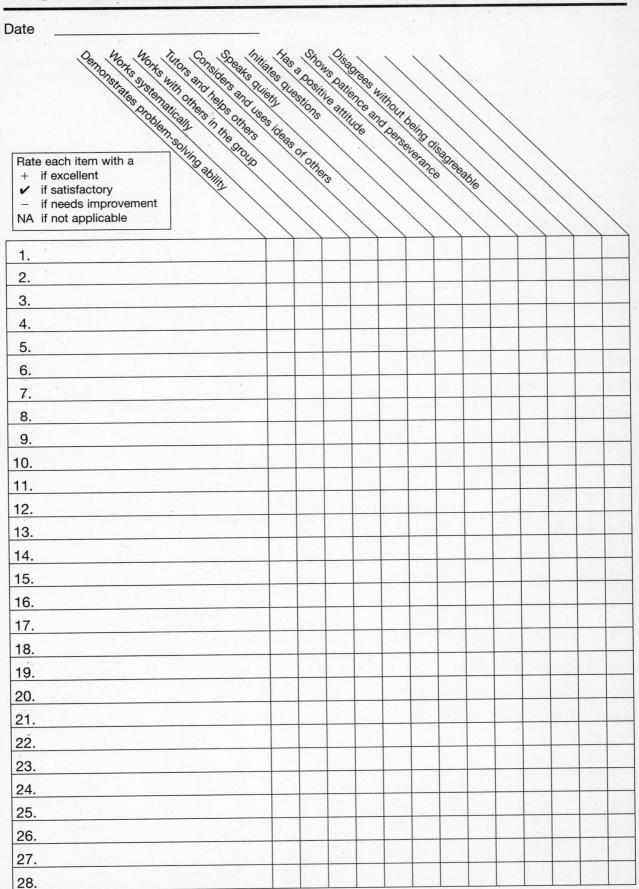

Rate each item with a
+ if excellent
✔ if satisfactory
– if needs improvement
NA if not applicable

	Demonstrates problem-solving ability	Works systematically	Works with others in the group	Tutors and helps others	Considers and uses ideas of others	Speaks quietly	Initiates questions	Has a positive attitude	Shows patience and perseverance	Disagrees without being disagreeable			
1.													
2.													
3.													
4.													
5.													
6.													
7.													
8.													
9.													
10.													
11.													
12.													
13.													
14.													
15.													
16.													
17.													
18.													
19.													
20.													
21.													
22.													
23.													
24.													
25.													
26.													
27.													
28.													

Individual Assessment Through Observation

Student _____ Date _____

	Frequently	Sometimes	Never
Understanding			
Demonstrates knowledge of skills	_____	_____	_____
Understands concepts	_____	_____	_____
Selects appropriate solution strategies	_____	_____	_____
Solves problems accurately	_____	_____	_____
Work Habits			
Works in an organized manner	_____	_____	_____
Works neatly	_____	_____	_____
Gets work in on time	_____	_____	_____
Works well with others	_____	_____	_____
Uses time productively	_____	_____	_____
Asks for help when needed	_____	_____	_____
Confidence			
Initiates questions	_____	_____	_____
Displays a positive attitude	_____	_____	_____
Helps others	_____	_____	_____
Flexibility			
Tries alternate approaches	_____	_____	_____
Considers and uses ideas of others	_____	_____	_____
Uses mental math and estimation	_____	_____	_____
Uses calculators and other technology	_____	_____	_____
Perseverance			
Shows patience and perseverance	_____	_____	_____
Works systematically	_____	_____	_____
Is willing to try	_____	_____	_____
Checks work without being told	_____	_____	_____
Other			
_____	_____	_____	_____
_____	_____	_____	_____

Overall Student Assessment

Date ______________________

Rate each item with a
- + if excellent
- ✔ if satisfactory
- – if needs improvement
- NA if not applicable

	Problem Solving	Cooperative Learning	Math Writing	Class Work	Homework	Participation in Discussion	Quiz Scores	Test Scores					
1.													
2.													
3.													
4.													
5.													
6.													
7.													
8.													
9.													
10.													
11.													
12.													
13.													
14.													
15.													
16.													
17.													
18.													
19.													
20.													
21.													
22.													
23.													
24.													
25.													
26.													
27.													
28.													

Project/Presentation Checklist

This form can be used to evaluate an oral or written student project made by one student or a group of students. This checklist also can be used to discuss successful methods for making presentations, or given to students to help guide them in planning their projects such as mathematical art, scientific experiments, data gathering for charts and graphs, computer demonstrations, skits, or oral and written research projects.

Student(s) _____

_____

Project _____

The Project

Rate each item with a
+ if excellent
✔ if satisfactory
– if needs improvement
NA if not applicable

_____ Demonstrates a mathematical concept properly

_____ Communicates math ideas clearly

_____ Shows a connection to another subject

_____ Shows time spent in planning and preparation

_____ Is original and/or creative

_____ Is colorful and neat

_____ Stimulates further investigation of the topic

_____ Includes a written report

_____ Lists resources used

_____ Shows a delegation of tasks among group members

The Oral Presentation

_____ Demonstrates a knowledge of the mathematical concept

_____ Is organized, and includes an introduction, main section, and conclusion

_____ Uses audio-visual props where appropriate

_____ Speaks clearly and paces presentation at proper speed

_____ Answers questions and stimulates further interest in the topic

_____ Demonstrates a positive problem-solving attitude

_____ Mentions resources used

Portfolio Assessment

Student _____ Date _____

	Required	Included	Comments
Table of Contents			
Letter from student • Explanation of contents • Criteria for selection			
Excerpt from Journal			
Working solution to an open-ended question			
Photo or sketch of problem worked with manipulatives			
Mathematical connections • Problems that work with more than one chapter • Problems that work with more than one area of math			
Subject-area connections • Problems that show connections with health, science, art, literature, data collection, social science, history, or geography			
Quiz, test, or homework; corrected or revised homework			
Projects			
Paragraph from student • How making a portfolio has been helpful			

Table of Contents for Test and Quizzes

Table of Contents for Tests and Quizzes *(continued)*

Using the Quizzes and Chapter Tests Forms A, B, C, D, E, and F

Assessment should be compatible with styles of learning and teaching. The *Assessment Sourcebook* offers several options for formal assessment. As teachers, you set the instructional styles for your classroom. The various forms of chapter tests help you incorporate assessment into whatever instructional styles you choose.

Teachers use written tests for many purposes. Particularly when a test is objective-referenced, it can be an efficient method of diagnosing the scope of a student's mathematical understanding. Tests can also provide valuable instructional feedback. And, of course, grades are a traditional instrument for reporting student achievement to parents, administrators, and the community. You may wish to have students show their work for all test forms. When there is limited space for this on the test page, ask that they include an additional sheet of paper with their work shown, or use the back of the test paper.

Quizzes (one per section)
There is a 1-page quiz for each section of the Student Edition. It covers each objective from the section.

Chapter Tests Forms A and B (free response)
Each test covers all of the objectives in the chapter of the Student Edition in a free-response format. Forms A and B are essentially parallel to each other. You can use Forms A and B together as pre- or post-tests. If you administer Form A and the test results show that students need additional instruction for particular objectives, you can reteach the objectives and then administer Form B.

The Item Analysis for Individual Assessment (in the Management Forms section of this *Assessment Sourcebook*) correlates these test items to objectives from the course, and it provides review options that you may use as needed.

While free-response tests are generally designed for written responses, they may also be used orally with individual students. An oral response approach might be especially helpful with students having special needs and with students who have limited proficiency in English.

Chapter Test Form C (multiple choice)
Test Form C is a 4–5 page multiple-choice test, which includes items that test every chapter objective. Because Test Form C is longer than Test Forms A and B, there are more items per objective. Even though Test Form C has a multiple-choice format, students taking these tests are not limited to performing calculations. Items, including word problems, are designed to assess understanding of concepts. In many school districts, students are required to take standardized tests. Using Test Form C provides students with practice in responding to multiple-choice questions, which are often used in standardized tests. You may want to have students use the Answer Form for Multiple-Choice Tests provided on page 266.

The Item Analysis for Individual Assessment (in the Management Forms section of this *Assessment Sourcebook*) correlates these test items to objectives from the course, and it provides review options that you may use as needed.

Chapter Test Form D (performance test)

This form is a 1-page performance test. The use of this form and its accompanying Evaluation Guide is discussed on page 29 of this *Assessment Sourcebook*.

Chapter Test Form E (mixed response)

This test is a 2–4 page mixed-response test, which includes free-response and multiple-choice items. At the end of each Test Form E, there is a performance task which requires students to apply mathematical concepts in a real-life application. Because Test Form E includes varied types of test items, you are able to use one test to evaluate understanding for students with varied learning and assessment styles.

The Item Analysis for Individual Assessment (in the Management Forms section of this *Assessment Sourcebook*) correlates these test items to objectives from the course, and it provides review options that you may use as needed.

Chapter Test Form F (cumulative chapter test)

This 2–4 page test is a mixed-response test designed to prepare students for standardized tests. About two-thirds of the test covers all of the objectives from the chapter at hand. The rest of the test covers important objectives from previous chapters. The test items are both free response and multiple choice.

There are three sections on each test. The first section, *Computation,* includes exercises designed to assess student ability to perform calculations. The second section, *Concepts,* assesses student understanding of mathematical ideas. The third section, *Applications,* provides opportunities for students to apply what they have learned in class to real-world situations.

The Item Analysis for Individual Assessment (in the Management Forms section of this *Assessment Sourcebook*) correlates these test items to objectives from the course, and it provides review options that you may use as needed.

Evaluating the Quizzes and Chapter Tests Forms A, B, C, E, and F

For Test Forms A and B, answers are displayed on reduced facsimiles of student pages. These answers begin on page 270. Answers for Quizzes and Test Forms C, E, and F begin on page 283. While many numerical answers are straightforward, it is important to keep in mind that a student may not use the exact wording given for problems requiring written explanations. Also, it is a good idea to refer to students' work and grant partial credit if the work is correct, but the answer is not. A Percent Table for Scoring is found on page 331 of this *Assessment Sourcebook*.

Using Chapter Test Form D (performance test)

> "Possessing mathematical power includes being able, and predisposed, to apply mathematical understanding in new situations, as well as having the confidence to do so."
>
> –NCTM Standards for School Mathematics

Students often wonder aloud when they will ever need to use a particular concept or skill. By using long term projects and performance tasks, teachers respond to students' need for meaningful learning experiences. As teachers expand their use of projects and other authentic tasks for teaching mathematics, performance assessment becomes a logical choice for assessing student understanding of mathematics.

For each chapter, the Assessment Sourcebook provides Test Form D, which is a performance assessment. Many of these tests provide information about a realistic situation and ask students to use new information along with their mathematics power to solve problems. Most of the problems are open ended, with an emphasis on finding meaningful solutions rather than calculating one and only one correct response.

The mathematical tasks included in Test Form D allow students to demonstrate a broad spectrum of abilities. By using performance assessment, you can evaluate how students:
- reason through problems;
- make and test conjectures;
- use number sense to predict reasonable answers;
- utilize alternative strategies.

Performance tests also give a way to assess student qualities of imagination, creativity, and perseverance.

Administering Chapter Test Form D
Managing performance assessment projects may be more difficult than managing other types of assessment. The following tips may help you with classroom management during performance assessment administration.

- Consider having students work in groups to complete a performance assessment.
- Move among students as they work to collect anecdotal information during the test. Ask questions that will give you information about thought processes.
- Spend time at the beginning of the test to be sure all students understand the purpose.
- You may wish to share the evaluation standards on the Evaluation Guide with students before they begin work.

Evaluating Chapter Test Form D
The Assessment Sourcebook provides a 1-page **Evaluation Guide** on the reverse side of each Test Form D. This page includes teacher notes that identify the mathematical concepts and skills involved in performing the assessment task.

For each test, a set of task-specific evaluation standards help you evaluate student work. These standards identify four levels of performance. Specific standards were created using the following characteristics of student performance as general guidelines.

Level 4: Accomplishes and extends the task; displays in-depth understanding; communicates effectively and completely.

Level 3: Substantially completes the task; displays minor flaws in understanding or technique; communicates successfully.

Level 2: Partially completes the task; displays one or more major errors in understanding or technique; communicates unclear and/or incomplete information.

Level 1: Makes an attempt; gives little evidence of understanding; communicates little relevant information.

Because performance assessments are open-ended, student responses may be as varied and individual as the students themselves. For that reason, you may find it helpful to use these general standards as well as the task-specific standards when evaluating student performance.

Using the Inventory Test and Quarterly Tests

Inventory Test
A four-page Inventory Test helps assess student skill levels at the beginning of the school year. The Item Analysis for Individual Assessment (in the Management Forms section of this *Assessment Sourcebook*) correlates these test items to objectives from the previous year, and it provides review options that you may use as needed.

Evaluating the Inventory Test
Answers for the Inventory Test are given on page 283. A Percent Table for Scoring is found on page 331 of this *Assessment Sourcebook*.

Quarterly Tests
Four Quarterly Tests (cumulative tests covering chapters 1–3, 1–6, 1–9, and 1–12, respectively) help maintain ongoing assessment of student mastery of the course objectives. The Item Analysis for Individual Assessment (in the Management Forms section of this *Assessment Sourcebook*) correlates these test items to objectives from the course, and it provides review options that you may use as needed.

Evaluating the Quarterly Tests
Answers for the Quarterly Tests are given sequentially after the answers for Test Form F for Chapters 3, 6, 9, and 12, respectively. A Percent Table for Scoring is found on page 331 of this *Assessment Sourcebook*.

Name _____

Date _____ Score _____

Give the letter of the correct answer.

1. Use the bar graph to find how many more students prefer cheese pizza than mushroom.

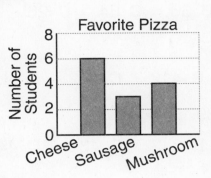

Favorite Pizza

A 6 students
B 4 students
C 3 students
D 2 students

1. _____

2. Give six hundred seven in standard form.

A 6,700   **B** 6,007   **C** 670   **D** 607

2. _____

3. Compare: 263 ● 236. Use <, >, or =.

A <   **B** >   **C** =

3. _____

4. Lydia began reading at 9:45 A.M. and finished 30 minutes later. What time did she finish?

A 9:15 A.M.   **B** 10:00 A.M.   **C** 10:15 A.M.   **D** Not here

4. _____

5. Estimate the sum of 28 and 63 by rounding.

A 90   **B** 80   **C** 40   **D** 30

5. _____

In 6–9, add.

6. 27 + 28

A 45   **B** 55   **C** 65   **D** Not here

6. _____

7. 285 + 172

A 457   **B** 357   **C** 113   **D** Not here

7. _____

8. 12 + 21 + 38

A 61   **B** 72   **C** 81   **D** Not here

8. _____

9. $4.64
     + 3.18

A $1.46   **B** $7.72   **C** $7.82   **D** Not here

9. _____

    Continued

Name _____

In 10–14, subtract.

10. 75 − 49

    A 44   **B** 36   **C** 34   **D** 26

11. 854 − 462

    A 392   **B** 412   **C** 492   **D** Not here

12. 621 − 289

    A 332   **B** 342   **C** 432   **D** 442

13.   7,335
    − 3,492

    A 4,943   **B** 4,843   **C** 3,943   **D** 3,843

14. $14.17
    − 12.24

    A $1.83   **B** $1.93   **C** $2.83   **D** $2.93

15. Carter buys a ball for $2.89. He gives the clerk $10.00. How much change does he receive?

    A $8.21   **B** $8.11   **C** $7.21   **D** Not here

16. Rochelle put 4 flowers in each vase. There are 8 vases. How many flowers are there in all? Choose the multiplication sentence that gives the answer.

    A 8 × 4 = 32   **B** 8 + 4 = 12
    C 8 − 4 = 4   **D** Not here

In 17–19, multiply.

17. 5 × 9

    A 45   **B** 35   **C** 40   **D** 42

18. 6 × 4

    A 36   **B** 28   **C** 24   **D** Not here

10. _____
11. _____
12. _____
13. _____
14. _____
15. _____
16. _____
17. _____
18. _____

Name _____

19. 8×7

    A 36   **B** 42   **C** 56   **D** 63

In 20–22, find each quotient.

20. $30 \div 5$

    A 6   **B** 7   **C** 8   **D** 9

21. $24 \div 4$

    A 4   **B** 5   **C** 6   **D** 8

22. $54 \div 6$

    A 6   **B** 7   **C** 8   **D** 9

23. Give the name for these lines

    A Parallel lines
    B Intersecting lines
    C Line segments

In 24–25, use the coordinate grid.

24. What is the ordered pair for point K?

    A (3, 3)   **B** (2, 1)
    C (1, 2)   **D** (1, 4)

25. Which letter is located at (3, 3)?

    A L   **B** M   **C** N

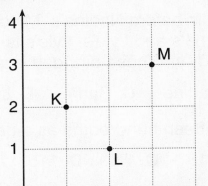

In 26–27, find each product.

26.   63
    $\times\ 7$

    A 421   **B** 441   **C** 541   **D** 564

27. $3.58
    $\times\ \ \ \ 4$

    A $14.36   **B** $14.32   **C** $14.06   **D** $12.02

19. _____

20. _____

21. _____

22. _____

23. _____

24. _____

25. _____

26. _____

27. _____

Name _____

In 28–29, find each quotient and remainder.

28. $4\overline{)18}$

    A 3 R6   **B** 4 R2   **C** 4 R4   **D** 5 R2

28. _____

29. $56 \div 6$

    A 7 R2   **B** 8 R2   **C** 9 R2   **D** Not here

29. _____

30. Estimate the amount that is shaded.

    A More than $\frac{1}{2}$

    B About $\frac{1}{2}$

    C Less than $\frac{1}{2}$

    D About $\frac{1}{4}$

30. _____

31. Give the fraction that tells what part of the set is ringed.

    A $\frac{1}{3}$ **B** $\frac{2}{3}$ **C** $\frac{1}{4}$ **D** $\frac{3}{4}$

31. _____

32. Moe's birthday is before Nadine's. Mindy's birthday is between Carrie's and Lyle's. Lyle's is after Nadine's but before Mindy's. Whose birthday is last?

    A Moe   **B** Nadine   **C** Carrie   **D** Lyle

32. _____

33. Give one and fifteen hundredths as a decimal.

    A 0.15   **B** 1.15   **C** 1.5   **D** 115

33. _____

In 34–36, choose the better estimate.

34. Length of a baseball bat

    A 1 meter   **B** 1 kilometer

34. _____

35. Capacity of a pitcher

    A 2 mL   **B** 2 L

35. _____

36. Is a sandwich less than or more than a kilogram?

    A Less than   **B** More than

36. _____

Name _____

Date _____ Score _____

Vocabulary: In 1–3, match each with its meaning.

1. coordinate grid

2. leaf

3. stem

a. shows the ones digit of a number in a stem-and-leaf plot

b. a graph used to locate points

c. shows the tens digit of a number in a stem-and-leaf plot

1. _____

2. _____

3. _____

Use the bar graph to answer 4–5.

4. How many students have a cat for a pet?

_____

5. How many more students have cats than have fish for pets?

_____

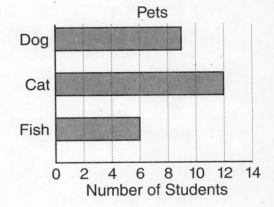

Pets

Number of Students

Use the line graph to answer 6–7.

6. During which week did the most people visit the zoo?

_____

7. Which operation would you use to find the number of visitors for all 5 weeks?

_____

Visitors to Petting Zoo

Visitors

Week

8. What does the ordered pair (3, 300) stand for?

_____

9. Use the line plot. How many students have no brothers or sisters?

_____

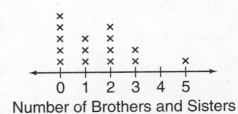

Number of Brothers and Sisters

Name _____

Date _____ Score _____

Vocabulary: In 1–2, match each with its meaning.

1. mode   **a.** the middle number when the data are put in order   1. _____

2. median   **b.** the number that occurs most often in the data   2. _____

3. Use the data in the table to complete the bar graph.

Top Speeds of Certain Animals

Animal	Speed (mi/hr)
Lion	50
Zebra	40
Elephant	25

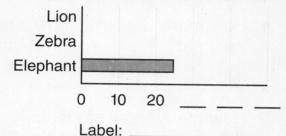

Top Speed of Certain Animals

Label: _____

4. Use the data in the table to complete the line plot.

Spelling Test Scores

Score	Number
100	1
96	3
92	4
88	2

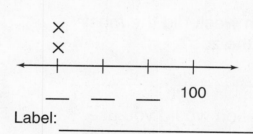

Label: _____

5. Find the range, median, and mode for the set of numbers: 1, 8, 5, 6, 15, 12, 5.

Range _____   Median _____   Mode _____

6. Complete the table. Write the rule.

_____

In	4	5	7	10	15
Out	8	9	11		

7. Kenny and Elena made 12 free throw shots all together. Kenny made two shots more than Elena. How many shots did each make? _____

Name _____

Date _____ Score _____

Vocabulary: In 1–3, match each with its meaning.

1. variable   a. a group of data that appear often on a line plot   1. _____

2. cluster   b. numbers that show the units on a graph   2. _____

3. scale   c. a letter that stands for a number or a range of numbers   3. _____

In 4–6, use the bar graph.

4. Which color was chosen most often?

   _____

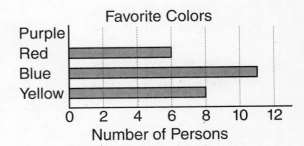

5. How many more people chose yellow than red?

   _____

6. Add a bar to show that 4 persons chose purple as their favorite color.

In 7–9, use the line graph.

7. What ordered pair shows the height of the plant for Day 6?

   _____

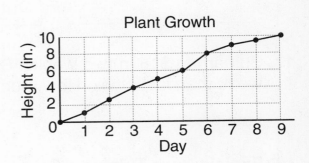

8. What was the plant's height on Day 3?

   _____

9. Which operation will you use to find how much the plant grew from Day 2 to Day 9?

   _____

Name _____

In 10–12, use the line plot.

10. How many students scored 90 points?

_____

11. What is the most common score?

_____

Game Scores (points)

12. Two students scored 105. Add their scores to the line plot.

In 13–14, use the stem-and-leaf plot.

13. How many birthdays are on the 20th day?

14. How many birthdays are shown in the plot?

Birthdays

stem	leaf
0	1 2 5 8 9
1	2 6 9 9 7
2	0 9 0 3 6 7 8 3

13. _____

14. _____

15. Find the range, median, and mode for the set of numbers. Use this set of numbers. 2 9 7 1 3 2 8

Range _____   Median _____   Mode _____

16. Complete the table. Write the rule.

_____

In	18	16	14	12	10
Out	15	13			7

17. Su earned $18 in two weeks. She earned $4 more this week than last week. How much did Su earn each week?

Last week _____   This week _____

18. Explain Your Thinking On a bar graph showing students' favorite sports, explain how you can tell the sport most often chosen.

_____

_____

Name _____

Date _____ Score _____

Vocabulary: In 1–3, match each with its definition.

1. line graph

a. graph that connects points to show how data change over time

1. _____

2. line plot

b. graph that uses pictures or symbols to show data

2. _____

3. pictograph

c. graph that shows data along a number line

3. _____

In 4–6, use the bar graph.

4. Which fruit is the least favorite?

_____

5. How many more people like bananas than kiwi?

_____

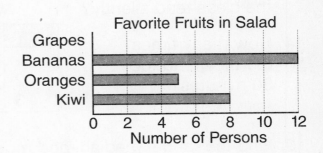

Favorite Fruits in Salad

Grapes
Bananas
Oranges
Kiwi

0 2 4 6 8 10 12
Number of Persons

6. Add a bar to show that 6 persons chose grapes as their favorite fruit.

In 7–9, use the line graph.

7. Which ordered pair shows the least number of students?

_____

8. Which years have the same number of students?

_____

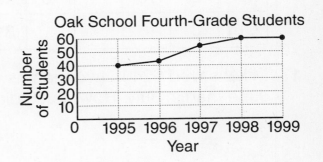

Oak School Fourth-Grade Students

Number of Students
60
50
40
30
20
10
0   1995 1996 1997 1998 1999
Year

9. Which operation will you use to find the total number of fourth graders in all five years?

_____

Name _____

In 10–12, use the line plot.

10. How many students read 5 books?

_____

11. How many books were read by
4 students?

_____

```
                        x
        x   x   x       x               x
        x   x   x   x   x   x           x
    x   x   x   x   x   x   x   x       x
  <-+---+---+---+---+---+---+---+---+---+->
    1   2   3   4   5   6   7   8   9   10
                  Books Read
```

12. Two more students read 6 books. Add this data to the line plot.

In 13–14, use the stem-and-leaf plot.

13. How many times did
the class read silently?

14. How many times
did they read for
30 minutes?

**Silent Reading
Minutes**

stem	leaf
1	5 5 8 0
2	0 5 0 0 5 8
3	5 0 5 3 0

13. _____

14. _____

15. Find the range, median, and mode for this
set of numbers: 9, 2, 4, 5, 1, 4, 3

Range _____   Median _____   Mode _____

16. Complete the table. Write the rule.

16. _____

In	2	10	12	19	25
Out	8	16			31

17. Mikal saved $24 in two months. He saved $6 less in
June than in July. How much did he save each month?

June _____   July _____

18. **Explain Your Thinking** On a pictograph showing
students' favorite colors, how can you tell the color least
often chosen.

_____

_____

Give the letter of the correct answer.

In 1–2, use the pictograph.

Animals Seen on Hike	
Deer	🐾 🐾 🐾
Squirrels	🐾 🐾 🐾 🐾 🐾
Rabbits	🐾 🐾 🐾 🐾 🐾

🐾 = 2 Animals

1. How many deer did the hikers see?

A 3 deer **B** 4 deer **C** 6 deer **D** 7 deer

1. _____

2. How many animals did the hikers see in all?

A 10 animals **B** 15 animals
C 20 animals **D** 25 animals

2. _____

In 3–6, use the bar graph.

Favorite Team Sport

Basketball
Soccer
Baseball
Floor hockey

0 2 4 6 8 10 12 14 16 18 20
Number of Votes

3. Which is the least favorite sport?

A Basketball **B** Soccer
C Baseball **D** Floor hockey

3. _____

4. How many people chose basketball?

A 12 people **B** 4 people
C 16 people **D** 18 people

4. _____

5. You decide to make the graph with vertical bars. Which sport will be the longest bar in your new graph?

A Basketball **B** Soccer
C Baseball **D** Not here

5. _____

6. You add a bar to show that 4 people voted for volleyball. Which bar will be shorter than this bar?

A Basketball **B** Soccer
C Baseball **D** Not here

6. _____

Continued **41**

Name _____

In 7–8, use the coordinate grid.

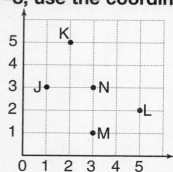

7. Name the ordered pair for point J.

   A (3, 1)   **B** (1, 3)   **C** (2, 5)   **D** (3, 3)

7. _____

8. Give the letter of point named by (5, 2).

   A K   **B** L   **C** M   **D** Not here

8. _____

In 9–10, use the line graph.

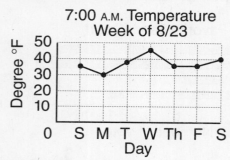

9. Which day had the lowest temperature reading?

   A Monday   **B** Tuesday
   C Wednesday   **D** Not here

9. _____

10. What was Monday's temperature?

   A 34 °F   **B** 36 °F   **C** 38 °F   **D** 30 °F

10. _____

11. Which operation would you use to find how many more pancakes Harry ate than Lisa ate?

   A Addition   **B** Subtraction
   C Multiplication   **D** Division

11. _____

12. Today, Liz practiced her piano for 15 minutes after school and for 20 minutes after dinner. How many minutes did she practice in all?

   A 5   **B** 15   **C** 20   **D** 35

12. _____

Continued

Name _____

Use the line plot for 13–16.

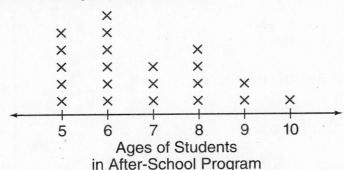

Ages of Students
in After-School Program

13. How many students are 10 years old?

 A 1 students   **B** 3 students
 C 4 students   **D** 7 students

14. What is the most common age of the students?

 A Age 3   **B** Age 4
 C Age 5   **D** Not here

15. On Monday, 3 students join the class. They are 9 years old. How many Xs will now be shown above age 9?

 A 2 Xs   **B** 4 Xs   **C** 5 Xs   **D** 6 Xs

16. A 5-year-old leaves the class. How does the number of Xs above the 5 in the line plot change?

 A There is one more X.   **B** There is one less X.

 C There is no change.   **D** Not here

In 17–18, use the stem-and-leaf plot.

17. What is the mode amount of pocket change?

 A 10¢
 B 25¢
 C 28¢
 D 30¢

Pocket Change

stem	leaf
0	7 8
1	0 2 5
2	5 5 5 8 2 0
3	5 0 3 0 4

18. How many people had more than 31¢?

 A 17 people   **B** 5 people
 C 3 people   **D** Not here

13. _____

14. _____

15. _____

16. _____

17. _____

18. _____

Name _____

19. What is the range for this set of numbers?
    8 12 18 11 20 9

A 20   **B** 9   **C** 12   **D** Not here

19. _____

20. What is the median for this set of numbers?
    2 8 4 3 15 7 14

A 13   **B** 7   **C** 8   **D** Not here

20. _____

21. What is the mode for this set of numbers?
    11 14 8 11 12 15 11

A 7   **B** 11   **C** 15   **D** Not here

21. _____

22. Which data set has the same mode, range, and median?

A 3, 4, 6, 8, 3, 4   **B** 2, 4, 5, 6, 4
C 1, 5, 6, 10, 4   **D** 7, 8, 3, 6, 1

22. _____

23. What is the rule for the table?

In	2	7	8	10
Out	7	12	13	15

A Add 5   **B** Subtract 5   **C** Add 6   **D** Not here

23. _____

24. What is the rule for this table?

In	8	10	5	16
Out	4	6	1	12

A $n + n$ **B** $n + 4$ **C** $n - 4$ **D** Not here

24. _____

25. The sum of two numbers is 17 and the difference is 5. Which is the larger number?

A 11   **B** 10   **C** 9   **D** 12

25. _____

26. Loni and Sam worked 45 minutes. Loni worked 5 minutes longer than Sam. How long did Sam work?

A 20 min   **B** 25 min   **C** 30 min   **D** Not here

26. _____

Some of your friends may have many brothers and sisters. Others may be only children. How do the sizes of the families of your friends and relatives compare?

a. Recording Data Make a list of the last names of 12 families. Write how many people are in each family after each name.

b. Recording Data Copy the line plot shown. Use your data to complete the line plot. Add more numbers to the number line if you need to.

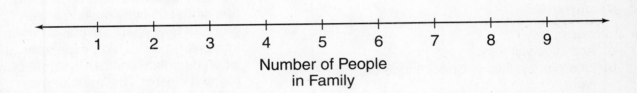

Number of People
in Family

c. Analyzing Data Use the line plot to answer these questions.

How many people are in the largest family?

What is the median family size?

What is the mode family size?

d. Think Critically

Do the data form a cluster? If so, describe the cluster.

Will your line plot look like other students' line plots? Explain.

e. Making Decisions You want to help raise money for school computers. How can you use your line plot to decide whether it would be better to raise money selling pizzas for $10 each or baseball tickets for $5 each to your family and friends? How might the size of the families influence your decision? Explain.

Teacher Notes

Concepts and Skills This activity requires students to:
- record information in a line plot.
- interpret information in a line plot.
- make decisions using real-life experiences.
- compare numbers.
- find measures of central tendency.

Guiding Questions
- Suppose you had data that included these numbers: 1, 2, 2, 3, 4, 5, 6, 7. How would you make a line plot for these numbers?
- Of the numbers above, which occurs most often?
- What does it mean when data is *clustered*?

Answers
a. Activities will vary.
b. Line plots will vary. Check students' work.
c. Answers will vary. Check students' work.
d. Answers will vary. Check students' answers. Many line plots may be similar, based on the size of the "average" family, but will differ based on the data gathered.
e. Answers will vary. Although from a cost perspective, a larger family might better afford to share a pizza than purchase a large number of baseball tickets.

Extension
Have students make a bar graph using the data. How are the line plot and the bar graph similar? How are they different?

Evaluation

Level	Standard to be achieved for performance of specified level
4	**Full Achievement** The student completes the line plot. He or she answers all questions correctly and is able to interpret and explain how data may vary and identify clusters.
3	**Substantial Achievement** The student is able to make and interpret the line plot. Most questions are correctly answered. He or she can interpret and explain how data may vary and identify clusters.
2	**Partial Achievement** The student has some difficulty making a line plot and may need assistance when interpreting a line plot, especially when deciding whether the data forms a cluster. The line plot may contain several errors. Some questions are incorrectly answered.
1	**Little Achievement** The student needs considerable help in completing and interpreting line plots. Answers to many questions are incomplete. The concept of clustering is not grasped. The student makes little attempt to explain why the line plots of different students may vary.

Name _____

Date _____ Score _____

In 1–3, use the bar graph.

1. How many students prefer pepperoni pizza?

_____

Pizza Preferences

Extra Cheese
Mushroom
Pepperoni
Sausage

0   2   4   6   8   10   12
Number of Students

2. How many more students prefer sausage pizza than mushroom pizza?

_____

3. Add a bar to show that 4 students prefer extra cheese.

In 4–5, use the coordinate grid.

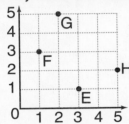

4. Which point is named by (2, 5)?

4. _____

5. Name the ordered pair for point E.

5. _____

A (5, 2)   **B** (2, 5)   **C** (3, 1)   **D** (1, 3)

In 6–8, use the line graph.

6. How many minutes did Ryan exercise on Thursday?

_____

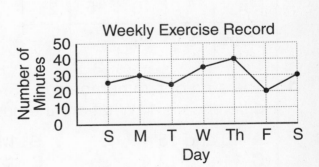

Weekly Exercise Record

Number of Minutes

50
40
30
20
10
0

S   M   T   W   Th   F   S
Day

7. On which day did he exercise for 20 minutes?

_____

8. Which operation will you use to find how many minutes he exercised in all?

_____

Name _____

In 9–11, use the line plot.

9. How many students receive
   $7 for allowance?

   _____

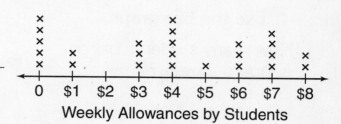

Weekly Allowances by Students

10. Which amount is not received
    by anyone?

    _____

11. New data show that 2 more students receive $5
    allowances. Add this data to the line plot.

In 12–13, use the stem-and-leaf plot.

12. What is the mode of
    Cecelia's scores?

    A 73
    B 89
    C 98
    D Not here

Cecelia's Test Scores	
stem	leaf
7	8 3
8	9 0 5 9
9	6 8 2

12. _____

13. What is the range of Cecelia's scores?

    A 98   **B** 73   **C** 25   **D** 89

13. _____

14. Complete the table. Write the rule.

In	5	10	15	25
Out	8	13		

14. _____

15. The sum of two numbers is 25. Their
    difference is 1. What are the numbers?

    A 10 and 15   **B** 14 and 11
    C 11 and 12   **D** 12 and 13

15. _____

16. **Performance Task** Explain how to find the
    median of a set of numbers.

    _____

    _____

Name _____

Date _____   Score _____

— Computation —

1. If ● = 10 pizzas, then how many pizzas do
   ● ● ● stand for?

   1. _____

2. 21 + 18 =

   A 49   **B** 39   **C** 38   **D** 37

   2. _____

3. 59 + 34 =

   A 83   **B** 25   **C** 93   **D** 85

   3. _____

4. 70 − 30 =

   A 100   **B** 100   **C** 50   **D** 40

   4. _____

5. 60 − 28 =

   A 32   **B** 42   **C** 88   **D** 38

   5. _____

— Concepts —

In 6–8, use the line graph.

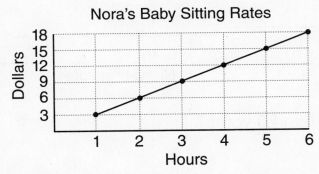

Nora's Baby Sitting Rates

6. What is the ordered pair of the last point on
   the graph (baby sitting 6 hours)?

   6. _____

7. How much will Nora earn if she baby sits
   2 hours on Monday and 2 hours on Tuesday?

   7. _____

8. Which operation would you use to find how much
   more Nora charges for 3 hours than for 1 hour?

   8. _____

   A Addition   **B** Subtraction
   C Multiplication   **D** Division

Name _____

In 9–10, use the stem-and-leaf plot.

9. What is the mode number of pushups?

Number of Pushups

stem	leaf
0	1 2 5 8
1	3 5 7 7
2	0 3 6 7 8
3	1 2 3 9

9. _____

10. What is the range in number of pushups?

10. _____

11. Write the rule for the numbers in the table.

In	6	8	16	18
Out	3	5	13	15

_____

12. John read 4 more chapters today than he read yesterday. He read 16 chapters in all. How many chapters did he read yesterday?

12. _____

▬ Applications ▬

13. Complete the bar graph.

Favorite lunch	Number of votes
Hamburgers	20
Hotdogs	15
Pizza	30

Title: _____

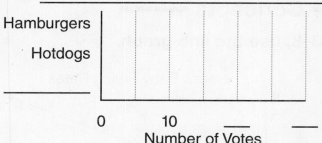

14. Which lunches received less than 20 votes? _____

15. Complete the line plot.

Touchdowns	Number of games
0	4
1	1
2	2
3	2

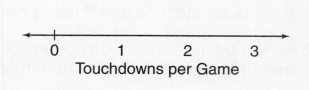

16. What is the median number of touchdowns?   16. _____

Date _____ Score _____

Vocabulary: In 1–3, match each with its example.

1. word name   **a.** 4,000 + 30 + 9   1. _____

2. standard form   **b.** 8,652,000   2. _____

3. expanded form   **c.** two thousand, two   3. _____

4. Write the value of the 8 in 80,675.   4. _____

5. Write the value of the 9 in 445,981.   5. _____

6. Write the value of the 2 in 4,016,128.   6. _____

7. Write the word name for 8,500. _____

8. Write the word name for 7,000,036. _____

**In 9–10, complete the table. Write how many
ones, tens, and hundreds are in each number.**

	Number	Hundreds	Tens	Ones
9.	400			
10.	2,700			

11. Write forty thousand two hundred ten   11. _____
    in standard form.

12. Write two million, four hundred thousand,   12. _____
    fifty-six in standard form.

13. Suppose you have 4 crayons: red, blue, yellow, and
    green. You can use 2 crayons to complete an art
    project. How many choices do you have? Make an
    organized list to show the ways.

_____

_____

Name _____

Date _____   Score _____

Vocabulary: In 1–3, match each with its meaning.

1. estimate   **a.** to place numbers from least to greatest and greatest to least

1. _____

2. compare   **b.** to find a number that is close to the exact number

2. _____

3. order   **c.** to decide which of two numbers is greater

3. _____

In 4–6, compare. Write >, <, or =.

4. 539 ■ 593

4. _____

5. 60,151 ■ 60,111

5. _____

6. 170,010 ■ 170,100

6. _____

7. Write the least number using the digits 3, 6, 1, 8, and 5.

7. _____

In 8–9, order the numbers from least to greatest.

8. 401,104   404,101   401,401   **9.** 6,542   5,642   652   4,652

_____   _____

10. Use the digits 8, 4, and 1. Create as many 3-digit numbers as you can. Order them from greatest to least.

_____

In 11–13, round each number to the nearest hundred.

11. 805   **12.** 683   **13.** 350

_____   _____   _____

In 14–16, round each number to the nearest thousand.

14. 5,499   **15.** 8,701   **16.** 2,450

_____   _____   _____

Vocabulary: In 1–3, match each with its meaning.

1. analog clock

a. a clock that displays just numbers

1. _____

2. digital clock

b. the difference between two times

2. _____

3. elapsed time

c. a clock with hands

3. _____

In 4–5, write each time two different ways.

4.

5. ┌─────────┐
     │ **8:50** │
     └─────────┘

4. _____
   _____

5. _____
   _____

6. Will a store open at 8:00 A.M. or 8:00 P.M.?

6. _____

In 7–8, compare. Write >, <, or =.

7. 2 days ■ 100 hours

7. _____

8. 3 years ■ 50 weeks

8. _____

In 9–12, write each elapsed time.

9. 4:30 P.M. to 4:30 A.M.

9. _____

10. 3:00 A.M. to 6:00 A.M.

10. _____

11. 3:45 P.M. to 4:30 P.M.

11. _____

12. 11:30 A.M. to 12:45 P.M.

12. _____

13. Which month is the third month of the year?

13. _____

14. What is the greatest number of days a month can have?

14. _____

Name _____

Date _____ Score _____

Vocabulary: In 1–3, match each with its example.

1. expanded form

a. the length of time between 3:30 A.M. and 6:00 A.M.

1. _____

2. digits

b. 1,000 + 500 + 30 + 9

2. _____

3. elapsed time

c. 0, 1, 2, 3, 4, 5, 6, 7, 8, 9

3. _____

In 4–7, write the value of the underlined digit.

4. 5,7<u>8</u>3

4. _____

5. 40,<u>7</u>19

5. _____

6. <u>2</u>26,855

6. _____

7. <u>6</u>,119,088

7. _____

8. Write the word name for 402,000. _____

9. Write fifty million, six hundred thirty-eight in standard form.

9. _____

In 10–11, complete the table. Write how many ones, tens, and hundreds are in each number.

	Number	Hundreds	Tens	Ones
10.	500			
11.	3,200			

In 12–14, compare. Write , „ or =.

12. 8,601 ■ 7,899   **13.** 33,812 ■ 33,182   **14.** 5,455 ■ 54,555

_____   _____   _____

15. How many different two-color outfits can Jere make if she has red and blue skirts and yellow, green, and white sweaters? Make an organized list to show the outfits.

_____

Name _____

In 16–17, order the numbers from least to greatest.

16. 36,551   63,155   36,515 _____

17. 701,107   707,101   701,701 _____

18. Round 5,601 to the nearest thousand.   **18.** _____

19. Round 3,482 to the nearest thousand.   **19.** _____

In 20–21, write each time two different ways.

20.

21. | 6:12 |

20. _____

_____

21. _____

_____

22. Does a store close at 9:00 A.M. or 9:00 P.M.?   **22.** _____

In 23–25, compare. Write >, <, or =.

23. 8 weeks ■ 3 months   **23.** _____

24. 200 minutes ■ 2 hours   **24.** _____

25. 18 months ■ 2 years   **25.** _____

In 26–28, write each elapsed time.

26. 5:15 P.M. to 5:15 A.M.   **26.** _____

27. 2:00 P.M. to 4:00 P.M.   **27.** _____

28. 1:45 P.M. to 2:15 P.M.   **28.** _____

29. Which month is the seventh month
of the year?   **29.** _____

30. How many months have 31 days?   **30.** _____

31. Explain Your Thinking Write a 3-digit and a 4-digit
number that round to the same number when rounded
to the nearest hundred. Explain.

_____

_____

Name _____

Date _____ Score _____

Vocabulary: In 1–3, match each with its example.

1. standard form   **a.** a year with 366 days   **1.** _____

2. ordinal number   **b.** 35,992,106   **2.** _____

3. leap year   **c.** fourth   **3.** _____

In 4–7, give the value of the underlined digit.

4. 6,<u>8</u>45   **4.** _____

5. 25,86<u>7</u>   **5.** _____

6. 622,7<u>5</u>4,013   **6.** _____

7. 32<u>4</u>,560,993   **7.** _____

8. Write the word name for 7,036. _____

9. Write forty-three million, two hundred thousand seven in standard form.   **9.** _____

In 10–11, complete the table. Write how many ones, tens, and hundreds are in each number.

	Number	Hundreds	Tens	Ones
10.	500			
11.	6,000			

In 12–14, compare. Write >, <, or =.

12. 8,992 ■ 8,299   **13.** 4,056 ■ 4,065   **14.** 55,319 ■ 55,391

_____   _____   _____

15. How many different outfits can Bob make if he has blue, green, and tan trousers and white and yellow sweaters? Make an organized list to show the outfits.

_____

Name _____

In 16–17, order the numbers from least to greatest.

16. 48,771   48,177   47,871 _____

17. 352,244   253,442   243,552 _____

18. Round 4,561 to the nearest thousand.   **18.** _____

19. Round 6,025 to the nearest thousand.   **19.** _____

In 20–21, write each time two different ways.

20.

21. $\boxed{2\!:\!51}$

20. _____

_____

21. _____

_____

22. Are your classes over at 3:30 A.M. or 3:30 P.M.?   **22.** _____

In 23–25, compare. Write >, <, or =.

23. 12 days ■ 2 weeks   **23.** _____

24. 2 hours ■ 250 minutes   **24.** _____

25. 2 years ■ 16 months   **25.** _____

In 26–28, write each elapsed time.

26. 2:30 P.M. to 5:30 P.M.   **26.** _____

27. 3:15 A.M. to 3:15 P.M.   **27.** _____

28. 3:15 P.M. to 4:45 P.M.   **28.** _____

29. Which month is the first month of the year?   **29.** _____

30. How many months have fewer than 31 days?   **30.** _____

31. Explain Your Thinking Write a 4-digit and a 5-digit number that round to the same number when rounded to the nearest hundred. Explain.

_____

_____

Give the letter of the correct answer.

1. Give the standard form for the number
six thousand, forty-two.

    A 6,420   **B** 6,402   **C** 6,042   **D** Not here

1. _____

2. Give the word name for 23,001.

    A Twenty-three thousand, one hundred
    B Twenty-three thousand, one
    C Two thousand, three hundred one
    D Not here

2. _____

3. Give the value of the 9 in 89,551.

    A 9   **B** 90   **C** 900   **D** 9,000

3. _____

4. Give the value of the 3 in 552,362.

    A 3   **B** 30   **C** 300   **D** 3,000

4. _____

5. Give the value of the 6 in 644,089.

    A 60   **B** 600   **C** 60,000   **D** 600,000

5. _____

6. Give the number of hundreds in 8,000.

    A 8   **B** 80   **C** 800   **D** 8,000

6. _____

7. Give the number of ones in 8,000.

    A 8   **B** 80   **C** 800   **D** 8,000

7. _____

8. Give the number of tens in 2,000.

    A 2   **B** 20   **C** 200   **D** 2,000

8. _____

9. Give the standard form for the number eighty-two
million, four hundred thousand, seventy-eight.

    A 82,404,078   **B** 82,400,078
    C 82,004,078   **D** Not here

9. _____

10. Give the word name for 30,050,020.   **10.** _____

    A Thirty million, fifty thousand, two
    B Three million, five thousand, twenty
    C Thirty million, fifty thousand, twenty
    D Thirty million, five hundred twenty

11. Give the value of the 2 in 123,559,604.   **11.** _____

    A 20,000   **B** 200,000   **C** 2,000,000   **D** 20,000,000

12. Give the value of the 6 in 21,603,449.   **12.** _____

    A 6,000   **B** 600,000   **C** 6,000,000   **D** 600,000,000

13. Give the value of the 7 in 33,507,448.   **13.** _____

    A 7,000   **B** 70,000   **C** 7,000,000   **D** 70,000,000

14. How many combinations of colors can be made   **14.** _____
using two colors of paint if you have red, blue,
yellow, and white paint?

    A 3 combinations   **B** 4 combinations
    C 5 combinations   **D** 6 combinations

15. How many outfits can Joel make using either black   **15.** _____
or navy jeans and a red T-shirt or a yellow T-shirt?

    A 2 outfits   **B** 3 outfits   **C** 4 outfits   **D** 5 outfits

16. Jo has a total of 25¢. How many combinations of   **16.** _____
coins could she have if she has only nickels and/or
dimes?

    A 1 combination   **B** 2 combinations
    C 3 combinations   **D** 4 combinations

17. Choose the correct comparison.   **17.** _____

    A 501 > 510   **B** 443 > 433
    C 339 > 393   **D** 621 < 612

18. Choose the correct comparison.   **18.** _____

    A 5,501 < 5,051   **B** 6,432 > 6,342
    C 2,099 > 3,000   **D** 4,661 < 4,616

Name _____

19. Choose the correct comparison.

    A $34{,}501 < 34{,}105$ **B** $56{,}792 > 65{,}792$
    C $43{,}550 > 4{,}355$ **D** $8{,}700 < 7{,}800$

19. _____

20. Which list shows the numbers in order from least to greatest?

    A 4,622 4,625 4,226   **B** 55,679 55,976 55,796
    C 81,234 82,134 84,123   **D** 3,402 4,203 2,403

20. _____

21. Which list shows the numbers in order from greatest to least?

    A 248 284 428   **B** 563 365 356
    C 490 409 940   **D** 221 112 122

21. _____

22. Which number shows 848 rounded to the nearest hundred?

    A 700   **B** 800   **C** 850   **D** 900

22. _____

23. Which number shows 3,099 rounded to the nearest thousand?

    A 3,000   **B** 3,100   **C** 4,000   **D** Not here

23. _____

24. Which number shows 2,500 rounded to the nearest thousand?

    A 2,000   **B** 2,500   **C** 3,500   **D** Not here

24. _____

25. What time is shown on the clock below?

    A 8 minutes before 2
    B 8 minutes after 2
    C 8 minutes before 3
    D 52 minutes after 1

25. _____

26. What time is shown on the clock below?

    A 20 minutes after 6
    B 40 minutes after 5
    C 20 minutes after 5
    D 40 minutes after 4

26. _____

27. Which is a reasonable time for you to be in school?   **27.** _____

    A 5:30 A.M.   **B** 5:30 P.M.   **C** 2:30 A.M.   **D** 2:30 P.M.

28. Choose the correct comparison.   **28.** _____

    A 6 weeks < 30 days   **B** 2 years < 600 days
    C 8 weeks < 3 months   **D** 3 years < 30 months

29. Choose the correct comparison.   **29.** _____

    A 80 minutes < 2 hours   **B** 2 days < 36 hours
    C 24 hours > 2 days   **D** 2 hours < 100 minutes

30. Give the elapsed time from 8:00 P.M. to 7:00 A.M.   **30.** _____

    A 1 hour   **B** 11 hours
    C 13 hours   **D** Not here

31. Give the elapsed time from 4:30 A.M. to 6:30 A.M.   **31.** _____

    A 2 hours   **B** 10 hours
    C 14 hours   **D** Not here

32. Give the elapsed time from 2:30 P.M. to 4:15 P.M.   **32.** _____

    A 1 hour and 15 minutes   **B** 1 hour and 45 minutes
    C 2 hours and 15 minutes **D** 2 hours and 45 minutes

33. Which months have 31 days?   **33.** _____

    A January, March, May
    B January, February, March
    C June, July, August
    D October, November, December

34. Which months have 30 days?   **34.** _____

    A February, April, June
    B September, October, November
    C April, June, September
    D June, August, October

35. How many days does a leap year have?   **35.** _____

    A 360 days   **B** 364 days
    C 365 days   **D** 366 days

How do you spend your time in one week? These are the activities that some fourth graders have listed.

being in school	sleeping	reading
doing homework	playing baseball	watching television
practicing piano	riding my bike	playing computer games
eating meals	playing with friends	roller blading

a. Recording Data First make a list of the things you usually do in one week during the school year. Then make a table like the one below. The number of rows depends on the number of activities in your list. Write your list in the Activities column and write the length of the activity to the nearest hour.

Hours I Spend on Activities During the School Year							
Activities	Sun.	Mon.	Tues.	Wed.	Thurs.	Fri.	Sat.
Total hours	24 hr	24 hr	24 hr	24hr	24 hr	24hr	24 hr

b. Recording Data Estimate the number of hours you spend on each activity each week. Write your estimates for each day in the table. Make sure that the sum in each column is 24 hours.

c. Analyzing Data Use the table to answer these questions.
Which activity takes the most time in a week?
Which activity takes the least time in a week?
Which days do you spend the most time in after-school activities?

d. Analyzing Data List the times you spend on the activities for one day from least to greatest.

e. Making Decisions Would you like to spend more or less time on any of the activities that you listed? Explain.

Teacher Notes

Concepts and Skills This activity requires students to:

- record data in a table.
- make decisions using real-life experiences.
- estimate amounts of time.
- find sums.
- compare and order numbers.
- evaluate personal scheduling of time.

Guiding Questions

- Suppose you practice piano 45 minutes each day. What estimate might you list in your table?
- What activities in your table should be considered after-school activities?

Answers

a. Activities will vary.
b. Estimates will vary. Check that students' totals for each day are 24 hours.
c. Check students' answers. Students will probably indicate that sleeping takes the most time each week, while practicing an instrument or reading might take the least time. Saturdays and Sundays most likely will have the greatest amount of time devoted to recreational activities.
d. Check students' answers.
e. Answers will vary.

Extension

Have students make a bar graph using the data in the last column of their table.

Evaluation

Level	Standard to be achieved for performance of specified level
4	**Full Achievement** The student is able to round times to the nearest hour and schedule time in a week. Each day column in the table totals 24 hours. All comparisons are correct and the explanations well written.
3	**Substantial Achievement** The student is able to round times to the nearest hour and schedule time in a week with only minor errors in computation or reasoning. Some errors may occur in the day totals. The ordering of the activities may contain some minor errors, and the explanation is basically well written.
2	**Partial Achievement** The student has some difficulty deciding on the activities to list and needs help estimating times. Totals for day column are not computed correctly. Ordering of activities contains major errors and explanations are incomplete.
1	**Little Achievement** The student demonstrates little if any understanding of the task at hand and needs considerable help identifying activities and times. The computation contains many errors, and the concepts of ordering are not grasped.

In 1 and 2, write the value of the 6 in each number.

1. 3,602

1. _____

2. 601,447,891

2. _____

3. Write the word name for 30,043. _____

4. Write sixty-one million, five hundred
   seventy-nine in standard form.

4. _____

In 5 and 6, complete the table. Write how many ones, tens, and hundreds are in each number.

	Number	Hundreds	Tens	Ones
5.	600			
6.	3,700			

In 7 and 8, compare. Write >, <, or =.

7. 56,801 ● 58,699

7. _____

8. 443,550 ● 443,505

8. _____

9. Use the table at the right.
   How many combinations of
   shirts and jeans can Maria
   choose from? List all the
   combinations.

Shirts	Jeans
Red	Black
Green	Navy
Yellow	

_____

10. Which numbers are ordered from least to greatest?

10. _____

   A 56,897 56,789 56,987 B 43,602 43,206 42,306
   C 32,145 32,451 32,541 D 82,903 89,203 83,902

11. Which numbers are ordered from greatest to least?

11. _____

   A 5,678 5,768 5,876   B 4,321 4,231 4,123
   C 7,801 4,602 5,891   D 859 2,341 5,568

12. Round 650 to the nearest hundred.

12. _____

13. Is 5,559 closer to 5,000 or 6,000?

13. _____

In 14 and 15, write each time two different ways.

14.

15. [8:09]

14. _____

_____

15. _____

_____

16. Choose the correct comparison.

16. _____

A 6 days > 1 week　　**B** 6 weeks > 1 month
C 6 months > 1 year　　**D** 6 minutes > 1 hour

17. Choose the correct comparison.

17. _____

A 50 days < 2 months　　**B** 50 minutes > 2 hours
C 50 weeks > 2 years　　**D** 50 seconds > 2 minutes

In 18 and 19, write each elapsed time.

18. 6:30 P.M. to 2:30 A.M.

18. _____

19. 1:30 P.M. to 7:00 P.M.

19. _____

20. How many months are in a year?

20. _____

21. What kind of year has more than 365 days?

21. _____

22. Which kind of number is used to tell order?

22. _____

A digit　　**B** ordinal number
C expanded number　　**D** standard number

23. Performance Task Explain how you would find the elapsed time from 10:45 A.M. to 1:25 P.M.

_____

_____

Name _____

Date _____ Score _____

— Computation —

1. Write the difference between the greatest value and the least value in this stem-and-leaf plot.

stem	leaf
1	2
2	3 3 5
3	5 6
4	2 8 9

1. _____

2. Which value is 3 times the least value in the stem-and-leaf plot?

2. _____

3. Choose the correct comparison.

A 20 minutes > half hour   **B** 7 weeks > 60 days
C 5 months < 40 weeks   **D** 20 minutes < 20 seconds

3. _____

4. Choose the correct comparison.

A 2 years < 30 months   **B** 2 months > 80 days
C 25 weeks > 1 year   **D** 12 hours < 60 minutes

4. _____

5. Write the elapsed time from 5:15 A.M. to 6:30 A.M.

5. _____

6. Write the elapsed time from 7:25 P.M. to 7:43 P.M.

6. _____

— Concepts —

7. Lemar can have a tuna, roast beef, or cheese sandwich. With his sandwich, he can have potato salad or cole slaw. How many different ways could he have his lunch?

A 2 ways   **B** 3 ways   **C** 5 ways   **D** 6 ways

7. _____

8. Which term describes the middle number in a list of numbers that are in order?

A average   **B** mode   **C** range   **D** median

8. _____

9. Find the mode in the data in Item 1.

9. _____

10. Find the median in the data in Item 1.

10. _____

Name _____

11. Write sixty-four thousand, one hundred eight in standard form.

11. _____

12. Write 3,000,000 + 40,000 + 500 + 60 + 1 in standard form.

12. _____

13. Write the value of the 8 in 482,039.

13. _____

14. Write the value of the 5 in 405,821,673.

14. _____

15. How many ones are in 2,300?

15. _____

16. How many tens are in 2,300?

16. _____

17. Which number is greater, 566,890 or 566,980?

17. _____

18. Which number is less, 35,021 or 34,998?

18. _____

19. Round 509 to the nearest hundred.

19. _____

20. Do you have dinner at 6:00 A.M. or 6:00 P.M.?

20. _____

21. Do you play baseball at 4:00 A.M. or 4:00 P.M.?

21. _____

22. Which of the following is not shown on a calendar?

    A days   **B** weeks   **C** months   **D** hours

22. _____

— Applications —

State	Land Area (square miles)	Population
Alaska (AK)	570,400	606,000
New York (NY)	47,200	18,200,000
Rhode Island (RI)	1,000	997,000
Texas (TX)	261,900	18,400,000

23. List the states in order from least population to greatest population.

23. _____

24. List the states in order from greatest area to least area.

24. _____

25. Have all the areas been rounded to the nearest hundred or nearest thousand?

25. _____

Vocabulary: In 1–3, match each with its meaning.

1. sum

a. number obtained by subtracting

2. difference

b. to find a number close to an exact answer

3. estimate

c. number obtained by adding

1. _____

2. _____

3. _____

In 4–5, complete each number sentence.

4. $30 + 40 = n$

$300 + 400 = n$

$3,000 + 4,000 = n$

5. $8 - 6 = n$

$80 - 60 = n$

$800 - 600 = n$

4. _____

   _____

   _____

5. _____

   _____

   _____

In 6–8, find each sum or difference. Use mental math.

6. $220 + 100$

7. $730 - 110$

8. $890 - 440$

6. _____

7. _____

8. _____

In 9–11, estimate each sum or difference. Round to the nearest thousand.

9. $3,798 + 2,144$

10. $1,828 + 5,422$

11. $7,210 - 899$

9. _____

10. _____

11. _____

12. You want to know if your have enough time to walk to the store and back before dinner. Do you need an exact answer or an estimate? Explain.

_____

Vocabulary: In 1–2, match each with its meaning.

1. addends

   a. a way to estimate by first looking at the leading digits.

2. front-end estimation

   b. numbers that are added together to make a sum

1. _____

2. _____

In 3–7, find each sum. Estimate to check.

3. 672 + 131

4. 521 + 685

3. _____

4. _____

5. $$\begin{array}{r} 2{,}727 \\ + 1{,}794 \\ \hline \end{array}$$

6. $$\begin{array}{r} 3{,}644 \\ 489 \\ + 65 \\ \hline \end{array}$$

7. $$\begin{array}{r} 4{,}567 \\ 9{,}012 \\ + 456 \\ \hline \end{array}$$

In 8–12, subtract.

8. 746 − 210

9. 815 − 465

8. _____

9. _____

10. $$\begin{array}{r} 4{,}489 \\ - 1{,}997 \\ \hline \end{array}$$

11. $$\begin{array}{r} 700 \\ - 461 \\ \hline \end{array}$$

12. $$\begin{array}{r} 5{,}200 \\ - 418 \\ \hline \end{array}$$

13. There are 49 campers. On Tuesday, 19 were playing basketball, 15 were playing volleyball, and the rest were painting. How many campers were painting?

13. _____

In 14–15, add or subtract mentally.

14. 628 − 202

15. 199 + 65

14. _____

15. _____

In 16–18, find each sum or difference.

16. $$\begin{array}{r} 2{,}993 \\ - 1{,}040 \\ \hline \end{array}$$

17. $$\begin{array}{r} 5{,}819 \\ + 2{,}426 \\ \hline \end{array}$$

18. $$\begin{array}{r} 50{,}035 \\ - 23{,}121 \\ \hline \end{array}$$

In 1–2, count the money. Write each amount with dollar sign and decimal point.

1. 3 $10 bills, 1 $5 bill, 3 $1 bills, 2 dimes

1. _____

2. 2 $20 bills, 3 $5 bills, 2 quarters, 1 nickel

2. _____

In 3–4, compare. Write <, >, or =.

3. $0.48 ⬤ $4.50

3. _____

4. $424.27 ⬤ $422.27

4. _____

In 5–10, add or subtract. Estimate to check.

5.	**6.**	**7.**
$8.40	$154.24	$ 5.49
+ 0.37	+ 19.67	3.47
		+ 12.16

8.	**9.**	**10.**
$6.20	$75.29	$82.00
− 2.44	− 10.99	− 6.78

11. Han-su bought tapes costing $12.75. He gave the cashier a $20 bill. What was his change?

11. _____

12. Lori bought 3 packages of film. Each package costs $2.50. She gave the cashier a $10 bill. What was her change?

12. _____

In 13–14, find the value for *n*.

13. $36 + n = 96$

13. _____

14. $700 = 200 + n$

14. _____

15. Continue the pattern. Then describe the pattern.

50, 70, 60, 80, 70, ■, ■, ■

Vocabulary: In 1–3, match each word with its meaning.

1. difference

    a. a way to estimate by first looking at the leading digits

2. estimate

    b. number obtained by subtracting

3. front-end estimation

    c. to find a number close to an exact amount

1. _____

2. _____

3. _____

In 4, complete each number sentence.

4. $7 + 2 = 9$

$70 + 20 = n$

$700 + 200 = 900$

$7,000 + 2,000 = n$

In 5–7, find each sum or difference. Use mental math.

5. $540 + 200$ **6.** $360 + 630$ **7.** $780 - 420$

_____   _____   _____

In 8–10, estimate each sum or difference. Round to the nearest hundred.

8. $768 - 284$ **9.** $933 - 645$ **10.** $529 + 255$

_____   _____   _____

11. Jay ran a 100-yard dash in 14 seconds. Is the time an exact amount or an estimate?

11. _____

In 12–15, find each sum. Estimate to check.

12. $723 + 538$

12. _____

13.
$$\begin{array}{r} 4,825 \\ + 987 \\ \hline \end{array}$$

14.
$$\begin{array}{r} 756 \\ 2,483 \\ + 4,309 \\ \hline \end{array}$$

15.
$$\begin{array}{r} 6,987 \\ 7,435 \\ + 123 \\ \hline \end{array}$$

16. Find $643 - 291$.

16. _____

Name _____

In 17–19, subtract. Add or estimate to check.

17. $\begin{array}{r} 829 \\ -\ 473 \\ \hline \end{array}$ 18. $\begin{array}{r} 4,071 \\ -\ 2,895 \\ \hline \end{array}$ 19. $\begin{array}{r} 6,001 \\ -\ 5,878 \\ \hline \end{array}$

20. Leo earned $290 mowing lawns and $340   20. _____
pulling weeds. He spent $125. How much
did he have left?

In 21–23, find the sum or difference.

21. $\begin{array}{r} 8,620 \\ -\ 4,000 \\ \hline \end{array}$ 22. $\begin{array}{r} 1,468 \\ +\ 3,929 \\ \hline \end{array}$ 23. $\begin{array}{r} 3,200 \\ +\ 4,704 \\ \hline \end{array}$

In 24–25, compare. Write <, >, or =.

24. $164 ● $16.40   24. _____

25. $7.49 ● $14.49   25. _____

In 26–28, add or subtract. Estimate to check.

26. $\begin{array}{r} \$24.65 \\ +\ \ 35.98 \\ \hline \end{array}$ 27. $\begin{array}{r} \$30.69 \\ +\ \ 29.77 \\ \hline \end{array}$ 28. $\begin{array}{r} \$57.00 \\ -\ \ 29.88 \\ \hline \end{array}$

29. Ana gives the cashier $5.00 for three items   29. _____
costing $1.50 each. How much change will
she receive?

In 30–31, find the value for each *n*.

30. $18 + n = 40$ 30. _____

31. $n + 400 = 700$ 31. _____

32. Tiger had $10. Then he saved $4 each week.   32. _____
How much money did he have after 5 weeks?

33. **Explain Your Thinking** Explain how Agatha
could use mental math to find 700 − 196.

_____

Vocabulary: In 1–3, match each with its meaning.

1. addends

a. a number obtained by adding

2. sum

b. numbers that are added together to make a sum

3. decimal point

c. a symbol that separates dollar and cent amounts

1. _____

2. _____

3. _____

In 4, complete each number sentence.

4. $4 + 3 = 7$

$40 + n = 70$

$400 + 300 = 700$

$4,000 + n = 7,000$

In 5–7, find each sum or difference. Use mental math.

5. $430 + 200$

6. $560 - 310$

7. $670 - 450$

_____   _____   _____

In 8–10, estimate each sum or difference. Round to the nearest hundred.

8. $568 + 291$

9. $255 + 640$

10. $928 - 799$

_____   _____   _____

11. David set a school record in pancake eating. Is the record an exact amount or an estimate?

11. _____

In 12–15, find each sum. Estimate to check.

12. $856 + 109$

12. _____

13.
$$\begin{array}{r} 2,964 \\ +\ \ 857 \\ \hline \end{array}$$

14.
$$\begin{array}{r} 627 \\ 4,521 \\ +\ 1,234 \\ \hline \end{array}$$

15.
$$\begin{array}{r} 8,296 \\ 928 \\ +\ 9,563 \\ \hline \end{array}$$

16. Find $679 - 231$.

16. _____

Continued **75**

Name _____

In 17–19, subtract. Add or estimate to check.

17.
```
  1,964
-   577
```

18.
```
  6,207
- 4,521
```

19.
```
  8,006
- 4,927
```

20. Toi earned $160 cleaning and $450 walking dogs. She spent $145. How much does she have left?

20. _____

In 21–23, find the sum or difference.

21.
```
  1,500
+ 3,260
```

22.
```
  5,970
- 3,000
```

23.
```
  8,236
- 4,389
```

In 24–25, compare. Write <, >, or =.

24. $17.76 ● $175.60

24. _____

25. $19.17 ● $16.20

25. _____

In 26–28, add or subtract. Estimate to check.

26.
```
  $27.66
+  94.29
```

27.
```
  $56.78
+   8.05
```

28.
```
  $59.00
-  39.37
```

29. Derek gives a cashier $10 for three items which cost $1.65 each. How much change will he receive?

29. _____

In 30–31, find the value for each *n*.

30. $n + 20 = 45$

30. _____

31. $60 = n + 10$

31. _____

32. Mariko had $15. Then she saved $5 each week. How much did she have after 4 weeks?

32. _____

33. **Explain Your Thinking** Explain how Deidre could use mental math to find 375 + 199.

Name _____

Date _____ Score _____

Give the letter of the correct answer.

1. Continue this number pattern: 3 + 4 = 7   1. _____
                                    30 + 40 = 70
                                    300 + 400 = 700

   A 300 + 40 = 340   **B** 300 + 40 = 340
   C 30 + 30 = 60   **D** 3,000 + 4,000 = 7,000

2. If 9 − 7 = 2, then 90 − 70 = ■.   2. _____

   A 2   **B** 20   **C** 160   **D** 200

3. Use a pattern to find the missing number.   3. _____
   5,000 − n = 3,000.

   A 200   **B** 5,000   **C** 2,000   **D** 1,000

In 4–7, find the sum or difference. Use mental math.

4. 220 + 200   4. _____

   A 440   **B** 400   **C** 420   **D** Not here

5. 380 + 110   5. _____

   A 480   **B** 270   **C** 470   **D** 490

6. 790 − 430   6. _____

   A 360   **B** 350   **C** 460   **D** 1,220

7. 870 − 560   7. _____

   A 210   **B** 310   **C** 1,330   **D** 301

8. Estimate 376 + 523. Round to the nearest hundred.   8. _____

   A 800   **B** 1,000   **C** 900   **D** 899

9. Estimate 4,586 + 3,175. Round to the   9. _____
   nearest thousand.

   A 8,000   **B** 7,761   **C** 7,000   **D** 9,000

Name _____

10. Estimate the difference. Round to the nearest thousand. **10.** _____
8,498 − 1,279

    A 8,000   **B** 6,000   **C** 9,000   **D** Not here

11. Kyle is training for a charity race. He uses a   **11.** _____
stopwatch to find the time it takes him to run a mile.
Will he use an estimate or an exact answer?

    A Estimate   **B** Exact answer

12. You have $5 and want to buy a magazine for $2.50   **12.** _____
and pretzels for $1.99. Can you estimate or do you
need an exact answer to figure out if you have
enough money?

    A Estimate   **B** Exact answer

In 13–20, add or subtract.

13. 540 +168   **13.** _____

    A 608   **B** 708   **C** 372   **D** 382

14.   3,269   **14.** _____
    + 7,385

    A 10,654   **B** 10,544   **C** 10,644   **D** 1,064

15.   7,218   **15.** _____
    1,968
    +   86

    A 8,272   **B** 9,262   **C** 9,272   **D** Not here

16. 694 + 73 + 4,387   **16.** _____

    A 5,054   **B** 4,154   **C** 5,154   **D** 5,144

17. 765 − 179   **17.** _____

    A 944   **B** 844   **C** 586   **D** 596

18.   7,643   **18.** _____
    − 2,892

    A 5,751   **B** 4,751   **C** 4,851   **D** 4,761

Name _____

19. 3,042
    − 1,956

A 2,086   **B** 1,186   **C** 1,096   **D** 1,086

19. _____

20. 14,080
    − 6,946

A 8,946   **B** 7,134   **C** 7,946   **D** 8,134

20. _____

21. Donya can use the classroom computer for 1 hour. She spends 15 minutes playing a math game and 25 minutes writing a story on the computer. How many minutes does she have left?

A 10 minutes   **B** 30 minutes
C 20 minutes   **D** Not here

21. _____

22. Howin wants to run 35 miles each week. He ran 3 miles on Monday and 5 miles on Tuesday. How many more miles does he have to run to make his goal?

A 43 miles   **B** 40 miles   **C** 30 miles   **D** 27 miles

22. _____

23. Add mentally: 99 + 62.

A 161   **B** 157   **C** 163   **D** 167

23. _____

24. Subtract mentally: 400 − 38.

A 372   **B** 438   **C** 362   **D** 368

24. _____

25. Which sum or difference would be the most difficult to solve using mental math?

A 27,000 − 20,000   **B** 48,000 + 20,000
C 42,000 − 12,000   **D** 48,796 + 29,948

25. _____

26. Find the sum: 1,422 + 2,015. Use any calculation method.

A 3,437   **B** 593   **C** 4,300   **D** 1,415

26. _____

27. How much money is there?
2 $10 bills, 1 $5 bill, 1 $1 bill, 2 quarters, 1 nickel

A $21.62   **B** $10.51   **C** $26.55   **D** $25.60

27. _____

Name _____

28. Which comparison is correct?

    A $12.65 < $12.56   **B** $12.65 = $12.56
    C $12.65 > $12.56   **D** $12.65 > $125.60

28. _____

29. Find $49.29 + 18.73.

    A $67.02   **B** $68.02   **C** $68.92   **D** $67.92

29. _____

30. Subtract. $78.49
          − 18.96

    A $59.53   **B** $5953.00   **C** $59.45   **D** $60.53

30. _____

31. Brian bought a CD for $14.65. He gave the cashier $20. How much change did he receive?

    A $34.65   **B** $6.65   **C** $5.35   **D** no change

31. _____

32. Alisha bought a dog toy for $3.75 and a bag of dog food for $8.50. She gave the cashier $15. How much change did she receive?

    A $2.75   **B** $6.50   **C** $27.25   **D** Not here

32. _____

33. Find the value for n. $845 + n = 895$.

    A 40   **B** 60   **C** 30   **D** 50

33. _____

34. Find the value for n. $600 = 450 + n$.

    A 150   **B** 100   **C** 250   **D** 200

34. _____

35. Continue the pattern: 5, 8, 7, 10, 9, 12, ■, ■, ■

    A 15, 18, 17   **B** 11, 14, 13
    C 10, 9, 12   **D** 5, 8, 7

35. _____

36. Jermaine planted a rose garden. He planted 4 rose bushes in the first row, 6 rose bushes in the second row, 8 rose bushes in the third row, and so on. How many rose bushes did he plant in the sixth row?

    A 10 rose bushes   **B** 12 rose bushes
    C 14 rose bushes   **D** Not here

36. _____

Name _____

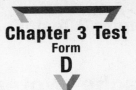

Date _____ Score _____

Your aunt will take you to two of the places shown in the table.

Busch Gardens	Child (ages 3–9) $29.75	Adult $36.15
Disney World	Child (ages 2–12) $32.68	Adult $40.81
Sea World	Child (ages (3–12) $32.80	Adult $39.95
Kennedy Space Center Tour	$8 per person (children under age 2 are free)	

a. Making Decisions Choose two places to visit.

b. Recording Data

How much will tickets cost for you and your aunt to visit one of the places you chose?

How much will it cost for tickets to the other place you chose?

How much will it cost for tickets for the two of you to visit both places?

c. Explain Your Thinking

How did you decide whether you needed a child's ticket or an adult's ticket?

How did you find the cost of two tickets to both places?

d. Making Decisions Your aunt gives you $10 to spend. Which items shown would you buy? How much will these items cost?

FLORIDA $7.22

FLORIDA $3.21

Pencil Case
FLORIDA
$4.26

$3.89

26¢

FLORIDA $4.78

FLORIDA $2.96

Teacher Notes

Concepts and Skills This activity requires students to:
- make decisions using real-life experiences.
- interpret data in a table.
- count money.
- add and subtract decimals, written as money amounts.

Guiding Questions
- Suppose you have two $5 bills. How will you find how much money you have in all?
- If a ball costs $2 and a bat cost $5, how will you find the cost of both items? If you have $6, do you have enough to buy both the ball and the bat? Explain.

Answers
a. Check students' answers.
b. Check students' answers.
c. Check students' answers. The decision on whether the student will purchase a child's ticket or an adult's ticket depends upon the student's age. The total cost to visit both attractions is the sum of the cost for each attraction.
d. Choices will vary.

Extension
Have students use a calculator to find the cost for their entire family to visit one of the attractions. Then encourage them to choose a souvenir for each person and find the total cost for the visit.

Evaluation

Level	Standard to be achieved for performance of specified level
4	**Full Achievement** The student understands addition of decimals written as money amounts and correctly computes the answers to the problems.
3	**Substantial Achievement** The student understands addition of decimals written as money amounts and computes correctly most of the answers.
2	**Partial Achievement** The student has some difficulty in adding decimals written as money amounts, and computations may contain some errors.
1	**Little Achievement** The student needs considerable help in adding decimals written as money amounts and may make many computation errors The concept of which items to buy given a set amount of money is not understood.

Name _____

Date _____ Score _____

1. Continue the number pattern. 6 + 2 = 8
60 + 20 = 80
600 + 200 = 800

1. _____

A 6,000 + 200 = 6,200 **B** 600 + 2,000 = 6,200
C 6,000 + 2,000 = 8,000 **D** 600 + 20 = 620

In 2–3, find each sum or difference. Use mental math.

2. 550 + 400

2. _____

3. 930 − 610

3. _____

In 4–5, estimate. Round to the nearest hundred.

4. 819 − 286

4. _____

5. 565 + 198

5. _____

A 800 **B** 700 **C** 400 **D** 100

6. Will you estimate or use an exact number to plan how
many people will attend a weekend fair? Explain.

_____

In 7–10, find each sum. Estimate to check.

7. 781 + 123

7. _____

8. 2,352
     + 654

9. 4,506
       500
     +   32

10. 8,009
        345
     + 1,225

In 11–14, subtract.

11. 973 − 456

11. _____

12. 7,862
      − 3,924

13. 6,008
      − 1,828

14. 7,090
      − 3,645

15. Add mentally. 5,609 + 235

15. _____

Name _____

16. Subtract mentally. 8,700 − 1,298   **16.** _____

17. Mia had a $20 bill. She bought glue for $2.99 and paint   **17.** _____
for $4.97. How much money does she have left?

   A $17.01   **B** $7.96   **C** $12.04   **D** Not here

**In 18–19, choose any calculation method to find the
sum or difference.**

18. 2,924 + 5,689   **18.** _____

   A 8,603   **B** 7,613   **C** 8,714   **D** Not here

19. 4,850 − 2,000   **19.** _____

   A 2,850   **B** 4,650   **C** 6,850   **D** Not here

In 20–21, compare the amounts. Write <, >, or =.

20. $12.54 ● $12.45   **20.** _____

21. $10.45 ● $10 bill + 4 dimes + 1 nickel   **21.** _____

In 22–24, add or subtract. Estimate to check.

22.	$1 2 9.4 4	**23.**	$2 7.4 7	**24.**	$7 8.0 0
−	6 6.7 3	+	6 8.7 3	−	2 9.4 3

25. Ryan bought 2 books. Each book costs $1.50. He gave   **25.** _____
the cashier a $20 bill. How much change did he receive?

   A $17.50   **B** $18.50   **C** $21.50   **D** Not here

26. Continue the pattern. Describe the pattern.
2, 6, 4, 8, 6, 10, 8, 12, 10, ■, ■, ■

_____

27. Performance Task Explain how to find the value of n
in $30 + n = 64$. How can you check your answer?

_____

_____

— Computation —

In 1–8, find each sum or difference.

1. 440 + 300

1. _____

2. 650 − 310

2. _____

3.   5,2 4 1
  + 8,8 6 9

4.   6 7 4
      6 1 3
    + 2,4 5 7

5.   3 6 2
     − 1 2 8

6.   7,0 6 1
  − 3,8 7 1

7. $9 6.3 1
  + 1 4.2 9

8. $1 0 0.1 9
  −   8 2.9 1

9. Add mentally. 821 + 698

9. _____

A 123   **B** 1,421   **C** 1,519   **D** 1,523

10. Subtract mentally. 999 − 425

10. _____

In 11–12, estimate. Round to the nearest hundred.

11. 687 − 278

11. _____

12. 365 + 198

12. _____

— Concepts —

13. Which operation would you use to find how many more apples are in one basket than in another?

13. _____

A Addition   **B** Subtraction
C Multiplication **D** Division

14. Which term describes the number that occurs the most often in a set of data?

14. _____

A mode   **B** median   **C** average   **D** range

15. What is the value of the 7 in 227,568?

15. _____

A 7   **B** 7,000   **C** 700   **D** 70,000

Continued

16. How would you write eighty-five thousand, two hundred seven in standard form?

    A 8,527   **B** 85,270   **C** 85,207   **D** 80,527

16. _____

17. Complete the number pattern. $5 + 3 = 8$
                                  $50 + 30 = 80$
                                  $500 + 300 = 800$

17. _____

    A $500 + 30 = 530$ **B** $5,000 + 3,000 = 8,000$
    C $5,000 + 300 = 5,300$ **D** $50,000 + 8,000 = 58,000$

18. Compare. Use $<$, $>$, or $=$.

    $6.34 ● 6 dollars, 2 quarters, 2 dimes

18. _____

19. Find the value for n in the number sentence.
    $20 = n + 8$.

19. _____

20. Continue this pattern: 8, 14, 20, 26, ■.

    A 30   **B** 34   **C** 28   **D** 32

20. _____

━ Applications ━

In 21–23, use the table.

Cafe Menu	
Sandwich $3.50	Soup $1.50
Salad $1.25	Drink $1.00

21. You order soup and a salad and pay with a $10 bill. How much change will you receive?

21. _____

22. Sue buys a sandwich and a salad. She gives the clerk a $5 bill. What are all the different ways she could receive the change, if she does not get any pennies?

_____

23. You have $10 and want to know if you have enough money for a sandwich, soup, a salad, and a drink. Will you need an exact amount or an estimate to make your decision?

23. _____

Give the letter of the correct answer.

In 1–3, use the line graph.

1. Which month had the least snowfall?

   A November
   B December
   C January
   D February

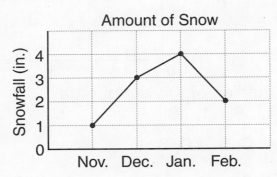

Amount of Snow

1. _____

2. Which month had 4 inches of snow?

   A November   **B** December
   C January   **D** February

2. _____

3. How much more snow fell in December than in February?

   A 1 inch   **B** 2 inches   **C** 3 inches   **D** 4 inches

3. _____

4. Which operation would you use to find how many more cars than trucks Ivan saw on the highway?

   A Addition   **B** Subtraction
   C Multiplication   **D** Division

4. _____

In 5–6, use the line plot that shows how many basketball points players made.

5. How many players made 23 points?

   A 4 players
   B 3 players
   C 2 players
   D Not here

5. _____

Points By Players

6. What is the mode number of points?

   A 20   **B** 21   **C** 22   **D** 23

6. _____

Name _____

7. Name the ordered pair for point *B*.

A (3, 2) **B** (4, 1)
C (1, 2) **D** (2, 3)

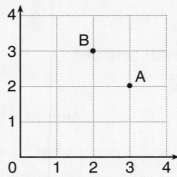

7. _____

8. What is the median of this set of data?
8, 5, 3, 4, 9, 1, 8

A 1 **B** 3 **C** 5 **D** 8

8. _____

9. Laura and Kendra have 24 merit badges all together. Kendra has 2 more badges than Laura. How many badges does Kendra have?

A 26 badges **B** 13 badges
C 11 badges **D** Not here

9. _____

10. Give the standard form for five hundred two thousand, sixty.

A 500,060 **B** 52,006
C 502,060 **D** Not here

10. _____

11. Give the value of the 7 in 47,091.

A 7 **B** 70 **C** 700 **D** 7,000

11. _____

12. Give the standard form for sixty-five million, two hundred thousand, forty-three.

A 65,200,043 **B** 65,243
C 650,243 **D** 65,243,000

12. _____

13. India has a blue skirt and a tan skirt. She also has a white blouse and a cream blouse. How many outfits can India make using these skirts and blouses?

A 1 outfit **B** 2 outfits **C** 3 outfits **D** Not here

13. _____

14. Which comparison is correct?

A 598 > 601 **B** 621 > 261
C 245 > 254 **D** 345 < 341

14. _____

Continued

Name _____

15. Which number shows 5,495 rounded to the nearest thousand?

A 5,000 **B** 5,500 **C** 6,000 **D** Not here

15. _____

16. What time is shown on the clockface?

A 25 minutes before 3
B 25 minutes after 3
C 25 minutes before 4
D 35 minutes after 3

16. _____

17. Which is a reasonable time for you to go to bed?

A 10:30 A.M.   **B** 12:30 P.M.
C 3:30 P.M.   **D** Not here

17. _____

18. Give the elapsed time from 9:30 A.M. to 11:15 A.M.

A 1 hour 45 minutes   **B** 2 hours 45 minutes
C 2 hours 15 minutes   **D** Not here

18. _____

19. Estimate the sum of 248 + 361. Round to the nearest hundred.

A 500 **B** 700 **C** 600 **D** Not here

19. _____

20. Estimate the difference of 582 − 319. Round to the nearest hundred.

A 100 **B** 200 **C** 300 **D** Not here

20. _____

In 21–23, find each sum.

21. 482
       + 365

A 787 **B** 847 **C** 867 **D** 747

21. _____

22. 5,217
       + 1,874

A 7,091 **B** 6,081 **C** 6,091 **D** 7,081

22. _____

23. 32 + 137 + 2,134

A 2,293 **B** 2,203 **C** 2,303 **D** 2,291

23. _____

In 24–28, find each sum or difference. Estimate to check.

24. 943 − 572

A 431   **B** 481   **C** 471   **D** 371

25. 4,194 − 2,527

A 2,473   **B** 2,677   **C** 1,667   **D** 2,667

26. 5,028
     − 3,082

A 2,066   **B** 2,046   **C** 1,946   **D** 2,946

27. $15.37
     + 14.59

A $29.86   **B** $29.96   **C** $29.77   **D** $21.28

28. $10.05
     − 3.49

A $13.54   **B** $7.64   **C** $4.76   **D** $6.56

29. Dean had $16.37 in his wallet. He put $7.50 in the bank and spends $3.79 at the mall. How much money does he have left in his wallet?

A $5.08   **B** $6.18   **C** $8.52   **D** $11.56

30. Add mentally: 49 + 34.

A 80   **B** 90   **C** 83   **D** Not here

31. Subtract mentally: 200 − 79.

A 120   **B** 121   **C** 100   **D** Not here

32. Danielle saves 1 penny on Monday, 3 pennies on Tuesday, and 5 pennies on Wednesday. If she follows the same pattern, how many pennies will she save on Friday?

A 6 pennies   **B** 7 pennies
C 8 pennies   **D** 9 pennies

24. _____
25. _____
26. _____
27. _____
28. _____
29. _____
30. _____
31. _____
32. _____

Name _____

Date _____ Score _____

Vocabulary: In 1–3, match each with its meaning.

1. factor   a. the number obtained after multiplying   1. _____

2. product   b. objects arranged in rows and columns   2. _____

3. array   c. numbers multiplied to form a product   3. _____

In 4–5, complete each number sentence.

4. ■ + ■ + ■ = ■   _____

5. ■ × ■ = ■   _____

Write a multiplication sentence and an addition sentence for problem 6. Then solve.

6. Jason eats 2 apples a day for 5 days. How many apples does he eat in all?

_____

7. Which are multiples of 2?   7. _____

   A 6, 9, 12   **B** 1, 2, 3   **C** 2, 4, 6   **D** 2, 5, 7

In 8–16, find each product.

8. 2×8 9. 5×7 10. 9×6

_____   _____   _____

11. 3×9 12. 8×0 13. 7×4

_____   _____   _____

14. 10×8 15. 11×9 16. 12×10

_____   _____   _____

17. Greg brushes his teeth 3 times a day. How   17. _____
    many times does he brush his teeth in a week?

Vocabulary: in 1–4, match each with its meaning.

1. dividend

    a. the answer to a division problem

1. _____

2. fact families

    b. the number by which a dividend is divided

2. _____

3. divisor

    c. a group of related facts using the same set of numbers

3. _____

4. quotient

    d. the number to be divided in a division number sentence

4. _____

In 5–7, divide.

5. $35 \div 7$

5. _____

6. $72 \div 8$

6. _____

7. $25 \div 5$

7. _____

8. Write a fact family for 35, 7, 5.

_____

In 9–12, find each quotient.

9. $63 \div 9$

9. _____

10. $45 \div 5$

10. _____

11. $0 \div 12$

11. _____

12. $24 \div 1$

12. _____

13. 3 is the divisor. 18 is the dividend. What is the quotient?

13. _____

14. What multiplication fact can help you find $49 \div 7$?

14. _____

15. There were 36 dancers in a parade. If there were 9 dancers in each row, how many rows were there?

15. _____

Vocabulary: in 1–4, complete each sentence with the correct word.

prime   composite   even   odd

1. A _____ number has only two factors, 1 and itself.

2. _____ numbers can be divided into two equal groups.

3. Whole numbers that have 1, 3, 5, 7, or 9 in the ones place are

   _____ numbers.

4. A _____ number has more than two factors.

In 5–10, find the quotient.

5. $4\overline{)24}$

6. $3\overline{)27}$

7. $4\overline{)36}$

8. $49 \div 7$

9. $54 \div 6$

10. $64 \div 8$

_____   _____   _____

In 11–13, write *odd* or *even* for each number.

11. 23

12. 48

13. 51

_____   _____   _____

14. List all the factors for 12. _____

In 15–17, write whether each number is prime or composite.

15. 12

16. 11

17. 14

_____   _____   _____

18. Lyle bought 2 tapes that cost $8.00 each. He   18. _____
    paid with a $20 bill. How much did Lyle spend?
    Is there too much or too little information to solve?

19. Juliette and Adam brought 15 photos to make   19. _____
    a collage. Juliette brought 3 more photos than
    Adam. How many photos did Adam bring?

Date _____ Score _____

Vocabulary: In 1–3, complete each sentence with the correct word.

| product fact family multiple divisor dividend quotient |

1. 12 is a __ of 2.

2. In $2 \times 3 = 6$, 6 is the __.

3. In $6 \div 2 = 3$, 6 is the __.

1. _____

2. _____

3. _____

In 4–5, complete each number sentence.

4. ■ + ■ + ■ + ■ = ■ _____

5. ■ × ■ = ■ _____

In 6–17, find each product.

6. $\begin{array}{r} 6 \\ \times 3 \\ \hline \end{array}$

7. $\begin{array}{r} 7 \\ \times 4 \\ \hline \end{array}$

8. $\begin{array}{r} 10 \\ \times 5 \\ \hline \end{array}$

9. $\begin{array}{r} 9 \\ \times 9 \\ \hline \end{array}$

10. 11×2

11. 7×6

12. 8×8

13. 9×7

_____

_____

_____

_____

14. 8×10

15. 12×12

16. 9×0

17. 10×11

_____

_____

_____

_____

18. What multiplication fact can help you to find $56 \div 7$?

18. _____

19. What multiplication fact can help you find $21 \div 3$?

19. _____

20. List all the factors of 9.

20. _____

Name _____

21. There are 20 singers in a chorus. If they stand **21.** _____
in 5 equal rows, how many singers will be in a row?

22. Write a fact family for this set of numbers: 4, 5, 20.

_____

In 23–31, find the quotient.

23. $2\overline{)18}$ **24.** $5\overline{)40}$ **25.** $9\overline{)45}$ **26.** $1\overline{)8}$

27. $0 \div 8$ **28.** $15 \div 3$ **29.** $48 \div 6$ **30.** $49 \div 7$

_____ _____ _____ _____

31. 4 is the divisor. 32 is the dividend. What is **31.** _____
the quotient?

In 32–35, write *odd* or *even* for each number.

32. 27   **33.** 58   **34.** 8   **35.** 45

_____ _____ _____ _____

In 36–38, write whether each number is prime or composite.

36. 13   **37.** 2   **38.** 22

_____ _____ _____

39. Elroy runs 5 miles and skates 3 miles each
week. How many miles does he run in 4 weeks?
Is there too much or too little information to solve? _____

40. Suzanne's softball team bought 24 bats and **40.** _____
mitts. They bought 4 more bats than mitts.
How many mitts did the team buy?

41. Explain Your Thinking How can you use patterns to tell
if your answer is reasonable when you multiply by 2?

_____

Name _____

Date _____ Score _____

Vocabulary: In 1–3, complete each sentence with the correct word.

| factor   fact family   multiple   quotient   divisor   dividend |

1. In 28 ÷ 7 = 4, 7 is the ___.

1. _____

2. 24 is a ___ of 4.

2. _____

3. In 8 × 2 = 16, 2 is a ___.

3. _____

In 4–5, complete each number sentence.

4. ■ + ■ + ■ + ■ = ■   _____

5. ■ × ■ = ■   _____

In 6–17, find each product.

6. 8
   × 4

7. 7
   × 3

8. 11
   × 5

9. 5
   × 9

10. 10 × 2

11. 7 × 8

12. 7 × 7

13. 8 × 6

_____   _____   _____   _____

14. 7 × 11

15. 12 × 10

16. 7 × 0

17. 11 × 12

_____   _____   _____   _____

18. What multiplication fact can help you find 72 ÷ 8?

18. _____

19. What multiplication fact can help you find 24 ÷ 4?

19. _____

20. List all the factors of 15.

20. _____

Name _____

21. There are 72 students at a baseball camp.   **21.** _____
If there will be 9 players on each team, how many
teams will there be?

22. Write a fact family for this set of numbers: 5, 7, 35.

_____

In 23–30, find each quotient.

23. $2\overline{)16}$ **24.** $5\overline{)25}$ **25.** $9\overline{)81}$ **26.** $9\overline{)9}$

27. $0 \div 6$ **28.** $36 \div 4$ **29.** $42 \div 7$ **30.** $54 \div 6$

_____   _____   _____   _____

31. 18 is the dividend. 3 is the divisor.   **31.** _____
What is the quotient?

In 32–35, write *odd* or *even* for each number.

32. 67   **33.** 38   **34.** 49   **35.** 32

_____   _____   _____

**In 36–38, write whether each number is prime
or composite.**

36. 30   **37.** 17   **38.** 25

_____   _____   _____

39. Tania lives 5 blocks from school and 3 blocks
from the mall. How many blocks does she
travel to and from school in 5 days? Is there
too much or too little information to solve? _____

40. Art has 18 model cars and ships. He has 8 more   **40.** _____
cars than ships. How many cars does he have?

41. Explain Your Thinking How can you use patterns to tell
if your answer is reasonable when you multiply by 5?

_____

Give the letter of the correct answer.

1. How can this multiplication sentence, $2 \times 4 = \blacksquare$, be written as an addition sentence?

A $4 + 4 = \blacksquare$
C $2 + 2 = \blacksquare$
B $4 + 2 = \blacksquare$
D $2 \times 2 = \blacksquare$

1. _____

2. How can $10 + 10 + 10 = \blacksquare$ be written as a multiplication sentence?

A $10 \times 10 = \blacksquare$
C 30
B $3 \times 10 = \blacksquare$
D $30 \times 3 = \blacksquare$

2. _____

3. Girard has football practice 2 hours each day. Which number sentence gives the number of hours of football practice he will have in 5 days?

A $5 \times 5 = 25$
C $2 \times 7 = 14$
B $5 + 2 = 7$
D Not here

3. _____

4. Which number sentence describes the picture?

A $3 \times 4 = 12$
C $5 \times 3 = 15$
B $4 \times 5 = 20$
D Not here

4. _____

In 5–9, find the product.

5. 5×9

A 40   **B** 45   **C** 50   **D** 54

5. _____

6. 8×0

A 0   **B** 8   **C** 80   **D** 1

6. _____

7. 9×2

A 9   **B** 11   **C** 18   **D** 22

7. _____

8. 9×1

A 8   **B** 10   **C** 9   **D** 1

8. _____

9. 7×5

A 30   **B** 32   **C** 36   **D** Not here

9. _____

Name _____

In 10–16, find the product.

10. 9 × 4   10. _____

    A 32   **B** 45   **C** 27   **D** Not here

11. 8 × 3   11. _____

    A 27   **B** 24   **C** 32   **D** 40

12. 8 × 6   12. _____

    A 36   **B** 48   **C** 64   **D** 46

13. 9 × 7   13. _____

    A 63   **B** 56   **C** 49   **D** Not here

14. 9 × 8   14. _____

    A 78   **B** 68   **C** 72   **D** 48

15. 10 × 10   15. _____

    A 100   **B** 20   **C** 10   **D** 1

16. 11 × 10   16. _____

    A 111   **B** 110   **C** 100   **D** 101

17. One class made 11 trays of peanut butter   17. _____
sandwiches for a picnic lunch. Each tray had 12
sandwiches. How many sandwiches did they make?

    A 121 sandwiches   **B** 131 sandwiches
    C 132 sandwiches   **D** 144 sandwiches

18. Which multiplication fact can help you find 24 ÷ 2?   18. _____

    A 24 × 2   **B** 2 × 12   **C** 2 × 3   **D** 3 × 4

19. Which multiplication fact can help you find 54 ÷ 6?   19. _____

    A 6 × 6   **B** 6 × 9   **C** 6 × 8   **D** 9 × 4

20. If 24 dancers form 4 circles with an equal number of   20. _____
dancers in each, how many dancers are in each circle?

    A 4 dancers   **B** 8 dancers   **C** 5 dancers   **D** 6 dancers

Name _____

21. Which number sentence would be in the fact family for 3, 9, and 27?

    A $3 \times 9 = 27$ **B** $9 \times 9 = 81$
    C $9 \div 3 = 3$ **D** Not here

21. _____

22. Which number sentence would be in the fact family for 4, 7, and 28?

    A $28 \div 4 = 7$ **B** $4 \times 7 = 28$
    C $7 \times 4 = 28$ **D** All of these

22. _____

In 23–32, find the quotient.

23. $45 \div 5$

    A 40   **B** 8   **C** 9   **D** 5

23. _____

24. $9\overline{)81}$

    A 72   **B** 8   **C** 9   **D** 90

24. _____

25. $2\overline{)16}$

    A 2   **B** 4   **C** 8   **D** 16

25. _____

26. $42 \div 7$

    A 49   **B** 35   **C** 7   **D** 6

26. _____

27. $0 \div 8$

    A 8   **B** 0   **C** 1   **D** Not here

27. _____

28. $6 \div 1$

    A 6   **B** 1   **C** 0   **D** Not here

28. _____

29. $4\overline{)36}$

    A 8   **B** 9   **C** 7   **D** 6

29. _____

30. $3\overline{)24}$

    A 6   **B** 7   **C** 9   **D** 8

30. _____

31. $56 \div 7$

    A 9   **B** 7   **C** 8   **D** 6

31. _____

Name _____

32. $64 \div 8$

   A 8   **B** 9   **C** 7   **D** 6

32. _____

33. 6 is the divisor. 48 is the dividend. What is the quotient?

   A 42   **B** 8   **C** 54   **D** 7

33. _____

34. Which is an odd number?

   A 31   **B** 30   **C** 62   **D** 18

34. _____

35. Which is an even number?

   A 61   **B** 23   **C** 85   **D** Not here

35. _____

36. Starting with 12, what are the next 4 even numbers?

   A 12, 13, 14, 15, 16   **B** 12, 11, 10, 9, 8
   C 12, 2, 4, 6, 8   **D** 12, 14, 16, 18, 20

36. _____

37. What are all of the factors of 16?

   A 4×4 **B** 1×6
   C 1, 2, 4, 8, 16   **D** 1, 4, 4, 16

37. _____

38. Which is a prime number?

   A 10   **B** 11   **C** 4   **D** 22

38. _____

39. Which is a composite number?

   A 17   **B** 27   **C** 11   **D** 2

39. _____

40. Kyra brought 30 apples and oranges for the class field trip. She brought 4 more apples than oranges. How many apples did she bring?

   A 17 apples   **B** 26 apples
   C 20 apples   **D** 34 apples

40. _____

41. Kobe collects models. He has 10 red cars, 10 blue cars, and 12 red trucks. How many model cars does he have in all?

   A 10 model cars   **B** 12 model cars
   C 20 model cars   **D** 32 model cars

41. _____

Your class is going to work in 4 small groups to make bead jewelry for a craft fair. Each group will be given one of the boxes of beads below.

Box A	Box B	Box C	Box D
25 strings	18 strings	42 strings	24 strings
45 round beads	72 round beads	49 round beads	36 round beads
40 square beads	81 square beads	63 square beads	48 square beads

a. **Making Decisions** Each group will have a different number of students. In each group students share the materials equally, with no materials left over. Decide how many will be in each group. (Hint: Think about basic facts of multiplication. There is only one possible answer for each box of beads.)

b. **Recording Data** Make and complete a table like the one below.

Group	Number of students	Box	Strings for each student	Round beads for each student	Square beads for each student
A		A			
B		B			
C		C			
D		D			

c. **Analyzing Data** Use the answers in the table.

In which group did each member get the most string?

In which group did each member get the least string?

In which group did each member get the most round beads?

d. **Making Decisions** Suppose you wanted to sell the jewelry at a craft fair. How would you decide what to charge? You want to make a profit.

Teacher Notes

Concepts and Skills This activity requires students to:
- recognize fact families.
- record information in a table.
- make decisions using real-life experiences.
- find quotients for basic division facts.
- use factors.
- compare numbers.

Guiding Questions
- Suppose you have counters to represent strings, round beads, and square beads. For Box A, what number divides evenly into 25, 45, and 40?
- Each of 2 groups has 20 strings to divide equally among its members. Which group will get more string? A group with 5 people or one with 10 people? Explain.

Answers
a. Group A will have 5 students.
Group B will have 9 students.
Group C will have 7 students.
Group D will have 6 students.

b.

Group	Number of students	Box	Strings for each student	Round beads for each student	Square beads for each student
A	5	A	5	9	8
B	9	B	2	8	9
C	7	C	6	7	9
D	6	D	4	6	8

c. C; B; A
d. Explanations will vary.

Extension
Have groups decide on different quantities and supplies that will go in the boxes and repeat the activity.

Evaluation

Level	Standard to be achieved for performance of specified level
4	**Full Achievement** The student clearly understands factors and division and identifies the number of students for each group. All computations and comparisons are correct. Student explains how to make a profit by discussing costs of materials and selling prices. Student mentions that selling prices must be higher than costs.
3	**Substantial Achievement** The student clearly understands the concept of division. He or she may make some errors in using factors but can describe the process clearly. Most computations and comparisons are correct. Student mentions cost of materials and selling price.
2	**Partial Achievement** The student may understand the concept of division but makes many computational errors. He or she also may make errors when using factors and making comparisons. Student does not show an understanding of profit.
1	**Little Achievement** The student demonstrates little understanding of the task at hand. The student makes many computational errors, and the concept of comparing is not grasped. Student does not attempt to explain how to make profit.

Name _____

Date _____ Score _____

In 1–2, complete each number sentence.

1. ■ + ■ + ■ = ■   1. _____

2. ■ × ■ = ■   2. _____

3. If it costs $3 per person to visit a museum,   3. _____
   how much will a family of 5 have to pay?

   A $3   **B** $15   **C** $35   **D** Not here

In 4–15, find the product.

4. $\begin{array}{r} 9 \\ \times\ 3 \\ \hline \end{array}$

5. $\begin{array}{r} 8 \\ \times\ 4 \\ \hline \end{array}$

6. $\begin{array}{r} 9 \\ \times\ 6 \\ \hline \end{array}$

7. $\begin{array}{r} 8 \\ \times\ 7 \\ \hline \end{array}$

8. 8×8

9. 9×0

10. 8×2

11. 9×5

_____   _____   _____   _____

12. 7×9

13. 6×10

14. 9×12

15. 8×11

_____   _____   _____   _____

16. 0, 3, 6, 9, and 12 are the first 5 multiples of: 16. _____

   A 12   **B** 0   **C** 6   **D** 3

17. Which multiplication fact can help you find $48 \div 8$?   17. _____

   A $8 \times 8 = 64$ **B** $6 \times 6 = 36$
   C $8 \times 6 = 48$ **D** $48 \div 6 = 8$

18. Fourteen girls want to play volleyball at   18. _____
    recess. If they want 2 equal teams, how
    many girls will be on each team?

19. Write a fact family for this set of numbers: 3, 7, 21.

_____

20. List all the factors of 14.

20. _____

In 21–28, find the quotient.

21. $2\overline{)10}$　　　　**22.** $5\overline{)40}$　　　　**23.** $9\overline{)45}$　　　　**24.** $6\overline{)0}$

25. $24 \div 3$　　　　**26.** $20 \div 4$　　　　**27.** $36 \div 6$　　　　**28.** $32 \div 8$

_____　　　_____　　　_____　　　_____

29. Which number is an even number?

29. _____

　　A 32　　**B** 41　　**C** 67　　**D** 95

30. Which is a composite number?

30. _____

　　A 24　　**B** 37　　**C** 29　　**D** 13

31. Which is a prime number?

31. _____

　　A 64　　**B** 14　　**C** 57　　**D** 59

32. Decide if the problem has too much or too little information. Solve, if possible; then write *too much* or *too little*.

In a music contest, Uri earned a perfect score of 10 points. Kris scored 8 points, and Linda received 9 points. How many more points did Uri score than Curt?

_____

33. Lauren and Rod brought 11 cartons of juice to the class party. Lauren brought 3 fewer cartons than Rod. How many cartons did Rod bring?

33. _____

34. Performance Task Start with 10, and name the next 4 even numbers. Explain how you know which numbers are even.

_____

_____

Name _____

Date _____ Score _____

━ Computation ━

1. Find 4,728 + 794 + 2,021.

1. _____

In 2–9, find the product.

2.　8
　　× 5

3.　7
　　× 9

4.　5
　　× 2

5.　6
　　× 4

6. 9 × 3

7. 7 × 8

8. 11 × 11

9. 10 × 4

_____　　_____　　_____　　_____

In 10–17, find the quotient.

10. 9)‾81‾

11. 2)‾0‾

12. 5)‾5‾

13. 3)‾27‾

14. 64 ÷ 8

15. 36 ÷ 6

16. 40 ÷ 5

17. 6 ÷ 2

_____　　_____　　_____　　_____

━ Concepts ━

18. Which number sentence describes the array?

18. _____

A 3 + 6 = 9
B 3 × 5 = 15
C 6 + 6 = 12
D Not here

✻ ✻ ✻ ✻ ✻ ✻
✻ ✻ ✻ ✻ ✻ ✻
✻ ✻ ✻ ✻ ✻ ✻

19. Write a fact family for this set of numbers 7, 9, 63.

_____

In 20–21, use the coordinate grid.

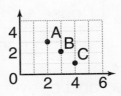

20. What letter is located at the ordered pair (3, 2)?

20. _____

21. What is the ordered pair at point *C*?

21. _____

Name _____

22. How would you write forty nine thousand, three hundred fifty-seven in standard form?

A 49,357   **B** 4,930,057
C 49,000,357   **D** 490,357

22. _____

23. Which multiplication fact can help you find 36 ÷ 4?

A 4 × 8 = 32   **B** 6 × 6 = 36
C 4 × 9 = 36   **D** Not here

23. _____

24. Is 23 a prime or composite number?

24. _____

25. Which term describes the middle number when the data are put in order?

A mode   **B** mean   **C** median   **D** range

25. _____

26. Round 78 to the nearest ten.

26. _____

━ Applications ━

27. Denise and 7 friends played 5 rap tapes and 3 rock tapes. How many tapes did they play in all? Is there too much or too little information to solve?

_____

28. Buster weighs 8 pounds more than Spot. Together they weigh 26 pounds. How much does Spot weigh?

28. _____

In 29–31, use the table.

Football Yards Rushed	
Hamilton High School	239 yd
Lincoln High School	235 yd
Roosevelt High School	241 yd
Washington High School	237 yd

29. Are the yards rushed odd or even numbers?

29. _____

30. How many yards did the schools rush in all?

30. _____

31. Order the yards rushed from greatest to least. _____

Vocabulary: In 1 and 2, match each with its meaning.

1. multiples of ten   **a.** data arranged in rows and columns   1. _____

2. array   **b.** 10, 20, 30, 40, and 50   2. _____

In 3–5, use a multiplication fact to help you find each product.

3. 6×40 3. _____

4. 7×80 4. _____

5. 3×90 5. _____

In 6 and 7, use patterns to find each product.

6. $5 \times 8 =$ _____ $5 \times 80 =$ _____ $5 \times 800 =$ _____

7. $4 \times 7 =$ _____ $4 \times 70 =$ _____ $4 \times 700 =$ _____

In 8–11, estimate each product.

8. 3×76 8. _____

9. 45×9 9. _____

10. 731×6 10. _____

11. 9×63 11. _____

In 12–13, find each product. Use the array to help.

12. $\begin{array}{r} 14 \\ \times\ 4 \\ \hline \end{array}$ 12. _____

13. $\begin{array}{r} 19 \\ \times\ 3 \\ \hline \end{array}$ 13. _____

In 1–8, find each product. Estimate to check.

1. 8×17

2. 5×74

3. 4×36

4. 6×58

5. $\begin{array}{r} 27 \\ \times\ 4 \\ \hline \end{array}$

6. $\begin{array}{r} 16 \\ \times\ 8 \\ \hline \end{array}$

7. $\begin{array}{r} 53 \\ \times\ 7 \\ \hline \end{array}$

8. $\begin{array}{r} 81 \\ \times\ 9 \\ \hline \end{array}$

In 9–16, multiply.

9. $\begin{array}{r} 307 \\ \times\ \ 5 \\ \hline \end{array}$

10. $\begin{array}{r} 416 \\ \times\ \ 7 \\ \hline \end{array}$

11. $\begin{array}{r} 809 \\ \times\ \ 3 \\ \hline \end{array}$

12. $\begin{array}{r} 723 \\ \times\ \ 6 \\ \hline \end{array}$

13. $\begin{array}{r} 7,000 \\ \times\ \ \ \ 5 \\ \hline \end{array}$

14. $\begin{array}{r} 3,006 \\ \times\ \ \ \ 8 \\ \hline \end{array}$

15. $\begin{array}{r} 2,468 \\ \times\ \ \ \ 3 \\ \hline \end{array}$

16. $\begin{array}{r} 9,034 \\ \times\ \ \ \ 4 \\ \hline \end{array}$

1. _____

2. _____

3. _____

4. _____

5. _____

6. _____

7. _____

8. _____

9. _____

10. _____

11. _____

12. _____

13. _____

14. _____

15. _____

16. _____

Name _____

Date _____ Score _____

In 1–3, find each product.

1. 4 × $1.45

2. 5 × $30.10

3. 7 × $42.85

In 4–7, use mental math to find each product.

4. 42 × 4

5. 9 × 51

6. 79 × 6

7. 7 × 38

In 8–10, find each product.

8. 4 × 5 × 9

9. 8 × 9 × 6

10. 6 × 11 × 3

1. _____

2. _____

3. _____

4. _____

5. _____

6. _____

7. _____

8. _____

9. _____

10. _____

In 11–12, write the factors in three different ways.

11. 4 × 7 × 5 _____

12. 2 × 8 × 6 _____

13. Cameron had $35.00. He bought two CDs for $13.50 each. How much money does he have left?

13. _____

14. A roll of nickels has 40 coins. Make a table to help you find the number of rolls you can make with 240 nickels.

14. _____

Number of rolls	1	2	3	4		
Number of nickels	40	80	120	160		

Name _____

Date _____ Score _____

Vocabulary: In 1–3, match each with its meaning.

1. product   **a.** data arranged in rows and columns   1. _____

2. array   **b.** multiplication answer   2. _____

3. factor   **c.** number being multiplied   3. _____

In 4-5, use a multiplication fact to help you find each product.

4. 8×20 4. _____

5. 9×70 5. _____

In 6–7, use patterns to find each product.

6. $7 \times 3 =$ _____ $7 \times 30 =$ _____ $7 \times 300 =$ _____

7. $5 \times 6 =$ _____ $5 \times 60 =$ _____ $5 \times 600 =$ _____

In 8–10, estimate each product.

8. 4×91 8. _____

9. 48×6 9. _____

10. 3×76 10. _____

11. Use the array to help you find the product.   11. _____

$$\begin{array}{r} 1\,7 \\ \times\ \ 4 \\ \hline \end{array}$$

In 12–14, find each product. Estimate to check.

12. 5×22 12. _____

13. 67×3 13. _____

14. 8×51 14. _____

Name _____

In 15–20, multiply.

15. $\begin{array}{r} 4\,1\,7 \\ \times\quad 9 \\ \hline \end{array}$

16. $\begin{array}{r} 3\,0\,7 \\ \times\quad 6 \\ \hline \end{array}$

17. $\begin{array}{r} 8,0\,0\,5 \\ \times\quad\quad 3 \\ \hline \end{array}$

18. $\begin{array}{r} 8,2\,0\,8 \\ \times\quad\quad 3 \\ \hline \end{array}$

19. $\begin{array}{r} \$3.7\,5 \\ \times\quad\quad 5 \\ \hline \end{array}$

20. $\begin{array}{r} \$1\,6.4\,1 \\ \times\quad\quad 6 \\ \hline \end{array}$

15. _____

16. _____

17. _____

18. _____

19. _____

20. _____

In 21-22, use mental math to multiply.

21. 5×52

22. 65×3

21. _____

22. _____

23. Write $4 \times 7 \times 5$ in three different ways. Then solve.

_____

24. Brenda and three friends went bowling. It cost each person $1.25 to rent shoes and $1.75 to play a game. They each bowled 2 games. How much did it cost the group altogether?

24. _____

25. Alice needs 48 plates. Plates come in packs of 8. Complete the table to find how many packs she needs.

25. _____

Number of packs	1	2	3			
Number of plates	8	16	24			

26. **Explain Your Thinking** Explain how multiplying money amounts is like multiplying whole numbers.

_____

_____

Vocabulary: In 1–3, match each with its meaning.

1. multiple   **a.** data arranged in rows and columns   1. _____

2. product   **b.** product of a given number and a whole number   2. _____

3. array   **c.** multiplication answer   3. _____

In 4–5, use a multiplication fact to help find each product.

4. 4×90 4. _____

5. 7×300 5. _____

In 6–7, use patterns to find each product.

6. $9 \times 3 =$ _____ $9 \times 30 =$ _____ $9 \times 300 =$ _____

7. $8 \times 5 =$ _____ $8 \times 50 =$ _____ $8 \times 500 =$ _____

In 8–10, estimate each product.

8. 6×82 8. _____

9. 57×6 9. _____

10. 3×48 10. _____

11. Use the array to help you find the product.   11. _____

$$\begin{array}{r} 1\,4 \\ \times\ 3 \\ \end{array}$$

In 12–14, find each product. Estimate to check.

12. 46×4 12. _____

13. 8×56 13. _____

14. 92×7 14. _____

Name _____

In 15–20, multiply.

15. $\begin{array}{r} 3\,2\,8 \\ \times\quad 7 \\ \hline \end{array}$

16. $\begin{array}{r} 5\,0\,2 \\ \times\quad 7 \\ \hline \end{array}$

17. $\begin{array}{r} 7{,}0\,6\,0 \\ \times\quad\quad 9 \\ \hline \end{array}$

18. $\begin{array}{r} 3{,}4\,0\,5 \\ \times\quad\quad 6 \\ \hline \end{array}$

19. $\begin{array}{r} \$6.3\,0 \\ \times\quad\quad 7 \\ \hline \end{array}$

20. $\begin{array}{r} \$1\,4.2\,4 \\ \times\quad\quad 8 \\ \hline \end{array}$

15. _____

16. _____

17. _____

18. _____

19. _____

20. _____

In 21–22, use mental math to find each product.

21. 5×73

22. 49×5

21. _____

22. _____

23. Write $2 \times 9 \times 5$ in three different ways. Then solve.

_____

24. Ray orders two medium cheese pizzas for $9.50 each and a large pepperoni pizza at $11.50. He uses a $3 coupon. How much does he need to pay?

24. _____

25. Brianna is planning a class party. She needs 150 napkins for the party. Napkins come in packs of 25. Complete the table to find how many packs of napkins she will need to buy.

25. _____

Number of packs	1	2	3			
Number of napkins	25	50	75			

26. **Explain Your Thinking** Explain why you place a decimal point in your answer when you multiply money amounts?

_____

_____

Name _____

Date _____   Score _____

Give the letter of the correct answer.

1. Use a multiplication fact to help you find 5×70.   1. _____

    A 360   **B** 350   **C** 420   **D** Not here

2. Use a multiplication fact to help you find 6×80.   2. _____

    A 540   **B** 560   **C** 480   **D** 380

3. Use patterns to find 5×900.   3. _____

    A 450   **B** 4,500   **C** 45,000   **D** Not here

4. Use patterns to find 8×500.   4. _____

    A 4,000   **B** 40,000   **C** 400   **D** Not here

5. Use patterns to find $7 \times 7,000$.   5. _____

    A 490   **B** 4,900   **C** 49,000   **D** Not here

6. Estimate the product of 37×8.   6. _____

    A 240   **B** 280   **C** 320   **D** 360

7. Estimate the product of 7×548.   7. _____

    A 350   **B** 3,500   **C** 4,200   **D** Not here

8. Estimate the product of 528 and 6.   8. _____

    A 3,000   **B** 3,600   **C** 30,000   **D** 5,000

9. Which describes the array?   9. _____

    A 3×16 **B** 3×17 **C** 4×16 **D** Not here

Name _____

10. Which describes the array?

    A 14 × 5 **B** 15 × 4 **C** 124 × 6 **D** Not here

In 11–23, multiply.

11.   2 8
    ×   4

    A 102   **B** 122   **C** 116   **D** Not here

12.   8 5
    ×   4

    A 320   **B** 380   **C** 340   **D** 260

13.   7 3
    ×   9

    A 657   **B** 637   **C** 587   **D** 747

14.   2 1 5
    ×   4

    A 840   **B** 850   **C** 860   **D** Not here

15.   3 0 6
    ×   7

    A 2,142   **B** 2,212   **C** 2,842   **D** Not here

16.   6 3 8
    ×   8

    A 5,104   **B** 5,004   **C** 4,834   **D** Not here

17.   7,0 0 8
    ×   6

    A 42,048   **B** 4,248   **C** 42,408   **D** 42,480

10. _____

11. _____

12. _____

13. _____

14. _____

15. _____

16. _____

17. _____

Continued

Name _____

18.   5,3 0 6
    $\times$ 6

A 30,836   **B** 31,836   **C** 31,216   **D** Not here

18. _____

19.   2,4 3 5
    $\times$ 3

A 6,305   **B** 7,295   **C** 7,315   **D** Not here

19. _____

20. $6.3 9
    $\times$ 4

A $24.56   **B** $25.36   **C** $25.56   **D** Not here

20. _____

21. $5 0.2 5
    $\times$ 4

A $200.10   **B** $201.00   **C** $210.00   **D** Not here

21. _____

22. $6 5.4 9
    $\times$ 8

A $523.92   **B** $513.92   **C** $523.82   **D** Not here

22. _____

23. $1 4.7 5
    $\times$ 7

A $113.25   **B** $93.25   **C** $103.25   **D** Not here

23. _____

24. Use mental math to find 9 $\times$ 31.

A 279   **B** 289   **C** 299   **D** Not here

24. _____

25. Use mental math to find 72 $\times$ 5.

A 350   **B** 360   **C** 310   **D** Not here

25. _____

26. Use mental math to find 4 $\times$ 41.

A 160   **B** 174   **C** 164   **D** Not here

26. _____

27. Find the product of (4 $\times$ 25) $\times$ 7.

A 100   **B** 175   **C** 700   **D** 675

27. _____

Name _____

28. Find the product of 8 × (5 × 4).   **28.** _____

    A 160   **B** 1,600   **C** 200   **D** Not here

29. Find the product of 60 × 5 × 6.   **29.** _____

    A 18,000   **B** 1,800   **C** 306   **D** Not here

30. Find the product of 50 × 6 × 3.   **30.** _____

    A 900   **B** 800   **C** 1,200   **D** Not here

31. Find the product of 9 × 3 × 3.   **31.** _____

    A 270   **B** 81   **C** 91   **D** Not here

32. Mary bought 3 pens at $1.29 each. She gave the   **32.** _____
clerk a $20 bill. How much change will she receive?

    A $3.87   **B** $18.71   **C** $16.13   **D** Not here

33. Patty orders 4 books from the book fair. Two books   **33.** _____
are $3.50 each. The other two books are each
$3.95. How much money does she need to pay
for the books?

    A $7.00   **B** $7.80   **C** $14.90   **D** Not here

34. Victoria has her collection of pewter animals on   **34.** _____
shelves in her room. Each shelf has 6 animals. Use
the table to help you find how many shelves she
uses to display her collection of 36 pewter animals.

Number of shelves	1	2	3	4		
Number of animals	6	12	18	24		

    A 6 shelves   **B** 9 shelves   **C** 12 shelves   **D** Not here

35. A roll of quarters costs $10. Use the table to help   **35.** _____
you find the number of quarters in a roll.

Number of quarters	4	8	16	24		
Number of dollars	1	2	4	6		

    A 40 quarters   **B** 36 quarters   **C** 32 quarters   **D** Not here

These groups will represent your school on Community Appreciation Day: 4 first graders, 5 second graders, 6 third graders, 7 fourth graders, and 8 fifth graders. You have been asked to schedule each group to visit one of the places listed below. Each group will visit a different place.

Place	Entrance Fee
City Hall	No cost
History Museum	$2 per student
Library	No cost
Art Museum	$3 per student
Planetarium	$10 per group

During the visit, each student is to choose 7 postcards costing $0.25 each to take back to class for a display. Lunch will cost $2.58 per student.

a. Making Decisions What would be a good way to select the students that will represent the school? Decide which group will visit each location.

b. Recording Data Copy and complete a table like the one below.

Grade	Number of Students	Place Visited	Cost of Postcards	Cost of Lunch	Total Cost of Visit

c. Analyzing Data How many postcards did the first graders and second graders buy in all? How many were bought by all 5 groups?

Which group spent the most money on its visit? The least money? What is the median cost per group?

d. Critical Thinking Suppose you want to spend the least amount of money possible. How would you decide which of the groups should be sent to each of the locations?

e. Making Decisions Suppose you only have $150 to spend. Could your entire class attend the event you chose for the fourth-grade group? If not, what could you do to make the trip happen for all fourth graders?

Teacher Notes

Concepts and Skills This activity requires students to:
- record data in a table.
- make decisions using real-life experiences.
- find products.
- find sums.
- explore budgeting.

Guiding Questions
- When deciding where to go, is the art museum a better choice for younger or older students? Explain.
- What operation can you use to find the cost for each person's lunch? The cost for 7 post cards?
- How much will it cost for the first graders to go to the history museum? [$8] Will the cost be greater or less than the cost for the fifth graders? [Less]

Answers
a. Decisions will vary.
b. Answers will vary.
c. 63 postcards; 210 postcards; Other answers will vary depending on the places selected and the number of students in the grade.
d. One way to cut costs is to send the group with the most members to the places where the entrance fee is the cheapest.
e. Answers will vary. A class of 30 students will spend $52.50 on postcards and $77.40 on lunch. So the choice of visiting city hall, the library, or the planetarium would keep the cost under budget.

Extension
Have students use a map to locate each of the places listed, either in your town or the city nearest your location. Then ask if that would change their decision about which group would visit each place.

Evaluation

Level	Standard to be achieved for performance of specified level
4	**Full Achievement** The student accurately and completely fills out the table and analyzes the data. The decision of whether or not the entire class can make the trip and what, if any, changes are needed to make the trip possible is clearly and concisely written with logical recommendations.
3	**Substantial Achievement** The student completes the table with only minor computational errors. The decision of whether or not the entire class can make the trip is well written with only minor discrepancies.
2	**Partial Achievement** The student has some difficulty completing the table and several computational errors were made. The reasons for deciding that the class can make the trip (or not make the trip) are incomplete or unclear.
1	**Little Achievement** The student needs help in completing the table and analyzing the data. The computation contains many errors. The student makes very little attempt to decide whether or not the entire fourth-grade class can make the trip and fails to find any of the requested costs.

In 1–3 find each product.

1. 7 × 40

1. _____

2. 9 × 2 = _____   9 × 20 = _____   9 × 200 = _____

3. 8 × 5 = _____   8 × 50 = _____   8 × 500 = _____

4. Estimate the product of 46 × 5.

4. _____

    A 200   **B** 225   **C** 250   **D** None of these

5. Estimate the product of 663 and 8.

5. _____

    A 5,600   **B** 8,000   **C** 4,800   **D** 4,200

6. Use the array to help you find the product.

6. _____

$$
\begin{array}{r}
1\,9 \\
\times\ \ 3 \\
\end{array}
$$

In 7–14, find each product.

7.
$$
\begin{array}{r}
7 \\
\times\ 5 \\
\end{array}
$$

8.
$$
\begin{array}{r}
8\,4 \\
\times\ \ 7 \\
\end{array}
$$

7. _____

8. _____

9.
$$
\begin{array}{r}
2\,3\,8 \\
\times\ \ \ \ 4 \\
\end{array}
$$

10.
$$
\begin{array}{r}
9\,0\,3 \\
\times\ \ \ \ 4 \\
\end{array}
$$

9. _____

10. _____

11. 6 × 3,025

11. _____

    A 18,150   **B** 1,815   **C** 18,050   **D** Not here

12. 3 × 5,429

12. _____

    A 17,187   **B** 15,287   **C** 16,387   **D** 16,287

13.
$$
\begin{array}{r}
\$4.8\,5 \\
\times\ \ \ \ \ 6 \\
\end{array}
$$

14.
$$
\begin{array}{r}
\$2\,0.1\,9 \\
\times\ \ \ \ \ \ 4 \\
\end{array}
$$

13. _____

14. _____

Name _____

In 15–16, use mental math to find each product.

15. 8 × 72   15. _____

16. 5 × 43   16. _____

17. Write 8 × 7 × 6 in three different ways. Then solve.

_____

18. Brittany buys a picture frame for $12.95, a   18. _____
card for $1.75, and wrapping paper for $1.95.
How much change will she receive from $20?

19. Rasheem picked 25 bushels of apples on   19. _____
Thursday and 36 bushels on Friday. On
Saturday, he sold 49 bushels to tourists.
How many bushels did he have left to sell?

20. Each token at the batting cages is good for   20. _____
15 pitches. How many tokens are needed
for 120 pitches?

Number of tokens	1	2	3					
Number of pitches	15	30	45					

21. Carlotta mixes 1 drop of blue paint with   21. _____
3 drops of yellow paint to get a green color.
How many drops of blue will she add if she
has 21 drops of yellow?

Drops of blue	1	2	3	4			
Drops of yellow	3	6	9	12			

22. Performance Task Explain how you would use mental
math to find 8 × 39.

_____

_____

— Computation —

1. 5 × 70

1. _____

2. Estimate the product of 7 × 29.

2. _____

3. Use patterns to find each product.

8 × 4 = _____   80 × 4 = _____   800 × 4 = _____

4. Use the array to help you find the product.

4. _____

3 × 18

5. Find the product of 7 and 75.

5. _____

A 425   **B** 525   **C** 625   **D** 455

6. Find the product of 9 and 806.

6. _____

A 7,254   **B** 7,245   **C** 6,454   **D** 5,472

7. Multiply: 4 × $32.72.

7. _____

A $140.88   **B** $120.88   **C** $130.08   **D** $130.88

8. Find the number of hours in 1 week.
(Hint: 1 day = 24 hours and 1 week = 7 days)

8. _____

9. Find the elapsed time between 3:45 P.M.
and 6:05 P.M.

9. _____

A 3 hours 40 minutes   **B** 3 hours 20 minutes
C 2 hours 30 minutes   **D** 2 hours 20 minutes

— Concepts —

10. Is 5 × 2,910 greater than or less than 15,000?

10. _____

11. Is 79 × 6 greater than or less than 480?

11. _____

12. Is 63 × 9 greater than or less than 540?

12. _____

Name _____

13. What do the parentheses in $(2 \times 5) \times 12$ tell you?

13. _____

_____

14. Which of the following will help you find the product $4 \times 9 \times 5$ mentally?

14. _____

A $(4 \times 5) \times 9$ **B** $(4 \times 9) \times 5$
C $4 \times (9 \times 5)$ **D** $4 \times (5 \times 9)$

15. Which is the number that occurs most often in a set of data?

15. _____

A Average   **B** Median   **C** Mode   **D** Range

16. Which is the middle number in a set of data when the data are in order?

16. _____

A Average   **B** Median   **C** Mode   **D** Range

17. Which number is less, 38,767 or 37,984?

17. _____

18. Which number is greater, 473,910 or 476,901?

18. _____

━━ Applications ━━

19. Jake's weekly allowance is $3.50. He has saved all his allowance for 4 weeks. How much will he have left if he spends $5.50 on a book?

19. _____

A $14.00   **B** $19.50   **C** $8.50   **D** $9.50

20. Jared buys a model car for $4.95 and a model airplane for $5.55. He gives the clerk $20. How much change will he receive?

20. _____

A $14.00   **B** $19.50   **C** $8.50   **D** $9.50

21. Tickets to the amusement park cost $12. How much would it cost for a group of 12 scouts to buy tickets for the amusement park during a "Buy One, Get One Free" sale?

21. _____

Number of tickets	2	4	6			
Cost	$12	$24	$36			

Vocabulary: In 1–3, match each with its definition.

1. multiple

a. the number obtained after multiplying

1. _____

2. product

b. numbers that are multiplied together to obtain a product

2. _____

3. factors

c. the product of a given whole number and any other whole number

3. _____

In 4–5, use patterns to find each product.

4. $40 \times 3 =$ _____

$40 \times 30 =$ _____

$40 \times 300 =$ _____

$40 \times 3,000 =$ _____

5. $50 \times 8 =$ _____

$50 \times 80 =$ _____

$50 \times 800 =$ _____

$50 \times 8,000 =$ _____

In 6–8, estimate each product.

6. 32×26

7. 34×47

8. 78×62

6. _____

7. _____

8. _____

In 9–14, find each product.

9. 54×50

10. 63×30

11. 85×70

12. 36×23

13. 27×45

14. $\begin{array}{r} 47 \\ \times\,19 \\ \hline \end{array}$

15. $\begin{array}{r} 38 \\ \times\,22 \\ \hline \end{array}$

9. _____

10. _____

11. _____

12. _____

13. _____

14. _____

15. _____

In 1–5, find each product.

  1. 17×18

  2. 24×15

  3. 34×22

  4.   44   **5.**   29
      $\times 39$ $\times 56$

  6. Multiply 36 and 51.

In 7–11, estimate each product.

  7. 284×25

  8. 416×72

  9. 809×33

  10. 316×43

  11. 249×71

In 12–16, find each product.

  12. $26 \times 2,431$

  13. $45 \times 2,075$

  14. $15 \times 1,324$

  15.   3,625   **16.**   4,507
     $\times$ 63 $\times$ 41

  17. Multiply 1,438 and 43.

  18. An orchard has 76 trees in each row. How many trees are in 45 rows?

1. _____

2. _____

3. _____

4. _____

5. _____

6. _____

7. _____

8. _____

9. _____

10. _____

11. _____

12. _____

13. _____

14. _____

15. _____

16. _____

17. _____

18. _____

In 1–8, find each product.

1. $1 0.4 5
    × 1 2

2. $3 0.7 5
    × 5 2

3. $3 5.0 9
    × 1 7

4. $4 1.5 5
    × 2 1

5. 15 × $8.75

6. 14 × $26.60

7. 25 × $17.23

8. 46 × $29.34

1. _____

2. _____

3. _____

4. _____

5. _____

6. _____

7. _____

8. _____

In 9, decide if you should overestimate or underestimate. Solve.

9. Joe's new tires need to be rotated every 6,000 miles. He drives about 298 miles every week. Will he need to rotate the tires in 18 weeks? Explain.

_____

_____

In 10–11, you can draw a picture to help you solve each problem.

10. The tallest plants in Dorothy's garden are in the 2 back rows. The midsized plants are in the 2 middle rows. The shortest plants are in the front 3 rows. There are 10 plants in each row. How many plants are in her garden?

10. _____

11. Anfernee counted 5 posts on each side of a square garden. If there is a post in each corner, how many posts are there in all?

11. _____

Vocabulary: In 1–3, match each with its meaning.

1. factors

a. the number obtained after multiplying

1. _____

2. multiple

b. numbers that are multiplied together to obtain a product

2. _____

3. product

c. the product of a given whole number and any other whole number

3. _____

In 4–7, use patterns to find each product.

4. $70 \times 8 =$ _____

$70 \times 80 =$ _____

$70 \times 800 =$ _____

$70 \times 8,000 =$ _____

6. $40 \times 7 =$ _____

$40 \times 70 =$ _____

$40 \times 700 =$ _____

$40 \times 7,000 =$ _____

5. $50 \times 4 =$ _____

$50 \times 40 =$ _____

$50 \times 400 =$ _____

$50 \times 4,000 =$ _____

7. $90 \times 5 =$ _____

$90 \times 50 =$ _____

$90 \times 500 =$ _____

$90 \times 5,000 =$ _____

In 8-14, estimate each product.

8. 84×23

9. 66×56

10. 29×78

11. 53×67

12. 246×58

13. 709×88

14. 395×31

8. _____

9. _____

10. _____

11. _____

12. _____

13. _____

14. _____

Name _____

In 15–24, find each product.

15.	72 ×30		**16.**	53 ×80	**15.**	_____

16. _____

17.	41 ×28		**18.**	57 ×43	**17.**	_____

18. _____

19. 95 × 32   **19.** _____

20. 42 × 39   **20.** _____

21. 32 × 1,247   **21.** _____

22. 2,371 × 16   **22.** _____

23. 15 × $14.95   **23.** _____

24. 12 × $24.08   **24.** _____

In 25, decide if you should overestimate or underestimate. Solve.

25. Marty plans to deposit $4.50 into his bank account each week. Estimate to see if he will have saved $50 to pay for a computer game at the end of 21 weeks.

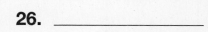

In 26, draw a picture to help you solve each problem.

26. Larry is in a bike race. There are 12 bikes in each row. There are 4 rows in front of him and 8 rows behind him. How many racers are there in all?   **26.** _____

27. Explain Your Thinking Describe the steps you would follow to find the product of 1,258 and 47.

Name _____

Date _____ Score _____

Vocabulary: In 1–3, match each with its meaning.

1. multiple

    a. numbers that are multiplied together to obtain a product

1. _____

2. product

    b. the product of a given whole number and any other whole number

2. _____

3. factors

    c. the answer in multiplication

3. _____

In 4–7, use patterns to find each product.

4. $80 \times 6 =$ _____

    $80 \times 60 =$ _____

    $80 \times 600 =$ _____

    $80 \times 6,000 =$ _____

5. $60 \times 5 =$ _____

    $60 \times 50 =$ _____

    $60 \times 500 =$ _____

    $60 \times 5,000 =$ _____

6. $90 \times 8 =$ _____

    $90 \times 80 =$ _____

    $90 \times 800 =$ _____

    $90 \times 8,000 =$ _____

7. $30 \times 9 =$ _____

    $30 \times 90 =$ _____

    $30 \times 900 =$ _____

    $30 \times 9,000 =$ _____

In 8–14, estimate each product.

8. 56×22

9. 49×63

10. 73×58

11. 34×94

12. 376×78

13. 298×66

14. 345×28

8. _____

9. _____

10. _____

11. _____

12. _____

13. _____

14. _____

Name _____

In 15–24, find each product.

15.   6 4
       × 2 0

16.   8 5
       × 5 0

17.   3 2
       × 5 3

18.   6 5
       × 3 4

19. 46 × 85

20. 56 × 36

21. 1,328 × 32

22. 2,485 × 19

23. $20.95 × 12

24. $15.05 × 19

15. _____

16. _____

17. _____

18. _____

19. _____

20. _____

21. _____

22. _____

23. _____

24. _____

In 25, decide if you should overestimate or underestimate. Solve.

25. Billy Bob needs to buy 5 notebooks. Each notebook costs $1.75. Estimate to see how much money he needs to give to the clerk.

_____

In 26, draw a picture to help you solve the problem.

26. Gina is in a charity fun run. She is in the seventh row. Altogether there are 15 rows with 14 runners in each row. How many runners are in the rows behind her?

26.

27. Explain Your Thinking Describe the steps you would follow to find the product of 3,425 and 46.

_____

_____

Give the letter of the correct answer.

1. Find the product of 30 × 40.

   A 120   **B** 1,200   **C** 12,000   **D** Not here

1. _____

2. Find the product of 60 × 400.

   A 24,000   **B** 2,400   **C** 240   **D** 240,000

2. _____

3. Find the product of 40 × 7,000.

   A 28,000   **B** 27,000   **C** 2,800,000   **D** Not here

3. _____

In 4–11, estimate each product.

4. 51 × 26

   A 150   **B** 1,500   **C** 15,000   **D** 1,000

4. _____

5. 38 × 82

   A 3,200   **B** 2,400   **C** 32,000   **D** Not here

5. _____

6. 57 × 48

   A 1,600   **B** 2,500   **C** 3,000   **D** Not here

6. _____

7. 24 × 76

   A 14,000   **B** 16,000   **C** 1400   **D** Not here

7. _____

8. 406 × 58

   A 2,400   **B** 24,000   **C** 240,000   **D** Not here

8. _____

9. 683 × 78

   A 42,000   **B** 49,000   **C** 48,000   **D** 56,000

9. _____

10. 947 × 56

   A 45,000   **B** 54,000   **C** 50,000   **D** 60,000

10. _____

11. 358 × 41

   A 12,000   **B** 16,000   **C** 20,000   **D** 15,000

11. _____

Name _____

In 12–26, find each product.

12. 27 × 80

    A 2,160   **B** 2,060   **C** 216   **D** Not here

12. _____

13. 42 × 70

    A 294   **B** 1,940   **C** 2,940   **D** Not here

13. _____

14. 35 × 24

    A 740   **B** 850   **C** 840   **D** Not here

14. _____

15. 29 × 31

    A 116   **B** 699   **C** 899   **D** Not here

15. _____

16.   4 6
    × 5 3

    A 2,538   **B** 3,438   **C** 2,448   **D** Not here

16. _____

17.   4 2
    × 3 7

    A 1,600   **B** 1,554   **C** 1,454   **D** 2,554

17. _____

18.   2 5
    × 4 5

    A 1,025   **B** 1,125   **C** 1,325   **D** Not here

18. _____

Name _____

19. 370 × 25

    A 9,250   **B** 8,950   **C** 2,590   **D** Not here

19. _____

20. 2,460 × 16

    A 38,360   **B** 49,360   **C** 39,360   **D** Not here

20. _____

21. 3,289
    ×   32

    A 105,248   **B** 115,248   **C** 125,248   **D** Not here

21. _____

22. 2,073
    ×   35

    A 62,555   **B** 72,455   **C** 72,555   **D** Not here

22. _____

23. $4.04 × 15

    A $24.24   **B** $60.60   **C** $61.60   **D** Not here

23. _____

24. $5.19 × 27

    A $46.71   **B** $139.13   **C** $373.68   **D** Not here

24. _____

25. $30.75
    ×   22

    A $676.50   **B** $686.50   **C** $776.50   **D** Not here

25. _____

26. $6.41
    ×   18

    A $115.38   **B** $125.38   **C** $116.38   **D** Not here

26. _____

Name _____

27. You are planning a field trip to a zoo. The admission is $3.45 per student. Would you overestimate or underestimate the total cost of admission for 28 students?

A Overestimate   **B** Underestimate

27. _____

28. You are planning to use 12 feet of ribbon on each of 26 costumes. Would you overestimate or underestimate how much ribbon to buy?

A Overestimate   **B** Underestimate

28. _____

29. Vanessa counted 8 rows of seats in front of her row, 6 rows of seats behind her row, 3 seats to her right and 3 seats to her left. Every row has the same number of seats. How many seats are in the theater? You can draw a picture to help you.

A 20 seats   **B** 848 seats   **C** 98 seats   **D** Not here

29. _____

30. The first 6 pages of Matt's album are filled with baseball cards. The last 7 pages are filled with basketball cards. There are 3 blank pages in the middle. Each page can hold 4 sports cards. How many cards can the album hold in all? You can draw a picture to help you.

A 64 cards   **B** 504 cards   **C** 12 cards   **D** Not here

30. _____

31. Bike racers line up in rows. There are 14 racers in each row. There are 4 rows in front of Jessica and 12 rows behind her. How many racers are in the rows behind her? You can draw a picture to help you.

A 56 racers   **B** 168 racers   **C** 238 racers   **D** Not here

31. _____

You are helping complete an order for the school store. You will be ordering paper, pencils, and painting supplies.

```
1 dozen = 12
1 gross = 12 dozen, or 144
1 ream = 500 sheets
```

a. Making Decisions Think about how many students are in your grade at school. Estimate how many pencils, paintbrushes, sheets of paper, and bottles of tempera paint are needed for the school year. Record your estimates in the first column of the table below.

b. Recording Data Copy and complete the order form.

	Estimated number of items needed	Number per box	Number of boxes	Cost per box	Total cost
Pencils				$2.69	
Paintbrushes				$4.00	
Sheets of paper				$24.35	
Tempera paint				$18.27	

c. Analyzing Data

How many pencils are in one box?
How many paintbrushes are in one box?
How many sheets of paper are in one box?
What is the total cost of all the items you are ordering?

d. Explain Your Thinking

Explain how you decided how many of each item to order.

e. Making Decisions Suppose your are ordering items for the entire school. How will you change your order? Explain. Estimate the total cost for the new amounts ordered.

Teacher Notes

Concepts and Skills This activity requires students to:
- record data in a table.
- make decisions using real-life experiences.
- estimate amounts of school items needed.
- find sums.
- find products.

Guiding Questions
- Suppose there are 100 children in your class. About how many pencils do you think they will use in one school year?
- How will you find the numbers for the Total Cost column?
- How will you find the total cost of all the items you ordered?

Answers
a. Estimates will vary.
b. Answers will vary. Check students' computations.
c. There are 144 pencils in one box. There are 30 paint brushes in one box. There are 500 sheets of paper in one box. Answers concerning total cost will vary depending on the estimates of number of items needed.
d. Explanations will vary.
e. Answers will vary.

Extension
Have students make a list that shows how many sheets of paper they use each day in each class. Then have them estimate how much paper they use in a school year. Is it more than a ream of paper? More than two reams of paper? Encourage them to compare their figures with the estimates used in the project.

Evaluation

Level	Standard to be achieved for performance of specified level
4	**Full Achievement** The student completes the table accurately making no computational errors. The total estimated cost for the school is reasonable.
3	**Substantial Achievement** The student completes the table, making only minor computational errors. The total estimated cost for the school is reasonable.
2	**Partial Achievement** The student has some difficulty with the multiplication and addition of whole numbers and decimals and completes the table, making many computational errors. The explanation of how they decided how to order for their class and for the whole school is not well written. The total estimated cost for the school is not reasonable.
1	**Little Achievement** The student needs help in completing the table and makes many computational errors. The total estimated cost for the school either is not completed at all or is not reasonable.

Name _____

Date _____ Score _____

In 1–2, use patterns to find each product.

1. 60 × 2 = _____

60 × 20 = _____

60 × 200 = _____

60 × 2,000 = _____

2. 80 × 3 = _____

80 × 30 = _____

80 × 300 = _____

80 × 300 = _____

In 3–6, estimate each product.

3. 34 × 58

A 1,500   **B** 2,400   **C** 1,800   **D** 2,000

4. 75 × 37

A 2,100   **B** 3,200   **C** 2,400   **D** 2,800

5. 54 × 239

6. 44 × 365

3. _____

4. _____

5. _____

6. _____

In 7–17, find each product.

7. 63 × 70

8. 48 × 30

9. 3 8
     × 1 5

A 228   **B** 470   **C** 560   **D** 570

10. 8 4
      × 3 1

A 2,604   **B** 336   **C** 2,504   **D** Not here

11. 2 3
      × 4 3

A 889   **B** 989   **C** 161   **D** 999

7. _____

8. _____

9. _____

10. _____

11. _____

Continued

Name _____

12. 5 4
    × 2 7   12. _____

    A 586 **B** 1,358 **C** 2,458 **D** Not here

13. 3,141 × 16   13. _____

    A 50,256 **B** 49,256 **C** 60,256 **D** Not here

14. 5,0 2 0
    ×   2 5   14. _____

    A 17,187 **B** 35,140 **C** 125,500 **D** Not here

15. $2.94 × 35   15. _____

    A $101.90 **B** $2,352 **C** $92.90 **D** Not here

16. $2.2 6
    ×   2 4   16. _____

17. $1 2.2 7
    ×   1 1   17. _____

18. Jack earns some money each time he   18. _____
    mows the lawn. He plans to save for a
    new bike. Should Jack overestimate or
    underestimate how much he will earn to
    be sure he has enough money?

19. The school band stands on steps for the
    yearbook picture. Each row has 11 band   19. _____
    members. There are 11 rows. Jean is
    exactly in the middle of the picture. Which
    row is she standing in? You can draw a
    picture to help.

20. **Performance Task** Explain how you would estimate the
    product of 283 × 54.

    _____

    _____

    _____

— Computation —

In 1–2, use patterns to find each product.

1. 50 × 8 = _____

 50 × 80 = _____

 50 × 800 = _____

 50 × 8,000 = _____

2. 70 × 2 = _____

 70 × 20 = _____

 70 × 200 = _____

 70 × 200 = _____

In 3–4, estimate each product.

3. 48 × 72

4. 353 × 47

 A 2,000   **B** 20,000
 C 15,000   **D** Not here

3. _____

4. _____

In 5–9, find each product.

5. 38 × 70

6. 45 × 27

 A 1,315   **B** 1,205
 C 1,215   **D** Not here

7. 5 6
 × 3 3
 _____

 A 1,748   **B** 2,984
 C 1,948   **D** Not here

8. 3,042 × 23

 A 69,966   **B** 68,966
 C 70,966   **D** Not here

9. Find 12 × $30.89.

10. Find 2,503 − 956.

11. Find 29 + 46 + 38.

5. _____

6. _____

7. _____

8. _____

9. _____

10. _____

11. _____

Name _____

— Concepts —

12. Write twenty-nine thousand, ten in standard form.

12. _____

13. Give the value of 8 in 4,850,732.

13. _____

14. Round 4,149 to the nearest thousand.

A 4,000   **B** 5,000   **C** 4,200   **D** 4,100

14. _____

15. Is your bedtime 9:00 A.M. or 9:00 P.M.?

15. _____

16. Which of the following will help you find the product $6 \times 9 \times 5$ mentally?

A $(6 \times 5) \times 9$ **B** $(6 \times 9) \times 5$
C $6 \times (9 \times 5)$ **D** $6 \times (5 \times 9)$

16. _____

— Applications —

17. A van's gas tank holds 14 gallons of gasoline. The van travels about 28 miles per gallon. You need to know how far the van can travel before stopping for more gasoline. Would it be better to overestimate or underestimate the driving distance? Explain.

_____

18. The chorus was arranged on steps in 12 rows of 10 singers. Nicole is in the row below the top row. How many singers are in the rows lower than Nicole? You can draw a picture to help.

18. _____

19. Gerald runs 2 miles every day. On Tuesday, he practices the piano for 40 minutes. How many miles will he run in one week?

19. _____

Name _____

Date _____ Score _____

Give the letter of the correct answer.

In 1–2, use the bar graph.

1. Which subject was chosen by the most students?

   A Math
   B Language Arts
   C Social Studies
   D Science

1. _____

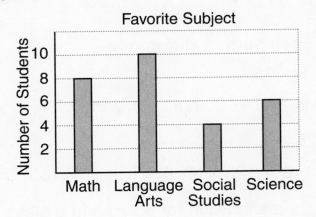

Favorite Subject

2. How many more students chose Language Arts than chose Science?

   A 2 students   **B** 4 students   **C** 6 students   **D** students

2. _____

3. What is the range for this set of data?
   3, 4, 9, 8, 5, 8, 8, 2, 2

   A 5   **B** 7   **C** 8   **D** Not here

3. _____

4. The sum of two numbers is 22. Their difference is 6. Which is the larger number?

   A 14   **B** 16   **C** 18   **D** Not here

4. _____

5. Give the standard form for one hundred forty-five thousand, three hundred six.

   A 145,000,306   **B** 145,360   **C** 145,306   Not here

5. _____

6. Which list shows the numbers in order from least to greatest?

   A 245, 542, 452
   C 542, 245, 452
   B 452, 245. 542
   D 245, 452, 542

6. _____

7. Find the elapsed time from 2:35 P.M. to 3:15 P.M.

   A 1 hour 20 minutes
   C 45 minutes
   B 40 minutes
   D 1 hour 10 minutes

7. _____

Name _____

8. Kim has a total of 35 cents. She only has nickels and dimes. How many combinations of coins can she make?

    A 1 way   **B** 2 ways
    C 3 ways   **D** 4 ways

8. _____

In 9–10, find each sum or difference.

9. $489 + 351 + 75$

    A 705   **B** 805   **C** 915   **D** 715

9. _____

10. $7,039 - 254$

    A 6,785   **B** 7,125   **C** 6,975   **D** 7,185

10. _____

11. Dick bought a sandwich for $5.75 and a glass of juice for $2.19. How much change will he receive from a ten-dollar bill?

    A $3.94   **B** $7.84   **C** $3.16   **D** $2.06

11. _____

12. Which comparison is correct?

    A $13.74 < $13.47   **B** $13.75 = $13.47
    C $13.74 > $13.47   **D** Not here

12. _____

13. A CD costs $12.99 and a cassette tape costs $3.50. Do you need an exact answer or an estimate to see if $20 is enough money to buy both items?

    A Exact answer   **B** Estimate

13. _____

In 14–19, find the product.

14. 3×8

    A 11   **B** 18   **C** 21   **D** Not here

14. _____

15. 7×6

    A 49   **B** 42   **C** 36   **D** Not here

15. _____

16. 4×7

    A 27   **B** 21   **C** 28   **D** Not here

16. _____

Continued

Name _____

17. 9×8

    A 64   **B** 72   **C** 81   **D** Not here

17. _____

18. 3×4

    A 7   **B** 15   **C** 12   **D** Not here

18. _____

19. 6×9

    A 63   **B** 56   **C** 54   **D** Not here

19. _____

In 20–25, find the quotient.

20. $4 \div 1$

    A 5   **B** 4   **C** 3   **D** Not here

20. _____

21. $12 \div 4$

    A 3   **B** 8   **C** 4   **D** 16

21. _____

22. $18 \div 3$

    A 7   **B** 5   **C** 6   **D** 4

22. _____

23. $0 \div 7$

    A 7   **B** 1   **C** 10   **D** Not here

23. _____

24. $64 \div 8$

    A 6   **B** 7   **C** 8   **D** 9

24. _____

25. $42 \div 6$

    A 8   **B** 7   **C** 6   **D** Not here

25. _____

26. At the mall, Chuck buys a musical greeting card for $4.35 and a pop-up card for $5.95. He spends $0.79 on a soda. How much did he pay for the cards?

    A $9.20   **B** $10.30   **C** $11.09   **D** Not here

26. _____

27. Estimate 76×4.

    A 210   **B** 280   **C** 360   **D** 320

27. _____

Name _____

In 28–30, find each product.

28. 7 × 35

    A 245   **B** 215   **C** 285   **D** Not here

28. _____

29. 6 × 328

    A 1,828   **B** 90   **C** 1,968   **D** Not here

29. _____

30. 5 × 3 × 9

    A 72   **B** 135   **C** 60   **D** Not here

30. _____

31. Ralph does 2 sit-ups on Monday, 5 sit-ups on Tuesday, and 8 sit-ups on Wednesday. If he follows this pattern, how many sit-ups will he do on Friday?

    A 7 sit-ups   **B** 14 sit-ups
    C 10 sit-ups   **D** 15 sit-ups

31. _____

32. Estimate 59 × 34.

    A 180   **B** 1,800   **C** 240   **D** 2,400

32. _____

In 33–35, find each product.

33. 74 × 32

    A 2,368   **B** 2,358   **C** 2,258   **D** Not here

33. _____

34. 368 × 42

    A 17,463   **B** 14,909   **C** 15,456   **D** 17,744

34. _____

35. $13.49 × 23

    A $308.07   **B** $311.27   **C** 409.28   **D** Not here

35. _____

36. Jennifer stands in the fifth row of the marching band. There are 13 rows with 10 band members each. How many band members are in the rows behind her?

    A 80 members   **B** 50 members
    C 130 members   **D** 40 members

36. _____

In 1–10, use patterns to find each quotient.

1. 24 ÷ 3 =

    240 ÷ 3 =

    2,400 ÷ 3 =

2. 42 ÷ 7 =

    420 ÷ 7 =

    4,200 ÷ 7 =

1. _____

    _____

    _____

2. _____

    _____

    _____

3. 300 ÷ 6   **4.** 560 ÷ 8   **5.** 240 ÷ 6   **6.** 6,300 ÷ 9

_____   _____   _____   _____

7. 180 ÷ 9   **8.** 540 ÷ 6   **9.** 2,000 ÷ 5   **10.** 3,200 ÷ 4

_____   _____   _____   _____

In 11–16, estimate each quotient.

11. 290 ÷ 7

12. 130 ÷ 6

13. 463 ÷ 9

14. 437 ÷ 6

15. 238 ÷ 8

16. 262 ÷ 3

11. _____

12. _____

13. _____

14. _____

15. _____

16. _____

In 17–22, divide.

17. 28 ÷ 3   **18.** 45 ÷ 7   **19.** 63 ÷ 9

_____   _____   _____

20. 26 ÷ 4   **21.** 48 ÷ 9   **22.** 37 ÷ 8

_____   _____   _____

In 1–3, complete. You may use place-value blocks to help.

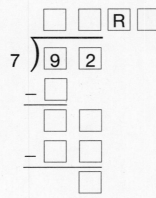

1. ☐ 3 R ☐
4 ⟌ 5 5
– 4
☐☐
– ☐☐
☐

2. ☐☐ R ☐
7 ⟌ 9 2
– ☐
☐☐
– ☐☐
☐

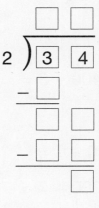

3. ☐☐
2 ⟌ 3 4
– ☐
☐☐
– ☐☐
☐

In 4–15, divide. Check your answer.

4. 6⟌96

5. 5⟌84

6. 3⟌71

7. 3⟌438

8. 2⟌368

9. 4⟌587

10. 4⟌235

11. 6⟌379

12. 2⟌295

13. 318 ÷ 3

14. 360 ÷ 2

15. 283 ÷ 4

_____ _____ _____

16. Tyler is making friendship pins. He has 50 beads. How many pins can Tyler make if he puts 7 beads on each pin?

16. _____

17. How many cars will you need to take 63 students on a field trip if each car can only hold 5 people?

17. _____

Name _____

Date _____ Score _____

Vocabulary: In 1–3, complete each sentence with one of the words listed.

1. Whole numbers that are not divisible by 2

   are _____.

2. Another word for mean is _____.

3. The numbers 2, 36, and 72 are _____.

In 4–6, complete. You may use play money to help.

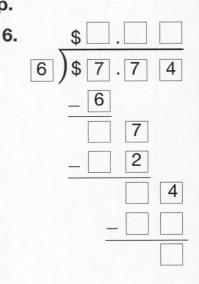

4.
```
       $ 0 . □ 4
  6 )$ 3 . 2  4
    - □ □
        □  4
      - □  4
        □
```

5.
```
       $ □ . 3 □
  7 )$ 9 . 6  6
    - 7
      □ □
    - 2  1
       5  6
     - 5  6
       □
```

6.
```
       $ □ . □ □
  6 )$ 7 . 7  4
    - 6
      □  7
    - □  2
       □  4
     - □  □
       □
```

In 7–8, divide and check.

7. 4)$6.24   7. _____

8. $4.59 ÷ 9   8. _____

In 9–10, find the mean of each set of numbers.

9. 9, 7, 8, 11, 10, 9   9. _____

10. 74, 76, 68, 76, 81   10. _____

11. Test 355 to see if it is divisible by 2, 3, or 5. _____
    If it is, write the quotient.

12. Dot spent $8. She has one ten-dollar bill   12. _____
    and two five-dollar bills left. How much
    money did she start with?

Vocabulary: In 1–4, complete each sentence with one of the words listed.

Word List
odd
even
mean
divisible

1. A number is _____ by another number if there is no remainder.

2. Whole numbers that are divisible by 2 are _____.

3. Average is another word for _____.

4. The numbers 3, 17, and 45 are _____.

In 5–10, use patterns to find each quotient.

5. $400 \div 8$

6. $540 \div 9$

7. $360 \div 4$

_____

_____

_____

8. $240 \div 3$

9. $420 \div 6$

10. $180 \div 9$

_____

_____

_____

In 11–13, estimate each quotient.

11. $351 \div 9$

12. $430 \div 5$

13. $294 \div 4$

_____

_____

_____

In 14–25, divide.

14. $6\overline{)37}$

15. $9\overline{)49}$

14. _____

15. _____

16. $23 \div 5$

17. $59 \div 8$

16. _____

17. _____

18. $3\overline{)37}$

19. $87 \div 6$

18. _____

19. _____

Name _____

20. 4)$\overline{536}$ **21.** 739 ÷ 5   **20.** _____

                                                         21. _____

22. 3)$\overline{92}$ **23.** 619 ÷ 6   **22.** _____

                                                         23. _____

24. 4)$\overline{\$\,5.12}$ **25.** $6.09 ÷ 3   **24.** _____

                                                         25. _____

26. Toby made 320 ounces of soup. How many   **26.** _____
9-ounce bowls can he fill?

In 27–28, find the mean of each set of numbers.

27. 7, 6, 9, 4, 7, 3   **27.** _____

28. 87, 76, 86, 88, 83   **28.** _____

**In 29–30, test if each number is divisible by
2, 3, or 5. If it is, then give the quotient.**

29. 273 _____

30. 578 _____

31. Jerry had some apple slices. He ate   **31.** _____
5 slices. He threw away 5 slices because
they were bruised. He has 3 slices left. How
many slices did Jerry start with?

32. Explain Your Thinking How many cars are needed to
carry 36 people if 5 people can ride in one car? Explain
how you know.

_____

_____

_____

Vocabulary: In 1–4, complete each sentence with one of the words listed.

1. Another word for mean is _____.

2. A number is _____ by another number if there is no remainder.

3. Whole numbers *not* divisible by 2 are

   _____.

4. The numbers 4, 22, and 36 are _____.

Word List
odd
even
average
divisible

In 5–10, use patterns to find each quotient.

5. $360 \div 6$ **6.** $320 \div 8$ **7.** $280 \div 4$

_____   _____   _____

8. $200 \div 5$ **9.** $630 \div 7$ **10.** $450 \div 9$

_____   _____   _____

In 11–13, estimate each quotient.

11. $251 \div 8$ **12.** $359 \div 6$ **13.** $429 \div 7$

_____   _____   _____

In 14–25, divide.

14. $6\overline{)43}$ **15.** $6\overline{)57}$ **14.** _____

                                                        15. _____

16. $35 \div 8$ **17.** $29 \div 7$ **16.** _____

                                                        17. _____

18. $2\overline{)47}$ **19.** $58 \div 4$ **18.** _____

                                                        19. _____

Name _____

20. 5)‾675‾ **21.** 845 ÷ 3 **20.** _____

21. _____

22. 5)‾54‾ **23.** 731 ÷ 7 **22.** _____

23. _____

24. 3)‾$4.53‾ **25.** $8.61 ÷ 7 **24.** _____

25. _____

26. Monica has 26 batteries. She plans to store them in bags that hold 8 batteries each. How many bags will Monica need to hold all the batteries? **26.** _____

In 27–28, find the mean of each set of numbers.

27. 8, 7, 9, 10, 6, 8 **27.** _____

28. 58, 57, 60, 65 **28.** _____

In 29–30, test if each number is divisible by 2, 3, or 5. If it is, then give the quotient.

29. 485 _____

30. 753 _____

31. Tonya gave 18 pieces of dried fruit to Tasha and put three pieces into a plastic bag. She has 5 pieces left. How many pieces did Tonya start with? **31.** _____

32. Explain Your Thinking Carl bought 128 inches of ribbon. How many 9-inch strips can he cut? Explain how you know.

_____

_____

_____

Give the letter of the correct answer.

In 1–3, use patterns to find each quotient.

1. 360 ÷ 9

   A 10   **B** 20   **C** 30   **D** 40

1. _____

2. 560 ÷ 7

   A 80   **B** 70   **C** 60   **D** 8

2. _____

3. 280 ÷ 7

   A 210   **B** 70   **C** 40   **D** 4

3. _____

In 4–7, estimate each quotient.

4. 371 ÷ 6

   A 60   **B** 80   **C** 100   **D** 90

4. _____

5. 224 ÷ 7

   A 200   **B** 230   **C** 30   **D** 60

5. _____

6. 448 ÷ 5

   A 450   **B** 90   **C** 400   **D** 50

6. _____

7. 196 ÷ 4

   A 200   **B** 90   **C** 190   **D** 50

7. _____

In 8–25, divide.

8. $6\overline{)32}$

   A 5 R2   **B** 6 R2   **C** 28   **D** Not here

8. _____

9. $5\overline{)18}$

   A 13   **B** 3   **C** 3 R3   **D** Not here

9. _____

Continued   **157**

10. 9)$\overline{76}$

    A 8 R4   **B** 8 R3   **C** 7 R13   **D** 9 R1

10. _____

11. 8)$\overline{67}$

    A 9 R 4   **B** 8 R3   **C** 7 R11   **D** Not here

11. _____

12. 5)$\overline{48}$

    A 8 R8   **B** 7 R3   **C** 9 R3   **D** Not here

12. _____

13. 7)$\overline{67}$

    A 9 R4   **B** 8 R1   **C** 9 R2   **D** 8 R10

13. _____

14. 8)$\overline{73}$

    A 9   **B** 8 R9   **C** 7 R1   **D** Not here

14. _____

15. 6)$\overline{82}$

    A 10 R2   **B** 16 R4   **C** 14 R2   **D** Not here

15. _____

16. 3)$\overline{459}$

    A 153   **B** 153 R1   **C** 153 R2   **D** 153 R3

16. _____

17. 5)$\overline{728}$

    A 145 R2   **B** 145 R3   **C** 145   **D** Not here

17. _____

18. 875 ÷ 4

    A 218   **B** 208 R3   **C** 218 R3   **D** 208

18. _____

19. 325 ÷ 3

    A 18 R1   **B** 78 R1   **C** 108 R1   **D** 174 R1

19. _____

20. 456 ÷ 8

    A 58   **B** 58 R2   **C** 57   **D** 57 R2

20. _____

Name _____

21. 483 ÷ 5

  A 96 R3   **B** 96 R2   **C** 96 R1   **D** 96

21. _____

22. 396 ÷ 5

  A 83 R 1   **B** 79 R1   **C** 78 R 7   **D** 79

22. _____

23. 4)‾40‾

  A 1 R8   **B** 10   **C** 12 R2   **D** Not here

23. _____

24. 5)‾518‾

  A 13 R8   **B** 103 R3   **C** 100 R8   **D** 103 R1

24. _____

25. 4)‾420‾

  A 120   **B** 104 R6   **C** 105   **D** 105 R6

25. _____

26. Barbara collected 39 plastic bottles. She put them in cartons that hold 6 bottles each. How many cartons did Barbara need?

  A 8 cartons   **B** 7 cartons
  C 6 cartons   **D** 5 cartons

26. _____

27. Gilbert collected 90 aluminum cans for recycling. He puts them in small boxes that hold 8 cans each. How many boxes can he completely fill?

  A 11 boxes   **B** 10 boxes
  C 13 boxes   **D** 9 boxes

27. _____

28. Ramona collected 70 cans. She put them in bags that hold 8 cans each. How many bags did Ramona need?

  A 6 bags   **B** 7 bags   **C** 8 bags   **D** 9 bags

28. _____

In 29–31, find each quotient.

29. 3)‾$6.81‾

  A $2.27   **B** $0.27   **C** $2.07   **D** Not here

29. _____

Name _____

30. 4)$\overline{\$7.32}$

    A $1.82   **B** $182   **C** $1.83   **D** $183

31. 9)$\overline{\$4.77}$

    A $5.30   **B** $530   **C** $0.53   **D** Not here

32. Find the mean for this set of data: 6, 8, 9, 5, 7.

    A 7   **B** 5   **C** 10   **D** 17

33. Find the mean for this set of data:
47, 40, 53, 56, 49, 37

    A 282   **B** 6   **C** 27   **D** 47

34. Is 154 is divisible by 2, 3, 5, or 6?

    A By 6   **B** By 5   **C** By 3   **D** By 2

35. Is 357 is divisible by 2, 3, 5, or 6?

    A By 2   **B** By 3   **C** By 5   **D** 6

36. Juan gave 2 bunches of grapes to Carlos and 4 bunches to Grace. He has 8 bunches of grapes left. How many bunches did he have to begin with?

    A 2 bunches   **B** 14 bunches
    C 6 bunches   **D** Not here

37. Mariah saves pennies. She gave 35 pennies to her sister on her birthday. Then her mother gave her 100 pennies. Mariah now has 316 pennies. How many pennies did she have to begin with?

    A 451 pennies   **B** 181 pennies
    C 251 pennies   **D** 381 pennies

38. Luanda spent $13. She has two one-dollar bills and three five-dollar bills left in her purse. How much did she have to begin with?

    A $20   **B** $4   **C** $30   **D** $16

You and eight or fewer friends picked the apples shown. There are red, yellow, and green apples.

a. Making Decisions

How many people are in your group?

Color the apples to show how many of each color you picked.

b. Recording Data You decide to share each color of apples equally. Complete the table to show how many of each color apple each person will pick. Don't forget to include yourself.

Apple Picking			
Kinds of Apples	Total Number	Number per Person	Number Left Over
Red apples			
Yellow apples			
Green apples			

c. Analyzing Data Use the table to answer these questions.

How many apples will each of you receive in all?
Which color of apple has the greatest number left over?
Did any color of apples have none left over?

d. Think Critically How many apples in all are left over? Can these be shared equally with your group? Explain.

e. Making Decisions Suppose you make apple pies with your apples. It takes 6 apples for a green apple pie. It takes 9 apples for a deep dish apple pie made with red or yellow apples. How many pies can you make? What kind of pies will they be?

Teacher Notes

Concepts and Skills This activity requires students to:
- record information in a table.
- make decisions using real-life experiences.
- find sums.
- find quotients.
- interpret remainders.

Guiding Questions
- If you have 30 apples and share them among 5 people, how will you find how many apples each person will receive? What is the answer?
- How will you find the number apples (red, yellow, and green) that each member of the group gets?

Answers
a. Answers will vary.
b. Answers will vary. Check students' computations.
c. Answers will vary.
d. Answers and explanations will vary.
e. Answers will vary.

Extension
Have students tell how many more apples they would need to make three deep dish pies than four green apple pies. (27 − 24 = 3; 3 more apples)

Evaluation

Level	Standard to be achieved for performance of specified level
4	**Full Achievement** The student accurately completes the table and determines the total number of apples for each person. He or she can interpret remainders to decide how many pies can be made.
3	**Substantial Achievement** The student completes the table, making some minor computational errors. He or she can interpret remainders to decide how many pies can be made.
2	**Partial Achievement** The student may need some help in order to complete the table, and makes several computational errors. He or she has difficulty deciding what to do with the left-over apples and determining how many pies can be made.
1	**Little Achievement** The student needs considerable help in completing the table, and makes many computational errors. He or she has difficulty deciding what to do with the left-over apples, and is unable to decide how many pies can be made.

In 1–3, use patterns to find each quotient.

1. 560 ÷ 7   **2.** 280 ÷ 4   **3.** 360 ÷ 6

_____   _____   _____

In 4–7, estimate each quotient.

4. 551 ÷ 6

   A 9   **B** 70   **C** 80   **D** 90

5. 368 ÷ 5

   A 70   **B** 100   **C** 700   **D** 800

6. 485 ÷ 7

   A 40   **B** 70   **C** 80   **D** 800

7. 250 ÷ 6

   A 80   **B** 70   **C** 60   **D** 40

4. _____

5. _____

6. _____

7. _____

In 8–21, divide.

8. 6)39   **9.** 5)27

10. 9)68   **11.** 4)63

12. 5)94   **13.** 33 ÷ 2

14. 3)369   **15.** 526 ÷ 4

16. 4)328   **17.** 476 ÷ 5

8. _____

9. _____

10. _____

11. _____

12. _____

13. _____

14. _____

15. _____

16. _____

17. _____

Name _____

18. 4)‾407   **19.** 6)‾653

18. _____

19. _____

20. 3)‾$4.56   **21.** 2)‾$6.08

20. _____

21. _____

22. Ricardo has 47 baseball cards. He wants to put them in display cases that hold 6 cards each. How many cases does Ricardo need?

22. _____

    A 8 cases   **B** 7 cases
    C 9 cases   **D** Not here

23. Lonato baked 39 cookies. He wants to give an equal number of cookies to each of 6 friends. How many cookies will he give each friend?

23. _____

    A 5 cookies   **B** 6 cookies
    C 7 cookies   **D** Not here

In 24–25, test if each number is divisible by 2, 3, or 5. If it is, then write the quotient.

24. 325 _____

25. 579 _____

26. Raneesha gave 4 jars of jam to each of 5 friends. She has 5 jars left. How many jars did she have to begin with?

26. _____

27. Performance Task Jerome is 48 in. tall. Marvin is 39 in. tall. Gavin is 45 in. tall. Explain how to find the mean height.

_____

_____

_____

Name _____

Date _____   Score _____

▬ Computation ▬

In 1–13, divide.

1. 280 ÷ 7

2. 44 ÷ 5

3. 23 ÷ 6

4. 6)‾87‾

5. 5)‾62‾

4. _____

5. _____

6. 3)‾428‾

7. 4)‾453‾

6. _____

7. _____

8. 4)‾389‾

9. 6)‾265‾

8. _____

9. _____

10. 9)‾96‾

11. 4)‾415‾

10. _____

11. _____

12. \$3.56 ÷ 4

13. \$5.16 ÷ 3

12. _____

13. _____

14. Find the sum. $\begin{array}{r} 3\,2 \\ 1\,4 \\ +\,2\,7 \\ \hline \end{array}$

14. _____

A 63 **B** 73 **C** 83 **D** Not here

15. Find the difference. $\begin{array}{r} 5\,7\,4 \\ -\,2\,8\,6 \\ \hline \end{array}$

15. _____

A 312 **B** 398 **C** 298 **D** 288

16. Find the product. $\begin{array}{r} 4\,8 \\ \times\,2\,3 \\ \hline \end{array}$

16. _____

A 984 **B** 1,004 **C** 1,104 **D** Not here

Continued

Name _____

━━ Concepts ━━

In 17–18, estimate each quotient.

17. 317 ÷ 8

18. 648 ÷ 9

19. Test if 735 is divisible by 2, 3, or 5.
If it is, find the quotient.

20. Find the mean for this set of data:
186, 189, 176, 182, 172

A 181   **B** 180   **C** 186   **D** Not here

21. Compare. Use <, >, or =.

$5.25 ● 5 dollars 2 dimes 2 nickels

A <   **B** >   **C** =

22. Find the value for n in $30 = n + 9$.

A $n = 39$ **B** $n = 48$
C $n = 21$ **D** $n = 11$

17. _____

18. _____

_____

20. _____

21. _____

22. _____

━━ Applications ━━

23. Austin has 38 comic books. He wants to
put them in boxes that hold 6 books each.
How many boxes will Austin need?

24. Sonya gave each of 12 friends 2 cups of
stew. She had 3 cups left. How many cups
of stew did she have before she served her
friends?

A 2 cups   **B** 5 cups
C 12 cups   **D** 27 cups

25. Baron buys 3 model cars for $2.98 each.
He pays the clerk with a $10 bill. How
much change does he receive?

23. _____

24. _____

25. _____

In 1–2, name the solid that each object looks like.

1.

2.

1. _____

2. _____

In 3–4, write the name of each polygon.

3.

4.

3. _____

4. _____

In 5–6, the lengths of the sides of a triangle are given. Name each triangle as scalene, isosceles, or equilateral.

5. 7 in., 10 in., 7 in.

6. 3 in., 3 in., 3 in.

5. _____

6. _____

In 7–8, name each triangle as right, acute, or obtuse.

7.

8.

7. _____

8. _____

In 9–10, tell whether each picture shows a slide, flip or turn.

9.

10.

9. _____

10. _____

In 11–12, write whether each set of figures is congruent, similar, or neither.

11.

12.

11. _____

12. _____

Vocabulary: choose the word that best completes each sentence.

1. A _____ is a straight path that goes on forever in both directions.

2. A _____ is a line segment, other than a side, connecting two vertices of a polygon.

3. A _____ is a part of a line with two end points.

In 4–5, write intersecting, parallel, or perpendicular for each.

4.

5.

4. _____

5. _____

In 6–7, write the name of each quadrilateral.

6.

7.

6. _____

7. _____

In 8–9, tell how many lines of symmetry each figure has.

8.

9.

8. _____

9. _____

10. Masud is standing in line after Alano and before Yoshi. Su-mi is directly after Yoshi. Who is first in line? You can use objects or any other strategy to solve.

10. _____

11. Kaya was standing to the left of Arnelle and to the right of Devon. Cody was standing to the left of Devon. Who was standing to the far right?

11. _____

Vocabulary: In 1–4, write *true* or *false*.

1. Area is the number of square units needed to cover a region.

2. Square inch is a measure of volume.

3. Perimeter is the distance around a figure.

4. Volume is the number of square units needed to cover a region.

1. _____

2. _____

3. _____

4. _____

In 5–6, find the perimeter of each polygon.

5. 4 in. / 4 in.

6. 3 in. / 5 in. / 4 in.

5. _____

6. _____

In 7–10, find the area of each rectangle.

7. 4 in. / 5 in.

8. 4 in. / 9 in.

9. 2 cm / 3 cm

10. 3 cm / 4 cm

7. _____

8. _____

9. _____

10. _____

In 11–12, find the volume of each rectangular prism.

11. 2 cm / 2 cm / 3 cm

12. 3 in. / 4 in. / 5 in.

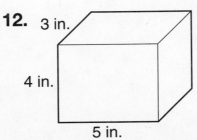

11. _____

12. _____

Vocabulary: In 1–2, match each with its meaning.

1. congruent

   a. a straight path that goes on forever in both directions

1. _____

2. line

   b. having the same size and shape

2. _____

In 3–4, name the solid that each object looks like.

3.

4.

3. _____

4. _____

In 5–6, write the name of each polygon.

5.

6.

5. _____

6. _____

In 7–8, the lengths of the sides of a triangle are given. Name each triangle as scalene, isosceles, or equilateral.

7. 4 cm, 7 cm, 4 cm

8. 5 cm, 8 cm, 3 cm

7. _____

8. _____

In 9–10, name each triangle as right, acute, or obtuse.

9.

10.

9. _____

10. _____

In 11–12, tell whether each picture shows a slide, flip, or turn.

11.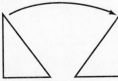

12.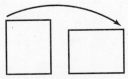

11. _____

12. _____

Name _____

13. Is the figure congruent, similar, or neither?

14. Are the lines parallel, intersecting, or perpendicular?

13. _____

14. _____

In 15–16, write the name of each quadrilateral.

15.

16.

15. _____

16. _____

In 17–18, tell how many lines of symmetry each figure has.

17.

18.

17. _____

18. _____

19. Norman stands behind Dennis. Dennis stands behind Rudy. Norman stands in front of Brad. Who is first in the line?

19. _____

In 20–21, a rectangle has length 5 cm and width 6 cm.

20. Find the perimeter of the rectangle.

20. _____

21. Find the area of the rectangle.

21. _____

22. A rectangular prism is 4 inches long, 3 inches wide, and 3 inches high. Find its volume.

22. _____

23. Explain Your Thinking The perimeter of a square measures 40 centimeters. Explain how you can find the length of each side. Then give the length.

_____

_____

_____

Name _____

Date _____ Score _____

Vocabulary: In 1–2, match each with its meaning.

1. polygon   **a.** a closed plane figure made of line segments

2. perimeter   **b.** the distance around a figure

1. _____

2. _____

In 3–4, name the solid each object looks like.

3.    4.

3. _____

4. _____

In 5–6, write the name of each polygon.

5.   6.

5. _____

6. _____

In 7–8, the lengths of the sides of a triangle are given. Name each triangle as scalene, isosceles, or equilateral.

7. 2 cm, 2 cm, 2 cm

8. 5 cm, 8 cm, 5 cm

7. _____

8. _____

In 9–10, name each triangle as right, acute, or obtuse.

9.   10.

9. _____

10. _____

In 11–12, tell whether each picture shows a slide, flip, or turn.

11. 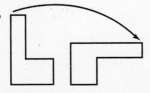   12.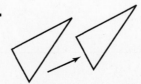

11. _____

12. _____

Name _____

13. Are the figures congruent, similar, or neither?

14. Are the lines parallel, intersecting, or perpendicular?

In 15–16, write the name of each quadrilateral.

15.

16.

15. _____

16. _____

In 17–18, tell how many lines of symmetry each figure has.

17.

18.

17. _____

18. _____

19. Jody is standing in a line before Marla and behind Pearl. Naomi is in front of Pearl. Who is last in the line?

19. _____

In 20-21, a rectangle has length 4 in. and width 3 in.

20. Find the perimeter of the rectangle.

21. Find the area of the rectangle.

22. A rectangular prism is 5 cm long, 3 cm wide, and 2 cm high. Find its volume.

20. _____

21. _____

22. _____

23. Explain Your Thinking The perimeter of a rectangle measures 14 inches. Two sides each measure 3 inches. Explain how to find the length of one of the other sides. Then give the length.

_____

_____

Give the letter of the correct answer.

1. Name the solid that the object looks like.

   A Cube   **B** Sphere
   C Cone   **D** Pyramid

   1. _____

2. Name the solid that the object looks like.

   A Pyramid   **B** Cylinder
   C Cone   **D** Rectangular prism

   2. _____

3. Name the solid that the object looks like.

   A Cone   **B** Cube
   C Cylinder   **D** Not here

   3. _____

4. What is the name of the polygon?

   A Triangle   **B** Octagon
   C Pentagon   **D** Hexagon

   4. _____

5. What is the name of the polygon?

   A Triangle   **B** Square
   C Pentagon   **D** Hexagon

   5. _____

6. What is the name of the polygon?

   A Square   **B** Octagon
   C Rectangle   **D** Hexagon

   6. _____

7. What type of triangle has sides with lengths 2 in., 2 in., and 2 in.?

   A Right   **B** Equilateral   **C** Scalene   **D** Isosceles

   7. _____

8. What type of triangle has sides with lengths 5 cm, 5 cm, and 3 cm?

   A Isosceles   **B** Equilateral   **C** Scalene

   8. _____

Name _____

9. What type of triangle has sides with lengths 3 in., 4 in., and 6 in.?

    A Isosceles   **B** Equilateral   **C** Scalene

9. _____

10. Name the type of triangle.

    A Right   **B** Obtuse
    C Acute

10. _____

11. Name the type of triangle.

    A Right   **B** Obtuse
    C Acute

11. _____

12. Does the picture show a slide, a flip, or a turn?

    A Slide   **B** Turn   **C** Flip

12. _____

13. Does the picture show a slide, a flip, or a turn?

    A Slide   **B** Turn   **C** Flip

13. _____

14. Tell whether the two figures appear to be congruent, similar, or neither.

    A Congruent   **B** Similar
    C Neither

14. _____

15. Tell whether the two figures appear to be congruent, similar, or neither.

    A Congruent   **B** Similar
    C Neither

15. _____

16. Are the lines intersecting, parallel, or perpendicular?

    A Intersecting   **B** Parallel
    C Perpendicular

16. _____

Continued

Name _____

17. Are the lines intersecting, parallel, or perpendicular?

    A Intersecting   **B** Parallel
    C Perpendicular

17. _____

18. What is the name of the quadrilateral?

    A Rectangle   **B** Square
    C Parallelogram **D** Trapezoid

18. _____

19. What is the name of the quadrilateral?

    A Rectangle   **B** Square
    C Parallelogram **D** Trapezoid

19. _____

20. How many lines of symmetry does the figure have?

    A 0 lines   **B** 1 line
    C 2 lines   **D** 3 lines

20. _____

21. How many lines of symmetry does the figure have?

    A 5 lines   **B** 4 line
    C 3 lines   **D** 2 lines

21. _____

22. Joe stood in front of Alison. Katie stood behind Alison and in front of Megan. Who was at the front of the line?

    A Megan   **B** Katie   **C** Alison   **D** Joe

22. _____

23. Julian put his red shirt at the left of his blue shirt. He then put his green shirt at the right of his blue shirt. What color was the shirt was to the far left?

    A Green   **B** Blue   **C** Red   **D** Not here

23. _____

24. Find the perimeter of the polygon.

    A 24 in.   **B** 24 square in.
    C 20 in.   **D** 20 square in.

4 in.

6 in.

24. _____

Name _____

25. Find the perimeter of the polygon.

    A 8 cm   **B** 8 square cm
    C 18 cm   **D** 18 square cm

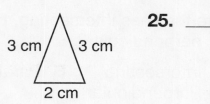

25. _____

26. Find the area of the rectangle.

    A 18 in.   **B** 18 square in.
    C 14 in.   **D** 14 square in.

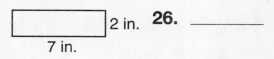

26. _____

27. Find the area of the rectangle.

    A 20 cm   **B** 20 square cm
    C 18 cm   **D** 18 square cm

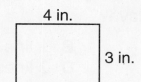

27. _____

28. Find the area of the rectangle.

    A 12 square in.   **B** 12 in.
    C 14 square in.   **D** 14 in.

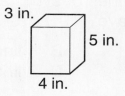

28. _____

29. Find the volume of the rectangular prism.

    A 60 in.   **B** 60 cubic in.
    C 12 in.   **D** 12 cubic in.

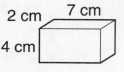

29. _____

30. Find the volume of the rectangular prism.

    A 13 cm   **B** 13 cubic cm
    C 56 cm   **D** 56 cubic cm

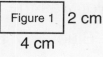

30. _____

31. Look at the two rectangles. They both have the same perimeter. Do they both have the same area? If not, which has the larger area?

    A Yes, they have the same area.
    B No, Figure 1 has a larger area.
    C No, Figure 2 has a larger area.

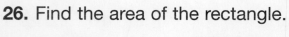

31. _____

Some artwork is made up of geometric figures. Look at the figures below.

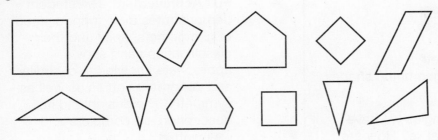

a. **Making Decisions** You will need two different colors to finish this test. Choose those colors. Do not color anything yet.

b. **Recording Data** Make a list of these figures: acute triangle, hexagon, obtuse triangle, octagon, parallelogram, pentagon, rectangle, square, and trapezoid. Tell how many of each figure there are.

c. **Analyzing Data**

How many triangles are there in all?

How many quadrilaterals are there in all?

Find the congruent figures. Color them with one of the colors you chose.

Find the similar triangles. Color them with a different color.

Which figures have no line of symmetry? Mark an X on them with a different color.

d. **Making Decisions** On a separate sheet of paper, create a design using some of the geometric figures shown above. Make a list of the figures you used. Color your design. Use as many different colors as you want.

e. **Critical Thinking** Write a paragraph that describes your artwork. Talk about the shapes in your artwork. Use words like *congruent, similar, symmetry.*

Teacher Notes

Concepts and Skills This activity requires students to:
- recognize geometric shapes.
- classify geometric shapes.
- identify congruent shapes.
- identify similar shapes.
- identify a line of symmetry.
- create a design using geometric shapes.

Guiding Questions
- Name the types of triangles we have studied. How are they alike? How are they different?
- Name the types of quadrilaterals we have studied. How are they alike? How are they different?
- Name any other types of shapes we have studied.

Answers
a. Decisions will vary.
b. Acute triangle, 3; hexagon, 1; obtuse triangle, 2; octagon, 0, parallelogram, 1 (You may want to point out that a square and a rectangle are considered to be parallelograms, so there are actually 5); pentagon, 1; rectangle, 1 (You may want to point out that a square is also considered to be a rectangle, so there are actually 4 rectangles.); square, 3; trapezoid, 0.
c. There are five triangles and five quadrilaterals. The two small squares are congruent. The two isosceles triangles are similar. The parallelogram and the scalene triangle have no lines of symmetry.
d. Check students' designs.
e. Answers will vary.

Extension
Ask why you could not add the number of parallelograms, rectangles, rhombuses, squares, and trapezoids to find the number of quadrilaterals.

Evaluation

Level	Standard to be achieved for performance of specified level
4	**Full Achievement** The student demonstrates a clear understanding of geometric shapes and their classifications and shows appropriate knowledge of similar and congruent figures as well as symmetry. The design and its description are complete and well written.
3	**Substantial Achievement** The student demonstrates a clear understanding of geometric shapes and their classifications and shows appropriate knowledge of similar and congruent figures, as well as symmetry. The design and its description are basically well written.
2	**Partial Achievement** The student has some difficulty deciding on how to classify various figures and needs help identifying the number of triangles and quadrilaterals. The student may confuse similar and congruent figures. The student can identify a figure that does not have a line of symmetry. The design and its description are not complete nor are they well written.
1	**Little Achievement** The student demonstrates little if any understanding of the task at hand and needs considerable help classifying and counting geometric shapes. Concepts such as congruence, similarity, and symmetry are not grasped. The student makes very little attempt to complete or describe a geometric piece of art.

Date _____ Score _____

In 1–2, name the solid that each object looks like.

1.   **A** Cone   **B** Sphere   1. _____
                           C Cube   **D** Pyramid

2.   **A** Cone   **B** Sphere   2. _____
                           C Cube   **D** Cylinder

In 3–4, what is the name of each polygon?

3.    **A** Hexagon   **B** Octagon   3. _____
                           C Triangle   **D** Pentagon

4.   **A** Hexagon   **B** Octagon   4. _____
                           C Triangle   **D** Pentagon

5. What type of triangle has sides   5. _____
   with lengths 6 cm, 6 cm, and 6 cm?

6. Is the triangle right,   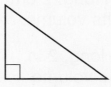   6. _____
   acute or obtuse?

7. Does the picture   7. _____
   show a slide,
   a turn, or a flip?

8. Do the two figures   8. _____
   appear to be congruent,
   similar, or neither?

Name _____

9. Are the lines intersecting, parallel, or perpendicular?

    A Intersecting
    B Parallel
    C Perpendicular

9. _____

10. What is the name of the quadrilateral?

10. _____

11. How many lines of symmetry does the figure have?

    A 4 lines   **B** 3 lines
    C 2 lines   **D** 1 line

11. _____

12. Paka and her friends fill up a bench. There are 4 friends sitting at Paka's left. Half as many friends are sitting at Paka's right. What is the total number of people sitting on the bench?

    A 4 people   **B** 5 people
    C 6 people   **D** Not here

12. _____

13. Find the perimeter of a rectangle whose length is 9 in. and whose width is 5 in.

13. _____

14. Find the area of a rectangle whose length is 7 cm and whose width is 4 cm.

14. _____

15. A rectangular prism is 3 cm long, 2 cm wide, and 4 cm high. Find its volume.

15. _____

16. A rectangular prism is 8 in. long, 2 in. wide, and 4 in. high. Find its volume.

16. _____

17. Performance Task Suppose you buy a 24-inch wood strip to make a picture frame. Describe how you can find the greatest area you can frame. Describe the figure.

_____

_____

_____

Date _____ Score _____

— Computation —

In 1-6, multiply, or divide.

1. 8×400

2. 36
      $\times\ \ 7$

3. 493
      $\times\ \ \ \ 9$

4. $28 \div 5$

5. $2\overline{)329}$

6. $7\overline{)354}$

1. _____

2. _____

3. _____

4. _____

5. _____

6. _____

— Concepts —

7. Name the solid that
the object looks like.

A Cone   **B** Sphere
C Cube   **D** Rectangular
                    prism

7. _____

8. Which polygon has 4 sides?

A Triangle   **B** Pentagon
C Hexagon   **D** Not here

8. _____

9. Which type of triangle has exactly two sides
of equal length?

A Scalene   **B** Isosceles
C Equilateral **D** Not here

9. _____

10. Is the triangle acute, right,
or obtuse?

10. _____

11. Does the picture show a slide,
a flip, or a turn?

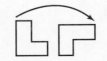

A Slide   **B** Flip   **C** Turn

11. _____

12. Tell whether the two figures appear to be congruent, similar, or neither.

12. _____

13. Are the lines intersecting, parallel, or perpendicular?

13. _____

14. How many lines of symmetry does the figure have?

14. _____

15. What is the name of the quadrilateral?

A Rhombus   **B** Square
C Rectangle   **D** Trapezoid

15. _____

— Applications —

16. Find the perimeter of a rectangular patio whose length is 12 ft and whose width is 6 ft.

16. _____

17. Find the area of a rectangular picture frame whose length is 5 in. and whose width is 3 in.

17. _____

18. Find the volume of a box whose length is 4 cm, width is 3 cm and height is 2 cm.

18. _____

19. Parker is standing to the left of Kristal. Kristal is standing to the left of Miguel. Zelda is standing to the right of Miguel. Who is on the far left?

19. _____

20. Melanie has 40 glass bottles. She wants to put them in cartons that hold 6 bottles each. How many cartons will she need to hold all the bottles?

20. _____

Name _____

Date _____   Score _____

Vocabulary: In 1–5, match each word with its meaning.

1. numerator

a. a number that has a whole number and a fractional part

2. fraction

b. a fraction in which the numerator is greater than or equal to the denominator

3. mixed number

c. the top number of a fraction

4. improper fraction

d. the bottom number of a fraction

5. denominator

e. a comparison of parts to a whole or to a set

1. _____

2. _____

3. _____

4. _____

5. _____

In 6–7, write a fraction for each shaded part.

6. 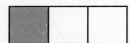   **7.**

6. _____

7. _____

8. What fraction of the set are flowers?

9. What fraction of the animals are striped?

8. _____

9. _____

In 10–11, write a fraction that shows about how full each container is.

10.

$\frac{1}{3}$ or $\frac{3}{4}$

11.

$\frac{1}{4}$ or $\frac{1}{2}$

10. _____

11. _____

12. _____

12. Write $\frac{7}{3}$ as a whole or mixed number.

13. Write $1\frac{2}{3}$ as an improper fraction.

13. _____

Vocabulary: In 1–2, complete.

Word List
equivalent fractions
simplest form

1. A fraction is in _____ when the numerator and the denominator have no common factors other than 1.

2. Fractions that name the same region, part of a set, or part of a segment, are

   called _____.

In 3–4, write a fraction for each shaded part. Then write an equivalent fraction.

3.   4.

3. _____

4. _____

In 5–6, multiply or divide to find equivalent fractions.

5. $\frac{4}{5}$

6. $\frac{10}{12}$

5. _____

6. _____

In 7–8, write each fraction in simplest form.

7. $\frac{3}{9}$

8. $\frac{4}{10}$

7. _____

8. _____

In 9–10, write <, >, or = in each ◯.

9. $\frac{3}{5}$ ◯ $\frac{2}{3}$ 10. $\frac{4}{5}$ ◯ $\frac{1}{3}$

In 11–12, order from least to greatest.

11. $\frac{2}{5}, \frac{3}{10}, \frac{4}{5}, \frac{1}{5}, \frac{1}{10}$

12. $\frac{3}{4}, \frac{3}{8}, \frac{1}{2}, \frac{3}{16}, \frac{5}{8}$

11. _____

12. _____

13. There were 28 shirts in a closet. One-fourth of them were red. How many shirts were red?

13. _____

In 1–2, choose the better measurement for each object.

1.

ERASER

2 in. or 2 ft

2.

MATH IS FUN!
Bulletin
Board

4 in. or 4 yd

1. _____

2. _____

In 3–6, write <, >, or = in ○.

3. 30 in. ○ 2 ft

4. 2 yd ○ 7 ft

5. 3 ft ○ 1 yd

6. 21 in. ○ 1 ft

In 7–8, measure the glue stick to the nearest:

7. $\frac{1}{2}$ in.

8. $\frac{1}{4}$ in.

GLUE STICK

7. _____

8. _____

In 9–10, measure the key to the nearest:

9. $\frac{1}{2}$ in.

10. $\frac{1}{4}$ in.

9. _____

10. _____

11. Dino's house is 10,000 feet from Tom's house. About how many miles apart are the houses?

11. _____

12. Pascal ran 3,000 feet on Monday, 5,000 feet on Tuesday, and 7,000 feet on Wednesday. About how many miles did Pascal run in all?

12. _____

13. Darla's playhouse is bigger than Maxine's but smaller than Connie's. Connie's playhouse is smaller than Brooke's. Who has the largest playhouse?

13. _____

Vocabulary: In 1–4, match each word with its meaning.

1. units of length

a. the top number of a fraction

1. _____

b. the bottom number of a fraction

2. simplest form

2. _____

c. when the numerator and denominator of a fraction have no common factors other than 1

3. numerator

3. _____

4. denominator

d. inch, foot, yard

4. _____

5. Write a fraction for the shaded part.

5. _____

6. Write a fraction that compares the squares to the whole set.

6. _____

In 7–8, write a fraction that shows about how full each container is.

7.

$\frac{1}{2}$ or $\frac{3}{4}$

7. _____

8.

$\frac{1}{4}$ or $\frac{2}{3}$

8. _____

9. Write $\frac{5}{4}$ as a whole number or mixed number.

9. _____

10. Write $2\frac{3}{5}$ as an improper fraction.

10. _____

In 11–12, write a fraction for each shaded part. Then write an equivalent fraction.

11.

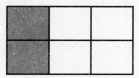

12.

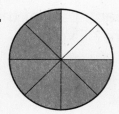

11. _____

12. _____

Name _____

In 13–14, multiply or divide to find equivalent fractions.

13. $\frac{4}{8}$ 13. _____

14. $\frac{2}{3}$ 14. _____

In 15–16, write each fraction in simplest form.

15. $\frac{2}{8}$ 15. _____

16. $\frac{8}{10}$ 16. _____

In 17–20, write <, >, or = in ◯.

17. $\frac{2}{3}$ ◯ $\frac{3}{4}$ 18. $\frac{3}{5}$ ◯ $\frac{1}{2}$

19. 28 in. ◯ 1 yd   20. 3 ft ◯ 1 yd

21. Order from least to greatest: $\frac{1}{2}, \frac{2}{5}, \frac{1}{5}, \frac{3}{10}, \frac{7}{10}$.   21. _____

22. Find $\frac{1}{5}$ of 25.   22. _____

In 23–24, measure the screw to the nearest:

23. $\frac{1}{2}$ in.   23. _____

24. $\frac{1}{4}$ in.   24. _____

25. Mt. Everest is 29,028 feet tall. About how   25. _____
many miles tall is the mountain?

26. Suke owns 3 more CDs than Marisa. If   26. _____
Nova buys 8 more CDs, she will own as
many CDs as Suke. Which girl owns more
CDs now, Marisa or Nova?

27. **Explain Your Thinking** Is each part of this
square $\frac{1}{6}$ of the whole square? Explain.

_____

_____

Vocabulary: In 1–4, match each with its meaning.

1. denominator

    a. when the numerator and denominator of a fraction have no common factors other than 1

2. simplest form

    b. inch, foot, yard

3. units of length

    c. the bottom number of a fraction

4. numerator

    d. the top number of a fraction

1. _____

2. _____

3. _____

4. _____

5. Write a fraction for the shaded part.

5. _____

6. Write a fraction that compares the circles to the whole set.

6. _____

In 7–8, write a fraction that shows about how full each container is.

7.

$\frac{1}{3}$ or $\frac{2}{3}$

8.

$\frac{1}{2}$ or $\frac{3}{4}$

7. _____

8. _____

9. Write $\frac{12}{4}$ as a whole or mixed number.

9. _____

10. Write $3\frac{2}{3}$ as an improper fraction.

10. _____

In 11–12, write a fraction for each shaded part. Then write an equivalent fraction.

11.

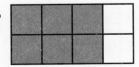

12.

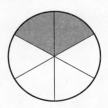

11. _____

12. _____

Name _____

In 13–14, multiply or divide to find equivalent fractions.

13. $\frac{2}{8}$

13. _____

14. $\frac{2}{5}$

14. _____

In 15–16, write each fraction in simplest form.

15. $\frac{2}{6}$

15. _____

16. $\frac{6}{9}$

16. _____

In 17–20, write <, >, or = in each ◯.

17. $\frac{1}{3}$ ◯ $\frac{1}{4}$ 18. 36 in. ◯ 1 yd

19. $\frac{2}{5}$ ◯ $\frac{1}{2}$ 20. 4 ft ◯ 2 yd

21. Order from least to greatest: $\frac{3}{4}, \frac{1}{2}, \frac{5}{16}, \frac{1}{4}, \frac{7}{8}$.

21. _____

22. Find $\frac{1}{4}$ of 24.

22. _____

In 23–24, measure the crayon to the nearest:

23. $\frac{1}{2}$ in.   24. $\frac{1}{4}$ in.

23. _____

24. _____

Crayon

25. Mt. McKinley is 20,310 miles high. About how many miles tall is the mountain?

25. _____

26. Yoki has 9 more marbles than Ruby. If Ana gives 3 marbles to Yoki, both girls will have the same number of marbles. Which girl has fewer marbles now?

26. _____

27. **Explain Your Thinking** Is each part of this square $\frac{1}{4}$ of the whole square? Explain.

_____

_____

Give the letter of the correct answer.

1. What fraction of the figure is shaded?

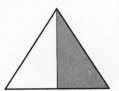

   A $\frac{1}{4}$ **B** $\frac{1}{3}$

   C $\frac{1}{2}$ **D** $\frac{1}{5}$

   1. _____

2. What fraction of the figure is shaded?

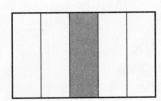

   A $\frac{1}{4}$ **B** $\frac{1}{3}$

   C $\frac{1}{2}$ **D** $\frac{1}{5}$

   2. _____

3. What fraction of the set are baseballs?

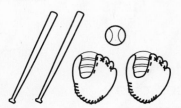

   A $\frac{1}{5}$ **B** $\frac{1}{2}$

   C $\frac{1}{3}$ **D** $\frac{1}{4}$

   3. _____

4. What fraction of the set are bats?

   A $\frac{1}{5}$ **B** $\frac{1}{2}$

   C $\frac{1}{3}$ **D** $\frac{1}{4}$

   4. _____

5. About how full is the container?

   A $\frac{1}{2}$ **B** $\frac{1}{4}$

   5. _____

6. About how full is the container?

   A $\frac{1}{3}$ **B** $\frac{2}{3}$

   6. _____

7. Give $\frac{13}{4}$ as a whole or mixed number.

   A $\frac{3}{4}$ **B** 3   **C** $3\frac{1}{4}$ **D** Not here

   7. _____

8. Give $\frac{12}{6}$ as a whole or mixed number.

   A $\frac{1}{3}$ **B** 2   **C** $2\frac{1}{6}$ **D** Not here

   8. _____

Name _____

9. Give $\frac{11}{3}$ as a whole or mixed number.

A $\frac{1}{3}$ **B** $3\frac{1}{3}$ **C** $2\frac{1}{3}$ **D** Not here

9. _____

10. Give $2\frac{5}{6}$ as an improper fraction.

A $\frac{13}{6}$ **B** $\frac{17}{6}$ **C** $\frac{7}{6}$ **D** Not here

10. _____

11. Give $1\frac{1}{3}$ as an improper fraction.

A $\frac{5}{3}$ **B** $\frac{4}{3}$ **C** $\frac{1}{4}$ **D** Not here

11. _____

12. Give a fraction for the shaded part. Then give the equivalent fraction.

A $\frac{6}{8}, \frac{3}{4}$ **B** $\frac{6}{10}, \frac{3}{5}$

C $\frac{4}{10}, \frac{2}{5}$ **D** $\frac{5}{10}, \frac{1}{2}$

12. _____

13. Give a fraction for the shaded part. Then give the equivalent fraction.

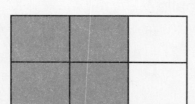

A $\frac{4}{6}, \frac{2}{3}$ **B** $\frac{8}{10}, \frac{4}{5}$

C $\frac{4}{6}, \frac{8}{16}$ **D** $\frac{3}{6}, \frac{1}{2}$

13. _____

14. Which is an equivalent fraction for $\frac{8}{12}$?

A $\frac{2}{3}$ **B** $\frac{3}{4}$ **C** $\frac{2}{4}$ **D** Not here

14. _____

15. Which is an equivalent fraction for $\frac{1}{4}$?

A $\frac{1}{3}$ **B** $\frac{2}{5}$ **C** $\frac{2}{8}$ **D** Not here

15. _____

16. Which is an equivalent fraction for $\frac{2}{6}$?

A $\frac{1}{2}$ **B** $\frac{1}{3}$ **C** $\frac{1}{4}$ **D** Not here

16. _____

17. Give the simplest form for $\frac{3}{15}$.

A $\frac{1}{3}$ **B** $\frac{5}{45}$ **C** $\frac{1}{5}$ **D** $\frac{1}{4}$

17. _____

18. Give $\frac{9}{12}$ in simplest form.

A $\frac{2}{3}$ **B** $\frac{3}{4}$ **C** $\frac{18}{24}$ **D** $\frac{1}{3}$

18. _____

Continued

Name _____

19. Give $\frac{3}{6}$ in simplest form.

    A $\frac{1}{2}$ **B** $\frac{1}{3}$ **C** $\frac{1}{4}$ **D** $\frac{1}{6}$

19. _____

20. Give $\frac{9}{15}$ in simplest form.

    A $\frac{3}{5}$ **B** $\frac{1}{2}$ **C** $\frac{2}{3}$ **D** $\frac{4}{7}$

20. _____

21. Use <, >, or = to compare: $\frac{1}{3}$ ● $\frac{1}{4}$

    A <   **B** >   **C** =

21. _____

22. Use <, >, or = to compare: $\frac{1}{2}$ ● $\frac{2}{3}$

    A <   **B** >   **C** =

22. _____

23. Order from least to greatest: $\frac{3}{10}, \frac{1}{10}, \frac{9}{10}, \frac{5}{10}, \frac{7}{10}$

    A $\frac{1}{10}, \frac{3}{10}, \frac{5}{10}, \frac{7}{10}, \frac{9}{10}$ **B** $\frac{1}{10}, \frac{5}{10}, \frac{3}{10}, \frac{7}{10}, \frac{9}{10}$

    C $\frac{9}{10}, \frac{7}{10}, \frac{5}{10}, \frac{3}{10}, \frac{1}{10}$ **D** $\frac{1}{10}, \frac{3}{10}, \frac{7}{10}, \frac{9}{10}, \frac{5}{10}$

23. _____

24. Order from greatest to least: $\frac{1}{6}, \frac{3}{4}, \frac{2}{3}, \frac{1}{2}, \frac{5}{6}$

    A $\frac{1}{6}, \frac{3}{4}, \frac{2}{3}, \frac{1}{2}, \frac{5}{6}$ **B** $\frac{5}{6}, \frac{1}{6}, \frac{3}{4}, \frac{2}{3}, \frac{1}{2}$

    C $\frac{1}{6}, \frac{1}{2}, \frac{2}{3}, \frac{3}{4}, \frac{5}{6}$ **D** $\frac{5}{6}, \frac{3}{4}, \frac{2}{3}, \frac{1}{2}, \frac{1}{6}$

24. _____

25. Find $\frac{1}{5}$ of 15.

    A 10   **B** 4   **C** 5   **D** 3

25. _____

26. Find $\frac{2}{3}$ of 12.

    A 6   **B** 18   **C** 12   **D** 8

26. _____

27. Find $\frac{3}{4}$ of 8.

    A 1   **B** 6   **C** 4   **D** Not here

27. _____

28. Use <, >, or = to compare: 15 ft ● 5 yd

    A <   **B** >   **C** =   **D** Not here

28. _____

29. Use <, >, or = to compare: 15 in. ● 1 yd

    A <   **B** >   **C** =   **D** Not here

29. _____

Name _____

30. Use <, >, or = to compare: 28 in. ● 2 ft

   A <   **B** >   **C** =   **D** Not here

31. Use <, >, or = to compare: 7 ft ● 3 yd

   A <   **B** >   **C** =   **D** Not here

31. _____

32. Measure the pencil below to the nearest $\frac{1}{2}$ inch.

32. _____

   A $4\frac{1}{4}$ in.   **B** 4 in.   **C** $4\frac{1}{2}$ in.   **D** Not here

33. Measure the pencil above to the nearest $\frac{1}{4}$ inch.

33. _____

   A $5\frac{1}{4}$ in.   **B** $4\frac{3}{4}$ in.   **C** 5 in.   **D** Not here

34. Ruth Ann climbed 5,000 feet up a mountain on Monday, 5,000 feet on Tuesday, and 10,000 feet on Wednesday. About how many miles did Ruth Ann climb in all?

34. _____

   A About 1 mile   **B** About 5 miles
   C About 3 miles   **D** About 4 miles

35. Marshall rode his bike 3,500 yards, then 7,000 yards, and then 7,000 more yards during a one-day trip. Which of these estimates is closest to the actual mileage?

35. _____

   A 7 miles   **B** 10 miles   **C** 1 mile   **D** Not here

36. Timothy, Pam, and Alan each own a boat. One of the boys owns a rowboat. The sailboat is parked next to Pam's boat. Timothy does not have a rowboat. Who is the owner of a canoe?

36. _____

   A Timothy   **B** Pam   **C** Alan

37. Dan, Diana, and Courtney each have a pet. One of the girls has a dog. The owner of a goldfish lives next to Dan. Courtney does not have a dog. Who has the goldfish?

37. _____

   A Dan   **B** Diana   **C** Courtney

Name _____

Date _____   Score _____

Chapter 9 Test
Form
D

How much do you know about your classmates? For example, even though you know some of them share your hair color, do you know what fraction of the class has the same hair color? Let's collect and analyze data to see!

a. **Recording Data** Complete the table. Use tally marks to show how many students are in each category. Then write the number of students in the second row.

Students In My Class				
	Red hair	Blonde hair	Brown hair	Black hair
Tally				
Number				

b. **Analyzing Data** Add another row to the table. Write a fraction for each hair color as shown below. Then write each fraction in simplest form.

■ ← Number of tally marks
■ ← Number of students in class

What fraction of the class has red hair? Blonde hair? Brown hair? Black hair?

c. **Thinking Critically** Write the fractions in order from greatest to least.

Which hair color do the most students have? The fewest students?

d. **Making Decisions** Think of another set of data that you can record about children in your class, such as eye color. Write questions about this data. Then order your fractions from greatest to least.

Teacher Notes

Concepts and Skills This activity requires students to:
- record information in a table.
- make decisions using real-life experiences.
- write fractions based on real-life data.
- compare and order fractions.
- create their own sets of data.

Guiding Questions
- How many students are there in this class?
- How do you write fractions in simplest form?

Answers
a. Answers will vary.
b. Answers will vary. Be sure students' answers are in simplest form.
c. Check students' answers.
d. Answers will vary.

Extension
Have students make a bar graph using the data in the second row of their table.

Evaluation

Level	Standard to be achieved for performance of specified level
4	**Full Achievement** The student can identify fractions as part of a set and is able to order fractions accurately.
3	**Substantial Achievement** The student can identify fractions as part of a set most of the time and can order fractions accurately with minimal errors.
2	**Partial Achievement** The student has some difficulty identifying fractions as part of a set and needs some help in ordering fractions.
1	**Little Achievement** The student needs considerable help in identifying, writing, and comparing fractions.

In 1–2, choose the fraction that shows the shaded part.

1.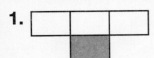

A $\frac{1}{3}$ **B** $\frac{1}{4}$

C $\frac{1}{2}$ **D** $\frac{1}{5}$

2.

A $\frac{1}{3}$ **B** $\frac{1}{4}$

C $\frac{1}{6}$ **D** $\frac{1}{5}$

1. _____

2. _____

3. What fraction of the set are skates?

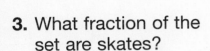

A $\frac{1}{4}$ **B** $\frac{1}{3}$

C $\frac{1}{2}$ **D** $\frac{2}{3}$

3. _____

4. About how full is the container?

$\frac{1}{3}$ or $\frac{1}{2}$

4. _____

5. Write $\frac{13}{6}$ as a whole or mixed number.

5. _____

6. Write $2\frac{1}{2}$ as an improper fraction.

6. _____

7. Give the name of the shaded part. Then give the equivalent fraction.

A $\frac{2}{12}, \frac{1}{6}$ **B** $\frac{2}{10}, \frac{1}{5}$ **C** $\frac{2}{8}, \frac{1}{4}$ **D** $\frac{3}{8}, \frac{1}{2}$

7. _____

In 8–9, multiply or divide to find equivalent fractions.

8. $\frac{8}{10}$

8. _____

9. $\frac{2}{3}$

9. _____

Name _____

In 10–11, give each fraction in simplest form.

10. $\frac{5}{10}$

    A $\frac{3}{5}$ **B** $\frac{1}{5}$ **C** $\frac{1}{2}$ **D** Not here

10. _____

11. $\frac{4}{12}$

    A $\frac{1}{4}$ **B** $\frac{2}{3}$ **C** $\frac{3}{4}$ **D** Not here

11. _____

In 12–15, write <, >, or =.

12. $\frac{1}{3}$ ◯ $\frac{5}{12}$ **13.** $\frac{2}{3}$ ◯ $\frac{1}{2}$

14. 4 ft ◯ 1 yd   **15.** 30 in. ◯ 3 ft

16. Find $\frac{2}{3}$ of 24.

    A 8   **B** 36   **C** 16   **D** Not here

16. _____

17. Order from least to greatest: $\frac{1}{2}, \frac{1}{4}, \frac{9}{16}, \frac{3}{8}, \frac{5}{16}$

_____

18. Measure the pencil to the nearest $\frac{1}{2}$ inch.

18. _____

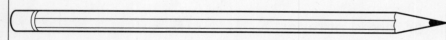

19. The distance from Tamara's home to her grandmother's house is 50,000 feet. About how many miles is this distance?

19. _____

20. Jolene, Aretha, and James each have a pet. Two of the pets are cats. The dog owner lives next to Jolene. What does Jolene own?

20. _____

21. **Performance Task** Name two equivalent fractions and explain how you know they are equal.

_____

_____

_____

— Computation —

1. 4,2 8 7
    +   5 2 8

2. 32 + 731 + 5,412

3. 8 3 4
    − 2 8 7

4. 4,519 − 2,370

5. 3 2 8
    ×   4

6. 12 × 49

7. 59 ÷ 8

8. $3\overline{)317}$

9. Find $\frac{3}{5}$ of 20.

1. _____

2. _____

3. _____

4. _____

5. _____

6. _____

7. _____

8. _____

9. _____

— Concepts —

10. What fraction of the
    figure is shaded?

    A $\frac{1}{3}$ **B** $\frac{1}{4}$

    C $\frac{1}{6}$ **D** $\frac{1}{8}$

10. _____

11. What fraction of the set
    are hockey sticks?

    A $\frac{1}{4}$ **B** $\frac{1}{3}$

    C $\frac{1}{2}$ **D** $\frac{2}{3}$

11. _____

12. About how full is the
    container?

    $\frac{2}{3}$ or $\frac{1}{3}$

12. _____

13. Write $\frac{15}{4}$ as a whole or mixed number.

13. _____

14. Write $2\frac{2}{5}$ as an improper fraction.

14. _____

15. Which polygon has three sides?

    A Square   **B** Cone   **C** Triangle   **D** Rhombus

15. _____

Name _____

16. Give the name of the shaded part.   **16.** _____
Then give an equivalent fraction.

A $\frac{4}{5}$, $\frac{8}{10}$ **B** $\frac{8}{12}$, $\frac{2}{3}$ **C** $\frac{4}{6}$, $\frac{2}{3}$ **D** Not here

17. Multiply or divide to find an equivalent   **17.** _____
fraction for $\frac{4}{6}$.

A $\frac{1}{2}$ **B** $\frac{3}{7}$ **C** $\frac{7}{8}$ **D** Not here

18. Write $\frac{8}{12}$ in simplest form.   **18.** _____

19. Write $\frac{3}{15}$ in simplest form.   **19.** _____

In 20–23, write <, >, or = in the ◯.

20. $\frac{3}{8}$ ◯ $\frac{1}{2}$ **21.** $\frac{2}{3}$ ◯ $\frac{3}{4}$

22. 22 in. ◯ 2 ft   **23.** 5 ft ◯ 3 yd

24. Order from least to greatest: $\frac{1}{2}$, $\frac{2}{3}$, $\frac{1}{6}$, $\frac{5}{6}$, $\frac{1}{3}$.

_____

25. Measure the nail to the nearest $\frac{1}{4}$ inch.   **25.** _____

▬ Applications ▬

26. The distance from Sparksville to Medora is   **26.** _____
30,000 feet. About how many miles is this
distance?

27. Melvin, Bonnie and Eric brought their lunch   **27.** _____
to school. Neither of the boys ate salad.
Melvin and the boy who ate the fish
sandwich are in different grades. Who ate
the hamburger?

28. Find the area of a rug whose length is 4 feet   **28.** _____
and width is 2 feet.

Name _____

Date _____ Score _____

Give the letter of the correct answer.

In 1–2, use the stem-and-leaf plot.

1. How many students spent 29 minutes on homework?

stem	leaf
1	5 1
2	8 9 9 4
3	4 1 5
4	2 8

   A 0   **B** 1   **C** 2   **D** 3

   1. _____

2. How many students spent less than 24 minutes on homework?

   A 2   **B** 3   **C** 5   **D** Not here

   2. _____

3. Dawn has 7 more necklaces than Eunice. They have 23 necklaces in all. How many necklaces does Dawn have?

   A 15 necklaces   **B** 16 necklaces
   C 30 necklaces   **D** Not here

   3. _____

4. Amber has three wigs–red, blond and brown. She also has gold and silver barrettes. How many different ways can she look?

   A 6 ways   **B** 5 ways   **C** 4 ways   **D** Not here

   4. _____

5. Compare: 3,785 ● 3,758. Use $<$, $>$, or $=$.

   A $<$ **B** $>$ **C** $=$

   5. _____

6. Joshua started piano practice at 5:15 P.M. He finished at 6:05 P.M. How long did he practice?

   A 50 minutes   **B** 45 minutes
   C 1 hour 20 minutes   **D** 1 hour 5 minutes

   6. _____

7. Ralph buys a notebook for $1.98, a pen for $0.79, and a package of stickers for $1.39. He pays with a $5 bill. How much change does he receive?

   A $3.96   **B** $2.84   **C** $0.84   **D** $0.94

   7. _____

Name _____

In 8–10, find each sum or difference.

8.   548
     + 391

   A 834   **B** 934   **C** 944   **D** Not here

9.   1,372
     −   491

   A 1,121   **B** 881   **C** 981   **D** Not here

10. $32.56
     + $41.75

   A $73.21   **B** 73.31   **C** $74.31   **D** 84.21

In 11–14, find each product or quotient.

11. 4 × 8

   A 32   **B** 36   **C** 40   **D** 28

12. 5 × 7

   A 49   **B** 35   **C** 36   **D** 25

13. 28 ÷ 4

   A 6   **B** 7   **C** 8   **D** 9

14. 63 ÷ 7

   A 8   **B** 7   **C** 6   **D** Not here

In 15–17, find each product. Estimate to check.

15. 47 × 8

   A 374   **B** 326   **C** 386   **D** Not here

16. 401 × 3

   A 123   **B** 1,203   **C** 1,230   **D** Not here

17. $15.21 × 3

   A $5.07   **B** $35.63   **C** $45.63   **D** Not here

8. _____

9. _____

10. _____

11. _____

12. _____

13. _____

14. _____

15. _____

16. _____

17. _____

Continued

Name _____

In 18–21, find each product.

18. $3 \times 8 \times 7$

    A 168   **B** 158   **C** 154   **D** Not here

18. _____

19. 36×41

    A 180   **B** 1,276   **C** 1,476   **D** Not here

19. _____

20. $12 \times 3,251$

    A 9,753   **B** 38,012   **C** 39,912   **D** Not here

20. _____

21. $\$2.96 \times 25$

    A $58.50   **B** $73.90   **C** $20.60   **D** Not here

21. _____

In 22–24, divide.

22. $7\overline{)83}$

    A 11 R5   **B** 10 R3   **C** 11 R6   **D** Not here

22. _____

23. $4\overline{)415}$

    A 101 R1   **B** 103 R3   **C** 131 R1   **D** Not here

23. _____

24. $385 \div 8$

    A 43 R1   **B** 48 R2   **C** 48 R1   **D** Not here

24. _____

25. Jason has 112 in. of ribbon. If it takes 38 in. of ribbon to trim a package, how many packages can he trim?

    A 1 package   **B** 2 packages
    C 3 packages   **D** 4 packages

25. _____

26. Leigh sold 3 bushels of oranges. Then she picked 2 more bushels. She now has 8 bushes. How many bushels did she have to begin with?

    A 13 bushels   **B** 3 bushels   **C** 9 bushels   **D** Not here

26. _____

27. Name the type of triangle

    A Right
    B Obtuse
    C Acute

27. _____

Name _____

28. Are the lines intersecting, parallel, or perpendicular?

    A Intersecting
    B Parallel
    C Perpendicular

28. _____

29. Find the perimeter of a rectangle whose length is 8 cm and whose width is 5 cm.

    A 13 cm   **B** 26 cm   **C** 40 cm   **D** Not here

29. _____

30. Find the area of a rectangle whose length is 5 in. and whose width is 3 in.

    A 8 square in.   **B** 16 square in.
    C 15 square in.   **D** Not here

30. _____

31. What fraction of the figure is shaded?

    A $\frac{1}{2}$ **B** $\frac{2}{3}$ **C** $\frac{3}{5}$ **D** $\frac{1}{6}$

31. _____

32. What fraction of the set are footballs?

    A $\frac{2}{3}$ **B** $\frac{3}{5}$ **C** $\frac{3}{10}$ **D** $\frac{1}{2}$

32. _____

33. Give $\frac{14}{5}$ as a mixed number.

    A $2\frac{4}{5}$ **B** $2\frac{11}{14}$ **C** $2\frac{3}{14}$ **D** Not here

33. _____

34. Multiply or divide to find a fraction equivalent to $\frac{6}{10}$.

    A $\frac{2}{3}$ **B** $\frac{3}{4}$ **C** $\frac{3}{5}$ **D** $\frac{5}{6}$

34. _____

35. Give $\frac{6}{8}$ in simplest form.

    A $\frac{1}{2}$ **B** $\frac{3}{4}$ **C** $\frac{2}{3}$ **D** Not here

35. _____

36. Compare: $\frac{5}{6}$ ● $\frac{4}{5}$. Use <, >, or =

    A <   **B** >   **C** =

36. _____

37. Gina, Ann, and Tom each own a stuffed animal. One of the girls has a lion. The owner of the tiger plays ball with Tom. Ann does not have a lion. Who has the tiger?

    A Gina   **B** Ann   **C** Tom

37. _____

Name _____

Date _____ Score _____

In 1–4 find each sum. Simplify.

1. $\frac{1}{4} + \frac{1}{4}$

2. $\frac{2}{5} + \frac{1}{5}$

3. $\frac{1}{10} + \frac{7}{10}$

4. $\frac{2}{3} + \frac{1}{3}$

In 5–7, find the value for *n*.

5. $\frac{2}{5} + n = \frac{4}{5}$

6. $n + \frac{1}{3} = \frac{2}{3}$

7. $\frac{3}{5} + n = 1$

In 8–14, find each sum. Simplify.

8. $\frac{1}{8} + \frac{1}{4}$

9. $\frac{2}{7} + \frac{3}{14}$

10. $\frac{1}{6} + \frac{1}{3}$

11. $\begin{array}{r} \frac{2}{3} \\ + \frac{1}{6} \\ \hline \end{array}$ 12. $\begin{array}{r} \frac{1}{4} \\ + \frac{3}{8} \\ \hline \end{array}$

13. $\begin{array}{r} \frac{2}{5} \\ + \frac{1}{10} \\ \hline \end{array}$ 14. $\begin{array}{r} \frac{1}{3} \\ + \frac{2}{9} \\ \hline \end{array}$

15. India has about $\frac{1}{6}$ of the world's population. The United States has about $\frac{1}{18}$ of the world's population. These two groups combined make up what fraction of the world's population?

1. _____

2. _____

3. _____

4. _____

5. _____

6. _____

7. _____

8. _____

9. _____

10. _____

11. _____

12. _____

13. _____

14. _____

15. _____

In 1–13, find the difference. Simplify.

1. $\frac{7}{9} - \frac{5}{9}$

2. $\frac{3}{4} - \frac{1}{4}$

3. $\frac{4}{5} - \frac{2}{5}$

4. $\frac{11}{12} - \frac{7}{12}$

5. $\frac{9}{10} - \frac{1}{5}$

6. $\frac{11}{15} - \frac{1}{3}$

7. $\frac{5}{8} - \frac{1}{4}$

8. $\begin{array}{r} \frac{13}{14} \\ -\ \frac{2}{7} \\ \hline \end{array}$

9. $\begin{array}{r} \frac{11}{12} \\ -\ \frac{3}{4} \\ \hline \end{array}$

10. $\begin{array}{r} \frac{3}{4} \\ -\ \frac{1}{4} \\ \hline \end{array}$

11. $\begin{array}{r} \frac{7}{8} \\ -\ \frac{1}{8} \\ \hline \end{array}$

12. $\begin{array}{r} \frac{2}{3} \\ -\ \frac{1}{9} \\ \hline \end{array}$

13. $\begin{array}{r} \frac{1}{2} \\ -\ \frac{3}{10} \\ \hline \end{array}$

1. _____

2. _____

3. _____

4. _____

5. _____

6. _____

7. _____

8. _____

9. _____

10. _____

11. _____

12. _____

13. _____

In 14–15, write the operation you would use. Then solve each problem.

14. Paula has $\frac{1}{6}$ cup of raisins. Her recipe calls for $\frac{1}{3}$ cup of raisins. How many more cups of raisins does she need?

_____

15. One-half of an atlas is made up of maps and $\frac{1}{4}$ is made up of pictures. What fraction of the atlas is made up of maps and pictures?

_____

In 1–5, choose the better estimate for each weight.

1. A fourth-grade student: 95 lb or 95 oz

2. A box of pencils: 8 oz or 8 lb

3. Your desk: 20 T or 20 lb

4. Your math book: 2 oz or 2 lb

5. A serving of applesauce: 6 oz or 6 lb

In 6–10, choose the better estimate for each capacity.

6. A lunch milk carton: 1 c or 1 gal

7. A lemonade pitcher: 2 c or 2 qt

8. A birdbath: 4 gal or 4 fl oz

9. A cereal bowl: 16 fl oz or 16 qt

10. A juice box: 8 c or 8 fl oz

In 11–16, complete.

11. 4 qt = ■ gal   **12.** 24 in. = ■ ft

13. 3 gal = ■ pt   **14.** 3 lb = ■ oz

15. 5 T = ■ lb   **16.** 6 ft = ■ yd

17. Complete the table. How many tickets could you buy for $20?

Tickets	1	2	4	6	8		
Cost	$2	$4	$8	$12		$20	$24

18. Find *n*.

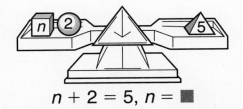

$n + 2 = 5, n =$ ■

1. _____

2. _____

3. _____

4. _____

5. _____

6. _____

7. _____

8. _____

9. _____

10. _____

11. _____

12. _____

13. _____

14. _____

15. _____

16. _____

17. _____

18. _____

In 1–16, find each sum or difference. Simplify.

1. $\frac{1}{5} + \frac{2}{5}$

2. $\frac{1}{8} + \frac{3}{8}$

3. $\frac{2}{3} - \frac{1}{3}$

4. $\frac{11}{12} - \frac{5}{12}$

5. $\frac{1}{6} + \frac{7}{12}$

6. $\frac{7}{10} - \frac{3}{10}$

7. $\frac{5}{8} - \frac{1}{4}$

8. $\frac{1}{15} + \frac{1}{3}$

9. $\begin{aligned} &\frac{5}{7} \\ -&\frac{3}{7} \end{aligned}$

10. $\begin{aligned} &\frac{1}{9} \\ +&\frac{1}{3} \end{aligned}$

11. $\begin{aligned} &\frac{14}{15} \\ -&\frac{2}{3} \end{aligned}$

12. $\begin{aligned} &\frac{2}{3} \\ +&\frac{1}{6} \end{aligned}$

13. $\begin{aligned} &\frac{3}{4} \\ -&\frac{1}{2} \end{aligned}$

14. $\begin{aligned} &\frac{5}{6} \\ -&\frac{1}{3} \end{aligned}$

15. $\begin{aligned} &\frac{9}{10} \\ -&\frac{3}{5} \end{aligned}$

16. $\begin{aligned} &\frac{1}{8} \\ +&\frac{3}{4} \end{aligned}$

1. _____

2. _____

3. _____

4. _____

5. _____

6. _____

7. _____

8. _____

9. _____

10. _____

11. _____

12. _____

13. _____

14. _____

15. _____

16. _____

17. Find the value of n for $n + \frac{2}{5} = \frac{4}{5}$.

17. _____

Name _____

In 18–19, write the operation you would use. Then solve.

18. Paolo ate $\frac{1}{8}$ of a pizza and Chandra ate $\frac{1}{4}$. How much of the pizza did they eat in all?

18. _____

19. Lashonda has $\frac{3}{4}$ yard of fabric. She uses $\frac{3}{8}$ yard to make dolls. How much fabric is left?

19. _____

In 20–24, choose the better estimate.

20. A box of pens: 8 oz or 8 lb

20. _____

21. A box of books: 16 oz or 16 lb

21. _____

22. A car: 2 lb or 2 T

22. _____

23. A kitchen sink filled with water: 10 pt or 10 gal

23. _____

24. A soda bottle: 16 c or 16 fl oz

24. _____

In 25–28, complete.

25. 2 qt = ■ pt   26. 36 ft = ■ yd

25. _____

27. 2 T = ■ lb   28. 2 lb = ■ oz

26. _____

29. How many granola bars could you get for $5?

27. _____

Granola Bars	2	4	6		
Cost	$1		$3	$4	

28. _____

29. _____

30. Find *n*.

30. _____

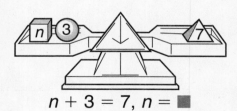

$n + 3 = 7, n =$ ■

31. **Explain Your Thinking** Explain why you multiply when you change a larger unit to a smaller unit.

_____

_____

In 1–16, find each sum or difference. Simplify.

1. $\frac{2}{7} + \frac{4}{7}$

2. $\frac{1}{6} + \frac{1}{6}$

3. $\frac{8}{9} - \frac{2}{9}$

4. $\frac{9}{10} - \frac{3}{10}$

5. $\frac{1}{4} + \frac{5}{12}$

6. $\frac{4}{5} - \frac{1}{5}$

7. $\frac{2}{3} - \frac{1}{9}$

8. $\frac{2}{15} + \frac{1}{3}$

9. $\begin{array}{r} \frac{2}{3} \\ -\ \frac{1}{3} \\ \hline \end{array}$

10. $\begin{array}{r} \frac{1}{10} \\ +\ \frac{1}{2} \\ \hline \end{array}$

11. $\begin{array}{r} \frac{14}{15} \\ -\ \frac{1}{5} \\ \hline \end{array}$

12. $\begin{array}{r} \frac{1}{4} \\ +\ \frac{5}{8} \\ \hline \end{array}$

13. $\begin{array}{r} \frac{5}{8} \\ -\ \frac{1}{2} \\ \hline \end{array}$

14. $\begin{array}{r} \frac{3}{4} \\ -\ \frac{1}{8} \\ \hline \end{array}$

15. $\begin{array}{r} \frac{5}{6} \\ -\ \frac{1}{3} \\ \hline \end{array}$

16. $\begin{array}{r} \frac{1}{5} \\ -\ \frac{1}{10} \\ \hline \end{array}$

1. _____

2. _____

3. _____

4. _____

5. _____

6. _____

7. _____

8. _____

9. _____

10. _____

11. _____

12. _____

13. _____

14. _____

15. _____

16. _____

17. Find the value of n for $n + \frac{1}{7} = \frac{2}{7}$.

17. _____

Name _____

**In 18–19, write the operation you would use.
Then solve.**

18. Rene has $\frac{3}{4}$ bushel of apples. He sells
$\frac{1}{2}$ bushel. How much does he have left?

18. _____

19. Joseph rode his bike $\frac{2}{5}$ mile on Saturday and
$\frac{3}{10}$ mile on Sunday. How far did he ride in all?

19. _____

**In 20–24, choose the better estimate for weight or
capacity.**

20. A truck: 4 lb or 4 T

20. _____

21. A can of fruit: 20 oz or 20 lb

21. _____

22. Your math book: 2 oz or 2 lb

22. _____

23. A glass of juice: 6 fl oz or 6 c

23. _____

24. A bathtub filled with water: 55 pt or 55 gal

24. _____

In 25–28, complete.

25. 8 qt = ■ gal   **26.** 12 ft = ■ yd

25. _____

27. 6,000 lb = ■ T   **28.** 2 lb = ■ oz

26. _____

29. How many tickets could you get for $50?

27. _____

Tickets	3	6			
Cost	$10		$30	$40	

28. _____

29. _____

30. Find *n*.

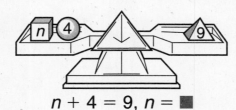

$n + 4 = 9, n =$ ■

30. _____

31. Explain Your Thinking Explain why you divide when you
change a smaller unit to a larger unit.

_____

_____

Give the letter of the correct answer.

In 12–16, add or subtract.

1. $\frac{3}{5} + \frac{1}{5}$

   A $\frac{4}{5}$ **B** $\frac{3}{5}$ **C** $\frac{1}{5}$ **D** $\frac{4}{10}$

1. _____

2. $\frac{3}{8} + \frac{1}{4}$

   A $\frac{4}{12}$ **B** $\frac{1}{3}$ **C** $\frac{5}{8}$ **D** Not here

2. _____

3. $\frac{8}{9} - \frac{5}{9}$

   A $\frac{1}{3}$ **B** $\frac{2}{9}$ **C** $\frac{13}{9}$ **D** Not here

3. _____

4. $\frac{5}{7} - \frac{2}{7}$

   A $\frac{7}{7}$ **B** $\frac{3}{14}$ **C** $\frac{1}{3}$ **D** Not here

4. _____

5. $\frac{1}{12} + \frac{1}{4}$

   A $\frac{1}{16}$ **B** $\frac{2}{12}$ **C** $\frac{4}{12}$ **D** $\frac{2}{16}$

5. _____

6. $\frac{2}{8} + \frac{1}{4}$

   A $\frac{3}{12}$ **B** $\frac{4}{8}$ **C** $\frac{3}{8}$ **D** $\frac{9}{12}$

6. _____

7. $\frac{7}{8} - \frac{1}{4}$

   A $\frac{5}{8}$ **B** $\frac{6}{8}$ **C** $\frac{2}{3}$ **D** $\frac{3}{4}$

7. _____

8. $\frac{3}{5} - \frac{1}{10}$

   A $\frac{2}{5}$ **B** $\frac{2}{10}$ **C** $\frac{3}{15}$ **D** $\frac{5}{10}$

8. _____

9. $\frac{4}{5} - \frac{1}{10}$

   A $\frac{3}{10}$ **B** $\frac{3}{5}$ **C** $\frac{7}{10}$ **D** Not here

9. _____

10. $\frac{1}{10} + \frac{1}{5}$

   A $\frac{2}{10}$ **B** $\frac{3}{10}$ **C** $\frac{4}{10}$ **D** $\frac{1}{5}$

10. _____

         Continued   **215**

Name _____

11. $\frac{5}{9} - \frac{1}{3}$

   A $\frac{4}{9}$ **B** $\frac{4}{3}$ **C** $\frac{1}{3}$ **D** $\frac{2}{9}$

12. $\frac{2}{15} + \frac{1}{3}$

   A $\frac{7}{15}$ **B** $\frac{4}{5}$ **C** $\frac{13}{15}$ **D** Not here

13. $\frac{5}{6} - \frac{2}{3}$

   A $\frac{1}{3}$ **B** $\frac{3}{6}$ **C** $\frac{1}{2}$ **D** Not here

14. $\frac{2}{3} + \frac{1}{6}$

   A $\frac{1}{2}$ **B** $\frac{5}{6}$ **C** $\frac{3}{9}$ **D** Not here

15. $\frac{1}{3}$

    $+ \ \frac{1}{6}$

   A $\frac{1}{6}$ **B** $\frac{2}{3}$ **C** $\frac{1}{2}$ **D** $\frac{2}{9}$

16. $\frac{11}{12}$

    $- \ \frac{1}{6}$

   A $\frac{3}{4}$ **B** $\frac{1}{3}$ **C** $\frac{5}{6}$ **D** $\frac{1}{6}$

In 17–18, give the value of *n*.

17. $\frac{3}{8} + n = \frac{4}{8}$

   A $\frac{7}{16}$ **B** $\frac{7}{8}$ **C** $\frac{1}{8}$ **D** 1

18. $n + \frac{2}{3} = 1$

   A $\frac{2}{3}$ **B** $\frac{3}{2}$ **C** 1   **D** $\frac{1}{3}$

19. Ty ran $\frac{9}{10}$ mile on Monday and $\frac{3}{5}$ mile on Tuesday. How many miles did he run in all? Choose the operation you would use to solve.

   A Addition   **B** Subtraction
   C Multiplication   **D** Division

11. _____

12. _____

13. _____

14. _____

15. _____

16. _____

17. _____

18. _____

19. _____

20. A football weighs $\frac{7}{8}$ pound. A soccer ball weighs $\frac{15}{16}$ pound. How much more does the soccer ball weigh? Choose the operation you would use to solve.

    A Addition   **B** Subtraction
    C Multiplication **D** Division

20. _____

21. One-third of the flowers on the parade float are red roses. One-sixth of the flowers are yellow roses. What fraction of the flowers are roses?

    A $\frac{1}{12}$ **B** $\frac{2}{9}$ **C** $\frac{1}{2}$ **D** Not here

21. _____

22. Joaquin had $\frac{5}{8}$ bushel of oranges. He gave Karen $\frac{1}{4}$ bushel. How many bushels did he have left?

    A $\frac{7}{8}$ **B** $\frac{3}{4}$ **C** $\frac{3}{8}$ **D** Not here

22. _____

In 23–28, choose the best estimate.

23. Weight of an apple

    A 4 lb   **B** 4 oz   **C** 4 T   **D** Not here

23. _____

24. Weight of a book

    A 1 lb   **B** 1 T   **C** 1 oz   **D** Not here

24. _____

25. Weight of a car

    A 2 lb   **B** 2 oz   **C** 2 T   **D** Not here

25. _____

26. Capacity of a fruit cup

    A 6 gal   **B** 6 fl oz   **C** 6 c   **D** 6 qt

26. _____

27. Capacity of a swimming pool

    A 5,000 pt   **B** 5,000 fl oz   **C** 5,000 c   **D** 5,000 gal

27. _____

28. Capacity of a cereal bowl

    A 12 fl oz   **B** 12 gal   **C** 12 c   **D** 12 pt

28. _____

In 29–32, choose the value for ■.

29. 9 ft = ■ yd

    A 1   **B** 2   **C** 3   **D** 4

29. _____

Name _____

30. 4 gal = ■ qt

    A 4   **B** 8   **C** 16   **D** 20

31. 4 T = ■ lb

    A 2000   **B** 4000   **C** 6,000   **D** 8,000

32. 48 oz = ■ lb

    A 4   **B** 3   **C** 2   **D** 1

30. _____

31. _____

32. _____

In 33–34, complete each table.

33. How many tickets could you get for $10?

33. _____

Tickets	1		3	4	
Cost	$2	$4		$8	

    A 2 tickets   **B** 4 tickets   **C** 5 tickets   **D** 10 tickets

34. How many apples could you get for $25?

34. _____

Apples	4	8	12		
Cost	$5		$15	$20	

    A 20 apples   **B** 12 apples   **C** 16 apples   **D** 4 apples

35. What is the value of n?

    A 3   **B** 4
    C 5   **D** 6

35. _____

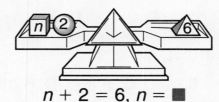

$n + 2 = 6, n = $ ■

36. What is the value of n?

    A 3   **B** 4
    C 5   **D** 6

36. _____

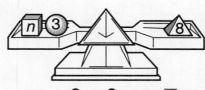

$n + 3 = 8, n = $ ■

You are helping plan a vegetable garden. The table at the right tells how many pounds of vegetables you will get from a 10-foot row.

One Row	
Vegetable	Yield
Cabbage	20 Pounds
Carrots	8 Pounds
Green Beans	6 Pounds
Lettuce	5 Pounds
Onions	10 Pounds
Peas	3 Pounds
Potatoes	7 Pounds
Radishes	10 Pounds
Tomatoes	50 Pounds

a. **Making Decisions** Decide what kinds of vegetables and how many rows of each you will have in your garden.

b. **Recording Data** Copy and complete the table.

Vegetable	Number of Rows	Yield in Pounds Per Row	Total Yield

c. **Analyzing Data** Use the table to answer these questions.

How many rows are in your garden?

How many pounds of vegetables will your garden yield?

Which kind of vegetable in your garden will have the greatest yield in pounds?

Write a fraction to describe the yield of each vegetable as part of the total yield.

d. **Making Decisions** Cabbage, lettuce, beans, carrots, and radishes grow very fast. They can be planted a second time to yield another crop. Which of these vegetables will you replant? Give the new totals for your vegetable garden.

Teacher Notes

Concepts and Skills This activity requires students to:
- read data in a table.
- make decisions using real-life experiences.
- multiply whole numbers.
- add whole numbers.
- create their own sets of data.

Guiding Questions
- Suppose a row yields 4 pounds. How much will 2 rows yield?
- How will you find the total number of pounds in the table?
- How will you find the totals at the bottom of the table?

Answers
a. Decisions will vary.
b. Answers will vary. Check students' tables.
c. Answers will vary.
d. Answers will vary. Check students' answers.

Extension
Have students make a bar graph using the data in the last column of their table.

Evaluation

Level	Standard to be achieved for performance of specified level
4	**Full Achievement** The student completes the table accurately and can write a fraction describing the yield.
3	**Substantial Achievement** The student completes the table, making only minor computational errors. He or she can write a fraction describing each yield.
2	**Partial Achievement** The student needs some help in completing the table accurately. He or she cannot write a fraction for each yield.
1	**Little Achievement** The student needs considerable help in completing the table and cannot write fractions describing yields. He or she may use inappropriate operations as well as make other computational errors.

Name _____

Date _____ Score _____

In 1–10, find the sum or difference. Simplify.

1. $\frac{3}{5} + \frac{1}{5}$

2. $\frac{7}{10} - \frac{3}{10}$

3. $\frac{5}{6} - \frac{3}{12}$

4. $\frac{4}{5} - \frac{3}{10}$

5. $\frac{1}{4} + \frac{1}{8}$

6. $\frac{1}{3} + \frac{1}{6}$

7. $\begin{array}{r} \frac{7}{15} \\ - \frac{1}{3} \\ \hline \end{array}$ **8.** $\begin{array}{r} \frac{1}{16} \\ + \frac{3}{4} \\ \hline \end{array}$

9. $\begin{array}{r} \frac{3}{8} \\ + \frac{1}{2} \\ \hline \end{array}$ **10.** $\begin{array}{r} \frac{5}{16} \\ - \frac{1}{4} \\ \hline \end{array}$

1. _____

2. _____

3. _____

4. _____

5. _____

6. _____

7. _____

8. _____

9. _____

10. _____

In 11–12, give the value of n.

11. $\frac{1}{5} + n = \frac{4}{5}$

   A $\frac{2}{5}$ **B** $\frac{1}{5}$ **C** $\frac{1}{4}$ **D** Not here

12. $n + \frac{5}{6} = 1$

   A 1   **B** $\frac{2}{3}$ **C** $\frac{1}{6}$ **D** Not here

11. _____

12. _____

In 13–14, choose the operation you would use. Then solve.

13. Doug walked $\frac{1}{5}$ mile before lunch and $\frac{3}{10}$ mile after lunch. How far did he walk in all?

   A Subtraction; $\frac{1}{5}$ mile   **B** Subtraction; $\frac{2}{5}$ mile
   C Addition; $\frac{4}{15}$ mile   **D** Addition; $\frac{1}{2}$ mile

13. _____

Name _____

14. Anita rowed her canoe $\frac{3}{4}$ mile. Geraldine rowed her canoe $\frac{1}{2}$ mile. How much farther did Geraldine row her canoe than Anita?

14. _____

   A Subtraction; $\frac{1}{2}$ mile   **B** Subtraction; $\frac{1}{4}$ mile
   C Addition; $\frac{2}{3}$ mile   **D** Addition; 1 mile

In 15–16, choose the better estimate for weight or capacity.

15. A computer monitor: 20 oz or 20 lb

15. _____

16. A soda can: 12 fl oz or 12 c

16. _____

In 17–19, complete.

17. 8 qt = ■ gal

17. _____

   A 1   **B** 2   **C** 3   **D** 4

18. 2 ft = ■ in.

18. _____

   A 4   **B** 6   **C** 24   **D** 36

19. 3 T = ■ lb

19. _____

   A 6,000   **B** 3,000   **C** 2,000   **D** Not here

20. Complete the table. How many peaches could you get for $15?

20. _____

Peaches	2	4	6		
Cost	$3	$6		$12	

21. Performance Task Explain how you can use the scale model to help you solve $5 + n = 7$. Then solve.

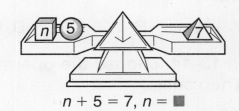

$n + 5 = 7, n = ■$

_____

_____

_____

Name _____

Date _____ Score _____

— Computation —

In 1–8, find the sum or difference. Simplify.

1. $\frac{1}{3} + \frac{1}{3}$

2. $\frac{7}{12} - \frac{5}{12}$

3. $\frac{1}{4} + \frac{3}{8}$

4. $\frac{2}{3} - \frac{1}{6}$

5. $\begin{array}{r} \frac{3}{5} \\ - \frac{1}{15} \end{array}$ 6. $\begin{array}{r} \frac{1}{4} \\ + \frac{1}{16} \end{array}$

7. $\begin{array}{r} \frac{5}{8} \\ - \frac{1}{4} \end{array}$ 8. $\begin{array}{r} \frac{2}{3} \\ + \frac{1}{9} \end{array}$

In 9–12, divide.

9. $39 \div 5$

10. $409 \div 4$

11. $7\overline{)732}$ 12. $4\overline{)\$6.24}$

1. _____

2. _____

3. _____

4. _____

5. _____

6. _____

7. _____

8. _____

9. _____

10. _____

11. _____

12. _____

— Concepts —

In 13–16, choose the better estimate for weight or capacity.

13. A potato: 8 oz or 8 lb

14. A dog: 16 lb or 16 T

15. A bucket of water: 5 gal or 5 pt

16. A drinking glass: 16 fl oz or 16 c

13. _____

14. _____

15. _____

16. _____

Name _____

In 17–20, complete.

17. 12 qt = ■ gal

    A 1   **B** 2   **C** 3   **D** 4

17. _____

18. 2 T = ■ lb

    A 6,000   **B** 3,000   **C** 2,000   **D** Not here

18. _____

19. Draw a scale for the number sentence and solve. $4 + n = 9$

19. _____

20. Harvey has three \$10 bills, two \$5 bills, 3 quarters, and 4 nickels. How much money does he have in all?

    A \$35.95   **B** 45.95   **C** \$35.70   **D** \$40.95

20. _____

— Applications —

21. Kati walked $\frac{3}{8}$ mile to school and $\frac{3}{8}$ mile back. How far did she walk? Choose the operation you would use. Then solve.

    A Addition; $\frac{6}{16}$ mile   **B** Addition; $\frac{3}{4}$ mile
    C Subtraction; $\frac{3}{16}$ mile   **D** Subtraction; $\frac{1}{2}$ mile

21. _____

22. Complete the table. How many apples can you buy for \$5?

22. _____

Apples	3	6	9		
Cost	\$1	\$2		\$4	

In 23–25, use the graph.

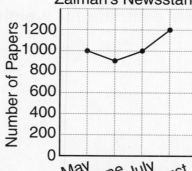
Zalman's Newsstand

23. In which month did Zalman sell the most papers?

23. _____

24. About how many papers did he sell in all?

24. _____

25. About how many more papers did he sell in May than in June?

25. _____

1. Write the word name, fraction, and decimal for the shaded part.

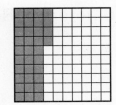

_____

_____

_____

In 2–3, write the decimal for each.

2. $3\frac{3}{10}$

2. _____

3. Seven and fifty-six hundredths

3. _____

4. Rewrite 0.6 in hundredths.

4. _____

5. Rewrite 0.90 in tenths.

5. _____

6. Suppose you have $1.35 in dimes and nickels. You have the same number of dimes as nickels. How many of each do you have?

6. _____

In 7–8, write <, >, or = in each ◯.

7. 0.65 ◯ 0.7

8. 1.02 ◯ 0.75

In 9–10, order the decimals from least to greatest.

9. 0.34, 1.02, 0.08, 1.35, 0.7

_____

10. 1.23, 1.14, 0.48, 0.24, 0.5

_____

In 11–13, round each decimal to the nearest whole number.

11. 2.4

11. _____

12. 0.62

12. _____

13. 4.50

13. _____

In 14–15, write the decimal for each fraction.

14. $\frac{7}{20}$

14. _____

15. $\frac{4}{25}$

15. _____

In 1–4, estimate each sum or difference. Round to the nearest whole number.

1. 7.93 + 4.12

2. 7.50 + 13.48

3. 18.25 − 7.98

4. 53.64 − 25.3

1. _____

2. _____

3. _____

4. _____

In 5–6, write the addition or subtraction sentence for each grid.

5.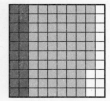

6.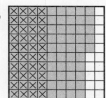

_____

_____

In 7–9, find each sum or difference. You can use hundredths grids to help.

7. 0.35 + 0.17

8. 0.94 − 0.23

9. 0.45 + 0.08

7. _____

8. _____

9. _____

In 10–13, find each sum or difference. Estimate to check your answer.

10. 2.71 + 3.2

11. 4.37 + 1.74

12. 8.74 − 3.06

13. 6.04 − 2.9

10. _____

11. _____

12. _____

13. _____

14. Nancy bought two packages of chicken. One package weighs 3.72 lb. The other weighs 2.93 lb. How many pounds of chicken did Nancy buy in all?

14. _____

Vocabulary: In 1–4, write what each word measures.

Word List
mass
length
capacity

1. centimeter   _____

2. gram   _____

3. kilometer   _____

4. liter   _____

In 5–6, choose the better unit of measure for each object.

5.

meters or decimeters

6.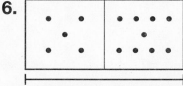

centimeters or meters

5. _____

6. _____

In 7–10, write <, >, or = for $\bigcirc$.

7. 70 cm $\bigcirc$ 7 m

8. 8 km $\bigcirc$ 800 m

9. 500 cm $\bigcirc$ 5 m

10. 30 m $\bigcirc$ 300 km

In 11–14, complete.

11. 3.7 m = ■ cm

11. _____

12. 250 cm = ■ m

12. _____

13. 3.4 kg = ■ g

13. _____

14. 7,800 g = ■ kg

14. _____

In 15–16, choose the better estimate of capacity for each.

15. Juice box: 250 mL or 250 L

15. _____

16. Kitchen sink filled with water: 50 mL or 50 L

16. _____

17. For every 100 miles you travel north, the temperature drops about 2°F. If it is 84°F at your house, what is the temperature 400 miles north?

17. _____

Vocabulary: In 1–3, write what each word measures.

Word List
mass
length
capacity

1. centimeter   _____

2. liter   _____

3. gram   _____

4. Suppose you have $1.05 in dimes and nickels. You have the same number of dimes as nickels. How many of each do you have?   4. _____

In 5–6, write the decimal for each.

5. $\frac{8}{10}$ 5. _____

6. Four and sixty-seven hundredths   6. _____

In 7–8, write <, >, or = for each ◯.

7. 0.98 ◯ 1.07   **8.** 0.87 ◯ 0.09

9. Order 0.32, 0.09, 1.04, 3.52, 0.7 from least to greatest.   _____

In 10–12, round each decimal to the nearest whole number.

10. 3.78   10. _____

11. 2.05   11. _____

12. 6.50   12. _____

In 13–14, write the decimal for each fraction.

13. $\frac{4}{5}$ 13. _____

14. $\frac{9}{20}$ 14. _____

In 15–16, estimate each sum or difference. Round to the nearest whole number.

15. 6.23 + 3.78   15. _____

16. 27.86 − 13.05   16. _____

Name _____

17. Write the addition or
subtraction sentence
for the grid.

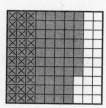

_____

In 18–22, find each sum or difference.

18. 0.48 + 0.23

19. 4.73 + 1.26

20. 0.87 − 0.24

21. 9.63 − 5.37

22. 7.34 − 2.28

18. _____

19. _____

20. _____

21. _____

22. _____

**In 23–24, choose the better unit of measure
for each object.**

23. Length of an eraser: centimeter or meter

24. Length of highway: meter or kilometer

23. _____

24. _____

In 25–26, complete.

25. 400 cm = ■ m   **26.** 3 m = ■ cm

In 27–28, write <, >, or = for each ◯.

27. 50 cm ◯ 5 m   **28.** 3 m ◯ 300 cm

25. _____

26. _____

In 29–30, choose the better estimate for each.

29. Nickel (a 5-cent coin): 5 g or 5 kg

30. Ice-cube tray: 380 mL or 380 L

29. _____

30. _____

31. A soup's temperature was 10.3°C before
it was heated. After being heated, its
temperature was 84.7°C. What was the
temperature change?

31. _____

32. Explain Your Thinking Explain how to write a decimal
in hundredths that is equal to 0.6.

Vocabulary: In 1–3, write what each word measures.

	Word List
	mass
	length
	capacity

1. meter _____

2. milliliter _____

3. kilogram _____

4. Suppose you have $1.10 in dimes and
   nickels. You have two more dimes than
   nickels. How many dimes do you have?   4. _____

In 5–6, write the decimal for each.

5. $\frac{7}{10}$ 5. _____

6. Five and forty-eight hundredths   6. _____

In 7–8, write <, >, or = in each $\bigcirc$.

7. 1.04 $\bigcirc$ 0.97   8. 1.23 $\bigcirc$ 1.08

9. Order 1.07, 0.67, 0.90, 0.5, 2.73
   from least to greatest: _____

**In 10–12, round each decimal to the nearest
whole number.**

10. 4.36   10. _____

11. 6.87   11. _____

12. 2.50   12. _____

In 13–14, write the decimal for each fraction.

13. $\frac{3}{10}$ 13. _____

14. $\frac{9}{25}$ 14. _____

**In 15–16, estimate each sum or difference. Round to
the nearest whole number**

15. 3.45 + 9.64   15. _____

16. 36.24 − 21.50   16. _____

Name _____

17. Write the addition or
subtraction sentence
for the grid.

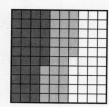

_____

In 18–22, find each sum or difference.

18. $0.27 + 0.71$

19. $5.43 + 3.29$

20. $0.78 - 0.36$

21. $8.71 - 3.48$

22. $9.62 - 3.29$

18. _____

19. _____

20. _____

21. _____

22. _____

**In 23–24, choose the better unit of measure
for each object.**

23. Width of a leaf: centimeter or meter

24. Height of a building: meter or kilometer

23. _____

24. _____

In 25–26, complete.

25. 600 cm = ■ m   **26.** 4 m = ■ cm

In 27–28, write <, >, or = in each ◯.

27. 40 cm ◯ 4 m   **28.** 6,000 cm ◯ 6 m

25. _____

26. _____

In 29–30, choose the better estimate for each.

29. Sack of potatoes: 5 g or 5 kg

30. Can of soda pop: 470 mL or 470 L

29. _____

30. _____

31. A pudding's temperature before it was put
into the refrigerator was 80.7°C. Its
temperature was 15.2°C when it was
served. What was the temperature change?

31. _____

32. Explain Your Thinking Explain how to write a decimal
in tenths that is equal to 0.70.

Give the letter of the correct answer.

1. What is the word name,
   fraction, and decimal
   for the shaded part?

   A Nine hundredths, $\frac{9}{100}$, 0.09

   B Nine tenths, $\frac{9}{10}$, 0.9

   C Four tenths, $\frac{4}{10}$, 0.4

   D Not here

   1. _____

2. What is the word name,
   fraction, and decimal
   for the shaded part?

   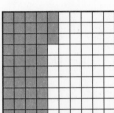

   A Forty-three hundredths, $\frac{43}{100}$, 0.43

   B Fifth-four hundredths, $\frac{54}{100}$, 0.54

   C Thirty-two hundredths, $\frac{32}{100}$, 0.32

   D Forty-six hundredths, $\frac{46}{100}$, 0.46

   2. _____

3. Rewrite 0.9 in hundredths.

   A 0.09   **B** 9.0   **C** 0.90   **D** Not here

   3. _____

4. Rewrite 0.10 in tenths.

   A 1.0   **B** 1.00   **C** 0.01   **D** Not here

   4. _____

5. Complete: 0.75 ● 0.9. Use <, >, or =.

   A <   **B** >   **C** =

   5. _____

6. Complete: 4.25 ● 4.05. Use <, >, or =.

   A <   **B** >   **C** =

   6. _____

7. Order 1.35, 1.7, 0.7, 1.62, 0.48 from least
   to greatest.

   A 0.7, 0.48, 1.7, 1.35, 1.62

   B 0.48, 0.7, 1.35, 1.7, 1.62

   C 0.48, 0.7, 1.35, 1.62, 1.7

   D 1.62, 1.35, 0.48, 1.7, 0.7

   7. _____

8. Round 4.21 to the nearest whole number.

   A 4.2   **B** 4.20   **C** 4   **D** 5

8. _____

9. Round 7.39 to the nearest whole number.

   A 7.4   **B** 7   **C** 7.40   **D** 8

9. _____

10. Round 4.9 to the nearest whole number.

   A 5   **B** 4   **C** 4.9   **D** 4.90

10. _____

11. Give the decimal for $\frac{3}{10}$.

   A 0.03   **B** 0.33   **C** 0.3   **D** 3.10

11. _____

12. Give the decimal for $\frac{4}{8}$.

   A 0.4   **B** 4.8   **C** 0.48   **D** 0.5

12. _____

13. Suppose you have $1.21 in dimes and pennies. You have the same number of dimes as pennies. How many of each do you have?

   A 10   **B** 9   **C** 11   **D** 8

13. _____

14. Suppose you have $1.26 in dimes and pennies. What is the fewest number of coins you can have?

   A 19 coins, 10 dimes and 9 pennies
   B 6 coins, 5 quarters and 1 penny
   C 12 coins, 6 dimes and 6 pennies
   D 18 coins, 12 dimes and 6 pennies

14. _____

In 15–16, estimate each sum or difference. Round to the nearest whole number.

15. 8.42 + 6.89

   A 14   **B** 15   **C** 16   **D** Not here

15. _____

16. 17.05 − 11.67

   A 3   **B** 4   **C** 5   **D** Not here

16. _____

Name _____

In 17–23, find each sum or difference.

17. $0.38 + 0.41$

    A 0.3841   **B** 0.13   **C** 0.49   **D** 0.79

17. _____

18. $1.45 + 3.28$

    A 4.63   **B** 4.73   **C** 4   **D** 5

18. _____

19. $\$12.38$
    $+\quad 1.97$

    A $10.45   **B** $14.75   **C** $14.35   **D** $13.25

19. _____

20. $0.76 - 0.24$

    A 0.5   **B** 1.2   **C** 0.52   **D** 0.42

20. _____

21. $7.52 - 3.29$

    A 5   **B** 4   **C** 4.33   **D** Not here

21. _____

22. 6.03
    $-\,4.21$

    A 2.82   **B** 1.82   **C** 2   **D** Not here

22. _____

23. $\$38.10$
    $-\,15.38$

    A $23.28   **B** $22.72   **C** $23.82   **D** $22.82

23. _____

24. Choose the best unit to measure the length of your playground.

    A Centimeter   **B** Meter   **C** Kilometer

24. _____

25. Choose the best unit to measure the width of a paperback book.

    A Centimeter   **B** Meter   **C** Kilometer

25. _____

26. Complete: 80 m ● 8 km. Use <, >, or =.

    A <   **B** >   **C** =   **D** Not here

26. _____

Name _____

27. Complete: 450 cm = ■ m.

    A 4,500   **B** 450   **C** 45   **D** 4.5

27. _____

28. Choose a reasonable unit of mass for a paper clip.

    A Gram   **B** Kilogram

28. _____

29. Choose a reasonable unit of mass for a pet dog.

    A Gram   **B** Kilogram

29. _____

30. Complete: 7,800 g = ■ kg.

    A 0.78   **B** 7.8   **C** 78   **D** 780

30. _____

31. Complete: 38 kg = ■ g.

    A 38,000   **B** 3,800   **C** 380   **D** 3.8

31. _____

32. Choose the better estimate of capacity for the gas tank of an automobile.

    A Milliliter   **B** Liter

32. _____

33. Choose the better estimate of capacity for an eyedropper.

    A 100 g   **B** 100 kg   **C** 10 mL   **D** 10 L

33. _____

34. Complete: 3,000 mL = ■ L.

    A 300   **B** 30   **C** 3   **D** Not here

34. _____

35. Complete: 2 L = ■ mL

    A 2   **B** 20   **C** 200   **D** 2,000

35. _____

36. Choose the better estimate of temperature for a snowy winter day.

    A –2°C   **B** 12°C

36. _____

37. If your temperature dropped from 101.9°F to 98.6°F, how much did it change?

    A 200.4°F   **B** 3.3°F   **C** 3.3°C   **D** Not here

37. _____

Name _____

Date _____ Score _____

Your bicycle club is sponsoring three rides. You are given the map below and need to decide which route to take.

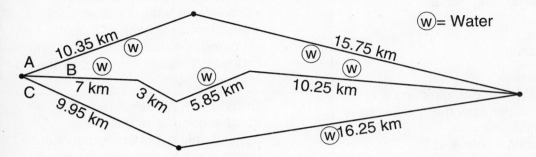

a. **Making Decisions** What do you need to know before you decide which route to take?

b. **Recording Data** Complete the table for each route.

Route	Distance	Number of Water Stations	Number of Turns
A			
B			
C			

c. **Analyzing Data** Use the table to answer these questions.

Which route is the longest?

Which route has the fewest water stations.

Which route has the most turns?

d. **Critical Thinking** Health and safety officials say that you must stop at each water station on your route. You also must slow down for each turn. How will this affect the time it takes to complete each route?

e. **Explain Your Thinking**

Which route will you choose? Explain why.

f. **Making Decisions** Suppose you find out that most of the riders are taking the route you plan to take. Would you change your route? Why or why not?

Teacher Notes

Concepts and Skills This activity requires students to:

- read data in a diagram.
- make decisions using real-life experiences.
- add decimals.
- compare decimals.

Guiding Questions

- If you ride 7.2 km in one direction and 6.25 km in another, how many miles have you ridden in all?
- Which is greater, 4.5 or 4.45?

Answers

a. Decisions will vary.
b. Route A: 26.1 miles, 2 water stations, 1 turn; Route B: 26.1 miles, 3 water stations, 3 turns; Route C: 26.2 miles, 1 water station, 1 turn.
c. Route C is longest and has fewest water stations. Route B has the most turns.
d. Answers will vary, but the more stops and turns on a route, the greater the impact on time.
e. Answers will vary.
f. Answers will vary.

Extension

Have students use a map and plan a bicycle race in their community. What other things could be provided for the riders besides water stops?

Evaluation

Level	Standard to be achieved for performance of specified level
4	**Full Achievement** The student completes the table that reflects the distance for each path with no computational errors. He or she has sound reasons to support the choice of path.
3	**Substantial Achievement** The student completes the table, making only minor computational errors and can offer good reasons to support the choice of path.
2	**Partial Achievement** The student needs some help in completing the table accurately and makes some computational errors. He or she may not be able to offer reasons for his or her choice of path.
1	**Little Achievement** The student needs considerable help in completing the table. He or she may use inappropriate operations as well as make other computational errors and cannot defend his or her choice of path.

In 1–3, write the decimal for each.

1. $4\frac{7}{10}$

2. Seven and six tenths

3. Three and fifty-eight hundredths

4. Rewrite 0.2 in hundredths.

5. Rewrite 0.80 in tenths.

1. _____

2. _____

3. _____

4. _____

5. _____

In 6–7, complete. Write < , >, or = for each ◯.

6. 1.03 ◯ 0.87

7. 0.45 ◯ 0.78

8. Order from least to greatest:
   1.03, 0.09, 0.78, 2.01, 1.3

   _____

In 9–10, round each decimal to the nearest whole number.

9. 4.21

10. 8.50

9. _____

10. _____

In 11–12, write the decimal for each fraction.

11. $\frac{3}{15}$

12. $\frac{4}{25}$

11. _____

12. _____

In 13–14, estimate each sum or difference. Round to the nearest whole number.

13. 4.78 + 8.2

   A 14   **B** 11   **C** 12   **D** 13

14. 7.05 − 4.87

   A 4   **B** 1   **C** 2   **D** 3

13. _____

14. _____

15. Suppose you have $1.47 in dimes and pennies. You have twice as many dimes as pennies. How many dimes do you have?

15. _____

Name _____

In 16–19, find each sum or difference.

16. $0.35 + 0.48$ 16. _____

17. $8.27 + 3.58$ 17. _____

18. $7.94 - 3.48$ 18. _____

19. $6.72 - 4.37$ 19. _____

In 20–21, choose the better unit to measure the object.

20. Distance from Chicago to Orlando: 20. _____
meter or kilometer

21. Length of a screwdriver: centimeter   21. _____
or meter

In 22–23, choose the symbol for ●.

22. 80 cm ● 8 m   22. _____

   A <   **B** >   **C** =

23. 8 km ● 8,000 m   23. _____

   A <   **B** >   **C** =

24. Complete: 4.8 m = ■ cm.   24. _____

25. Choose the better estimate of mass for a   25. _____
medium-sized dog: 39 g or 39 kg

26. Choose the better estimate of capacity for a   26. _____
coffeepot: 2 mL or 2 L

27. Choose the better estimate temperature for   27. _____
a warm, sunny summer day.

   A 100°C   **B** 85°C   **C** 30°C   **D** Not here

28. Performance Task Explain why you need to line up the
decimal points when adding and subtracting decimals.

_____

_____

_____

— Computation —

**In 1–2, estimate each sum or difference.
Round to the nearest whole number.**

1. $3.24 + 2.50$

    A 4   **B** 5   **C** 6   **D** 7

2. $6.75 - 3.21$

    A 3   **B** 4   **C** 5   **D** 6

In 3–10, find each sum or difference.

3. $0.23 + 0.68$

4. $7.58 + 5.46$

5. $8.73 - 2.49$

6. $7.63 - 3.48$

7. $\frac{1}{3} + \frac{1}{6}$

8. $\frac{1}{2} + \frac{1}{8}$

9. $\frac{2}{3} - \frac{1}{9}$

10. $\frac{3}{5} - \frac{3}{10}$

— Concepts —

11. Write a decimal for $6\frac{3}{10}$.

12. Write a decimal for four and thirty-five
hundredths.

13. Rewrite 0.40 in tenths.

14. Round 8.21 to the nearest whole number.

15. Round 3.52 to the nearest whole number

1. _____

2. _____

3. _____

4. _____

5. _____

6. _____

7. _____

8. _____

9. _____

10. _____

11. _____

12. _____

13. _____

14. _____

15. _____

Name _____

In 16–17, write the decimal for each fraction.

16 $\frac{9}{10}$ 16. _____

17. $\frac{6}{25}$ 17. _____

18. Complete: 0.98 ● 0.89. Use <, >, or =.   18. _____

19. Order from least to greatest:
0.56, 0.07, 1.21, 0.9, 1.03.   _____

20. Complete: 7 cm = ■ m.   20. _____

**In 21–22, choose the better unit of measure
for each object.**

21. Width of your desktop: centimeter or meter   21. _____

22. Length of a soccer field: meter or kilometer   22. _____

In 23–25, choose the better estimate for each.

23. Capacity of a water bucket: 16 mL or 16 L   23. _____

24. Weight of a canned ham: 3 g or 3 kg   24. _____

25. Temperature of a boiling pot of water   25. _____

   A 100°C   **B** 212°C   **C** 37°C   **D** Not here

26. Which of these numbers is prime?   26. _____

   A 0   **B** 8   **C** 10   **D** 17

━━ Applications ━━

27. Alicia has $2.50 in dimes and nickels. She   27. _____
has twice as many dimes as nickels. How
many dimes does she have?

   A 20 dimes   **B** 15 dimes   **C** 10 dimes   **D** 5 dimes

28. Dwayne weighs 10 more kilograms than   28. _____
Edward. Together they weigh 150 kilograms.
How much does Edward weigh?

In 1–5, find each quotient. Use mental math.

1. $80 \div 40$

2. $240 \div 60$

3. $630 \div 90$

4. $560 \div 70$

5. $280 \div 40$

In 6–8, estimate each quotient.

6. $729 \div 82$

7. $431 \div 74$

8. $477 \div 62$

9. Complete: $245 \div 80 \bullet 246 \div 80$.
Use $<$, $>$, or $=$.

10. Complete: $360 \div 6 \bullet 3{,}600 \div 60$.
Use $<$, $>$, or $=$.

In 11–17, divide and check.

11. $252 \div 40$

12. $576 \div 70$

13. $60 \overline{)429}$

14. $187 \div 91$

15. $337 \div 84$

16. $54 \overline{)498}$

17. $32 \overline{)293}$

18. Some spaceships travel 330 miles
in 55 seconds. How many miles
per second do they travel?

1. _____

2. _____

3. _____

4. _____

5. _____

6. _____

7. _____

8. _____

9. _____

10. _____

11. _____

12. _____

13. _____

14. _____

15. _____

16. _____

17. _____

18. _____

_____

Vocabulary: In 1–3, match each with its meaning.

1. certain   a. result of an action or event   1. _____

2. probability   b. definitely will happen   2. _____

3. outcome   c. the chance that an event   3. _____
                  will happen

In 4–5, write whether the event is impossible, unlikely, equally likely as unlikely, likely, or certain.

4. You will take a trip to Mars this year.   4. _____

5. A mosquito bite will be itchy.   5. _____

In 6, write whether the game is fair or unfair. If it is unfair, explain why.

6. Jamal gets one point if the spinner lands on A. Candy gets one point if the spinner lands on B.

_____

7. List all possible outcomes of tossing two pennies. Hint: a coin can land heads up or tails up.

_____

8. What is the probability of rolling a 4 on a number cube labeled 1–6? Write your answer as a fraction.   8. _____

9. In a survey of 20 students, 5 students say they prefer hamburgers to hot dogs. Based on this survey, how many students out of 200 would you expect to prefer hamburgers?   9. _____

10. Sean makes a sandwich with a slice of ham, a slice of cheese, a slice of lettuce, and a pickle. How many ways can he arrange his sandwich?   10. _____

Vocabulary: In 1–4, match each with its meaning.

1. unlikely

2. probability

3. impossible

4. outcome

a. the chance that an event will happen

b. result of an action or event

c. probably will not happen

d. definitely will not happen

1. _____

2. _____

3. _____

4. _____

In 5–7, find each quotient. Use mental math.

5. $180 \div 90$

6. $360 \div 60$

7. $210 \div 70$

5. _____

6. _____

7. _____

In 8–10, estimate each quotient.

8. $225 \div 72$

9. $468 \div 93$

10. $197 \div 48$

11. Complete: $276 \div 90 \bullet 275 \div 90$.
Use $<$, $>$, or $=$.

12. Complete: $640 \div 8 \bullet 6{,}400 \div 80$.
Use $<$, $>$, or $=$.

8. _____

9. _____

10. _____

11. _____

12. _____

In 13–18, divide and check.

13. $368 \div 40$

14. $429 \div 70$

15. $60\overline{)492}$

16. $132 \div 62$

17. $83\overline{)507}$

18. $94\overline{)756}$

13. _____

14. _____

15. _____

16. _____

17. _____

18. _____

Name _____

In 19–20, write whether the event is impossible, unlikely, equally likely as unlikely, likely, or certain.

19. The sun will rise tomorrow morning.

19. _____

20. It will snow in Washington, D.C., during January.

20. _____

In 21, write whether the game is fair or unfair. If it is unfair, explain why.

21. A box contains these letters: A, B, C, D, E, F. Kevin gets a point if he draws a vowel. Steve gets a point if he draws a consonant.

_____

22. A counter has a 1 on one side and a 4 on the other side. Another counter has a 3 on one side and a 7 on the other side. List all possible outcomes of flipping both counters.

22. _____

23. What is the probability of rolling an even number on a number cube labeled 1–6? Write your answer as a fraction.

23. _____

24. In a survey of 25 students, 5 students say they prefer to play basketball rather than baseball. Based on this survey, how many students out of 100 would you expect to play basketball?

24. _____

25. José has a model car, a model plane, a model tank, and a model boat. How many ways can he arrange them on a shelf?

25. _____

26. Explain Your Thinking Without finding the exact answer, tell whether 548 ÷ 90 will be greater than or less than 6. Explain.

_____

_____

_____

Name _____

Date _____ Score _____

Vocabulary: In 1–4, match each with its meaning.

1. certain

a. the chance that an event will happen

2. outcome

b. probably will happen

3. probability

c. result of an action or event

4. likely

d. definitely will happen

1. _____

2. _____

3. _____

4. _____

In 5–7, find each quotient. Use mental math.

5. $540 \div 60$

6. $480 \div 80$

7. $240 \div 80$

5. _____

6. _____

7. _____

In 8–10, estimate each quotient.

8. $628 \div 92$

9. $253 \div 41$

10. $463 \div 47$

8. _____

9. _____

10. _____

11. Complete: $480 \div 6 \bullet 4{,}800 \div 60$.
Use $<$, $>$, or $=$.

12. Complete: $812 \div 90 \bullet 815 \div 90$.
Use $<$, $>$, or $=$.

11. _____

12. _____

In 13–18, divide and check.

13. $368 \div 90$

14. $186 \div 20$

15. $70\overline{)423}$

16. $391 \div 76$

17. $38\overline{)235}$

18. $59\overline{)296}$

13. _____

14. _____

15. _____

16. _____

17. _____

18. _____

Name _____

In 19–20, write whether the event is impossible, unlikely, equally likely as unlikely, likely, or certain.

19. The Atlantic Ocean will dry up this year.

19. _____

20. Summer will be hot in New York City.

20. _____

In 21, write whether the game is fair or unfair. If it is unfair, explain why.

21. A box contains these letters: A, E, I, O, U. Ernesto gets a point is he draws a vowel. Isabel gets a point if she draws a consonant.

_____

22. A game tile has an A on one side and a B on the other side. A second tile has a C on one side and a D on the other. List all possible outcomes of flipping both counters.

22. _____

23. What is the probability of rolling a 4 on a number cube labeled 1–6? Write your answer as a fraction.

23. _____

24. In a survey of 30 students, 15 students say they prefer country music to rock music. Based on this survey, how many students out of 300 would you expect to prefer country music?

24. _____

25. Mercedes has a cooking book, a novel, a soccer book, and a dictionary. How many ways can she put the books on a shelf?

25. _____

26. **Explain Your Thinking** Without finding the exact answer, tell whether $419 \div 60$ will be greater than or less than 7.

_____

_____

_____

Give the letter of the correct answer.

In 1–5, find each quotient. Use mental math.

1. 60 ÷ 20

   A 30   **B** 3   **C** 20   **D** 2

1. _____

2. 320 ÷ 40

   A 8   **B** 80   **C** 90   **D** 9

2. _____

3. 640 ÷ 80

   A 80   **B** 8   **C** 60   **D** 6

3. _____

4. 720 ÷ 80

   A 80   **B** 8   **C** 90   **D** 9

4. _____

5. 210 ÷ 30

   A 3   **B** 30   **C** 7   **D** 70

5. _____

In 6–9, estimate each quotient.

6. 184 ÷ 91

   A About 2   **B** About 20   **C** About 90   **D** About 9

6. _____

7. 419 ÷ 52

   A About 80   **B** About 8   **C** About 90   **D** About 9

7. _____

8. 535 ÷ 64

   A About 80   **B** About 8   **C** About 90   **D** About 9

8. _____

9. 716 ÷ 87

   A About 7   **B** About 70   **C** About 8   **D** About 80

9. _____

10. Compare: 342 ÷ 80 ● 340 ÷ 80. Use <, >, or =.

   A <   **B** >   **C** =

10. _____

Name _____

In 11–18, divide and check.

11. 248 ÷ 40

    A 6   **B** 8 R8   **C** 6 R8   **D** Not here

11. _____

12. 166 ÷ 70

    A 2 R16   **B** 2 R26   **C** 2 R36   **D** Not here

12. _____

13. 375 ÷ 90

    A 4   **B** 4 R5   **C** 5 R5   **D** Not here

13. _____

14. 667 ÷ 94

    A 7   **B** 7 R11   **C** 7 R9   **D** Not here

14. _____

15. 513 ÷ 84

    A 6 R9   **B** 6 R13   **C** 6 R11   **D** Not here

15. _____

16. 76)‾387‾

    A 5 R17   **B** 5 R7   **C** 5 R87   **D** Not here

16. _____

17. 93)‾583‾

    A 6   **B** 6 R5   **C** 6 R15   **D** Not here

17. _____

18. 73)‾297‾

    A 4 R5   **B** 4 R15   **C** 4 R3   **D** Not here

18. _____

In 19–21, tell whether the event is impossible, unlikely, likely, or certain.

19. The sun shines brightly at night in Chicago.

    A Impossible   **B** Unlikely   **C** Likely   **D** Certain

19. _____

20. Three of your friends will go to the Arctic Circle.

    A Impossible   **B** Unlikely   **C** Likely   **D** Certain

20. _____

21. You will play with friends this weekend.

    A Impossible   **B** Unlikely   **C** Likely   **D** Certain

21. _____

Name _____

In 22–23, tell whether each game is fair or unfair.

22. Manuel gets one point
if the spinner lands on A.
Inge gets one point if
the spinner lands on B.

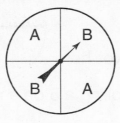

    A Fair   **B** Unfair

22. _____

23. Jackie gets one point if a number cube labeled 1–6
rolls an even number. Arlon gets one point if a
number cube rolls an odd number.

    A Fair   **B** Unfair

23. _____

24. A box contains 8 red tiles and 4 blue tiles. Zahara
chooses a tile without looking. She wins if the tile is
red. Clara wins if the tile is blue. How can you make
this game a fair game?

    A Add 6 blue tiles to the box.
    B Take away 4 blue tiles from the box.
    C Take away 4 red tiles from the box.
    D Add 6 yellow tiles to the box.

24. _____

25. A counter has a 1 on one side and a 2 on the other.
A second counter has a 3 on one side and a 4 on
the other. What are all possible outcomes of flipping
both counters?

    A 1, 2, 3, 4   **B** 1,3; 1,4; 2,3; 2,4
    C 1,2; 1,3; 1,4; 2,4 **D** 1,2; 2,3; 3,4; 4,1

25. _____

26. What are the possible
outcomes for spinning
both spinners together?

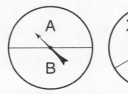

    A AB, XY, XZ   **B** AB, AX, AY, AZ, BX, BY, BZ
    C AX, AY, AZ, AB   **D** AX, AY, AZ, BX, BY, BZ

26. _____

27. Suppose you had a box with slips of paper
numbered from 1 to 10. If you select a slip without
looking, how many possible outcomes are there?

    A 1 outcome   **B** 11 outcomes   **C** 10 outcomes   **D** Not here

27. _____

Name _____

28. What is the probability of spinning a 3 on the spinner?

A $\frac{1}{2}$ B $\frac{1}{3}$ C $\frac{3}{4}$ D Not here

28. _____

29. What is the probability of rolling a 5 on a number cube labeled 1–6?

A $\frac{1}{6}$ B $\frac{5}{6}$ C $\frac{1}{2}$ D Not here

29. _____

30. What is the probability of drawing a black marble from a bag filled with 5 white marbles and 7 black marbles?

A $\frac{5}{6}$ B $\frac{5}{12}$ C $\frac{7}{12}$ D $\frac{5}{7}$

30. _____

31. In a survey of 40 students, 8 students say they prefer to ride their bikes to school. Based on this survey, how many students out of 400 would you expect to ride their bikes to school?

A 40 students   B 100 students
C 200 students   D 80 students

31. _____

32. In a survey of 40 students, 20 students say they prefer strawberry yogurt to vanilla yogurt. Based on this survey, how many students out of 400 would you expect to prefer strawberry yogurt?

A 200 students   B 25 students
C 150 students   D 15 students

32. _____

33. Isaac has a picture of his mother, a picture of his father, and a picture of his little sister. How many ways can Isaac arrange them on the wall?

A 6 ways   B 5 ways   C 3 ways   D Not here

33. _____

34. Caroline, Marcy, Hal, and Melvin are deciding in what order to line up for lunch. How many ways can they line up?

A 4 ways   B 8 ways   C 12 ways   D 24 ways

34. _____

35. Rhonda has 4 stuffed animals. How many ways can she arrange them on a shelf?

A 4 ways   B 8 ways   C 12 ways   D Not here

35. _____

As a reward for winning the school read-a-thon, the City Council awarded your class 525 tokens to use when playing games on Holiday Fair Day. The teacher distributes the tokens evenly among the students when you go to the fair.

At the end of the day, you and your classmates have played several games and have received 999 tickets that can be traded for prizes. The teacher distributes the tickets evenly among you and your classmates.

a. Recording Data Record the data in a table.

Number of students in class	Number of tokens	Number of tokens per student	Number of tickets	Number of tickets per student

b. Analyzing Data Use your table to analyze the data.

How many tickets will each student receive to exchange for prizes?

c. Think Critically The prizes you can get with tickets are shown below.

| ◦ 9 Tickets | ◦ 3 Tickets | ◦ 2 Tickets | ◦12 Tickets | ◦ 8 Tickets |

Which prizes will you choose to get with your tickets? How many of each prize will you get?

d. Making Decisions One of the games at the fair is shown below. Which spinner will you choose to play? Explain.

A = No Prizes
B = 10 Tickets
C = 1 Ticket
D = Spin Again

Teacher Notes

Concepts and Skills This activity requires students to:

- make decisions using real-life experiences.
- divide whole numbers, with and without remainders.
- multiply whole numbers.
- use probability to determine which game to play.

Guiding Questions

- If you have 12 prizes and want to share them with 3 people, will you multiply or divide to find how many to give each person?
- How do you estimate the answer to a division problem?
- How do you decide which outcome is most likely on a spinner?

Answers

a. Answers will vary depending upon the number of students in your class.

b. Check students' answers.

c. Answers will vary.

d. Answers will vary. The best chance of winning some tickets is with Spinners 1 and 4. However, Spinner 1 offers the best chances: a 1 in 4 chance of winning 1 ticket, a 1 in 4 chance of winning 10 tickets, and a 1 in 4 chance of spinning again.

Extension

Suppose these prizes were awarded for the spinners instead of tickets: A toy car; B ring; C puzzle; D no prize. Which spinner would you choose? Explain.

Evaluation

Level	Standard to be achieved for performance of specified level
4	**Full Achievement** The student completes the table with no errors and then selects a prize or prizes based upon logic within the given parameters. The choice of spinner at the arcade game illustrates an excellent understanding of probability outcomes.
3	**Substantial Achievement** The student completes the table and then selects prize selections, making few computational errors. He or she needs only minimal help in selecting the spinner that is the best choice and demonstrates a good understanding of probability outcomes.
2	**Partial Achievement** The student may need some help in completing the table and in making prize selections. Many computational errors occur. He or she cannot explain which spinner is the best choice and shows little understanding of probability outcomes.
1	**Little Achievement** The student needs considerable help in completing the table and cannot make prize selections logically and stay within the given number of tickets. He or she chooses a spinner at random and shows little understanding of probability outcomes.

In 1–4, find each quotient. Use mental math.

  1. $120 \div 40$ **1.** _____

  2. $420 \div 70$ **2.** _____

  3. $250 \div 50$ **3.** _____

  4. $180 \div 60$ **4.** _____

In 5–7, estimate each quotient.

  5. $437 \div 61$ **5.** _____

  6. $368 \div 72$ **6.** _____

  7. $831 \div 93$ **7.** _____

  8. Complete: $3{,}250 \div 80 \bullet 325 \div 8$.
      Use $<$, $>$, or $=$.   **8.** _____

In 9–14, divide and check.

  9. $429 \div 70$ **9.** _____

10. $647 \div 80$ **10.** _____

11. $354 \div 43$ **11.** _____

12. $437 \div 86$ **12.** _____

13. $97\overline{)308}$ **13.** _____

14. $81\overline{)578}$ **14.** _____

In 15–16, tell whether the event is impossible, unlikely, likely, or certain.

15. Comic book characters will come to life.   **15.** _____

    A Impossible   **B** Unlikely   **C** Likely   **D** Certain

16. It will snow during the month of July in Seattle.   **16.** _____

    A Certain   **B** Likely   **C** Unlikely   **D** Impossible

Name _____

In 17–18, write whether the game is fair or unfair. If it is unfair, explain why.

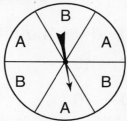

17. Gloria gets one point if the spinner lands on A. Wesley gets one point if the spinner lands on B.

_____

18. A counter is red on one side and white on the other side. A second counter is blue on one side and green on the other side. List all possible outcomes of flipping both counters.

_____

19. What is the probability of rolling a 2 on a number cube labeled 1–6? Write your answer as a fraction.

19. _____

A $\frac{1}{2}$ **B** $\frac{2}{6}$ **C** $\frac{2}{5}$ **D** Not here

20. What is the probability of drawing a blue gumball from a bag containing 4 red gumballs and 5 blue gumballs?

20. _____

A $\frac{4}{5}$ **B** $\frac{4}{9}$ **C** $\frac{5}{9}$ **D** Not here

21. In a survey of 50 students, 10 students say they like to read mystery books. Based on this survey, how many students out of 300 would you expect to prefer reading mystery books?

21. _____

22. Coley, Judy, Adela, and Laurel are deciding in what order to line up to have their picture taken. How many ways can they line up?

22. _____

A 4 ways   **B** 5 ways   **C** 6 ways   **D** Not here

23. Performance Task Carlene divided a number by 21 and wrote the answer as 5 R23. She decided her answer was not reasonable. Explain why.

_____

_____

— Computation —

In 1–2, find each quotient. Use mental math.

  1. $280 \div 70$ **1.** _____

  2. $300 \div 50$ **2.** _____

In 3–4, estimate each quotient.

  3. $329 \div 43$ **3.** _____

  4. $348 \div 53$ **4.** _____

  5. Complete: $245 \div 60 \bullet 243 \div 60$.   **5.** _____
     Use $<$, $>$, or $=$.

In 6–11, divide and check.

  6. $286 \div 40$ **6.** _____

  7. $569 \div 70$ **7.** _____

  8. $341 \div 83$ **8.** _____

  9. $392 \div 47$ **9.** _____

10. $73\overline{)593}$ **10.** _____

11. $65\overline{)328}$ **11.** _____

12. Find the product of 45×38.   **12.** _____

13. Find the product of $4 \times 3 \times 5$.   **13.** _____

— Concepts —

14. Give the elapsed time from 8:25 A.M. to 9:15 A.M.   **14.** _____

    A 1 hr 10 min   **B** 1 hr 15 min
    C 50 min   **D** Not here

15. Margaret has a 39-inch piece of lace.   **15.** _____
    How many 9-inch pieces can she cut to
    trim party favors?

Name _____

16. Continue the pattern: 3, 7, 5, 9, 7, ■, ■, ■.

16. _____

    A 8, 9, 10   **B** 4, 8, 5   **C** 11, 8, 12   **D** Not here

17. Write whether the following event is impossible, unlikely, equally likely as unlikely, likely, or certain. There will be no school during the month of May.

17. _____

    A Certain   **B** Likely   **C** Unlikely   **D** Impossible

18. Tell whether this game is fair or unfair. If it is unfair, explain why. Players toss a number cube with the numbers 1 through 6 on it. Dean gets one point if he tosses a 1, 2, or 3. Kayla gets one point if she tosses a 4 or 5.

_____

19. A counter has a 10 on one side and a 20 on the other side. A second counter has a 30 on one side and a 40 on the other side. List all possible outcomes of flipping both counters.

19. _____

    A 10, 20, 30, 40   **B** 10,20; 10,40; 30,20; 30,40
    C 10,30; 10,40; 20,30; 20,40   **D** Not here

20. What is the probability of rolling a 5 on a number cube labeled 1–6? Write your answer as a fraction.

20. _____

    A $\frac{1}{5}$ **B** $\frac{1}{6}$ **C** $\frac{1}{2}$ **D** Not here

21. Which is the better estimate of capacity for a pitcher of iced tea: 1 L or 1 mL?

21. _____

— Applications —

22. In a survey of 25 students, 5 students say they would rather watch cartoons than sports. Based on this survey, how many students out of 350 would you expect to prefer cartoons?

22. _____

23. Joan has 4 books. How many different ways can she put them on a shelf?

23. _____

    A 4 ways   **B** 8 ways   **C** 12 ways   **D** 24 ways

Name _____

Date _____ Score _____

Give the letter of the correct answer.

1. Which team scored the fewest number of points?

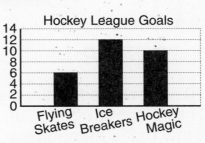

Hockey League Goals

A Flying Skates
B Ice Breakers
C Hockey Magic

1. _____

2. How many more goals did the Ice Breakers score than the Flying Skates?

A 2 goals   **B** 4 goals   **C** 6 goals   **D** 28 goals

2. _____

3. Give the value of the underlined digit in $\underline{7}2,468$.

A 700   **B** 7,000   **C** 70,000   **D** 700,000

3. _____

4. Give the elapsed time from 2:15 P.M. to 3:10 P.M.

A 1 hr 5 min   **B** 55 min
C 5 hr 25 min   **D** 1 hr 55 min

4. _____

5. Find $3,125 + 378 + 92$.

A 3,485   **B** 3,585   **C** 3,595   **D** Not here

5. _____

6. Find $4,139 - 2,742$.

A 2,397   **B** 1,497   **C** 2,817   **D** 1,397

6. _____

7. Continue the pattern: 4, 7, 5, 8, 6, 9, ■, ■, ■

A 7, 10, 8   **B** 12, 10, 13   **C** 10, 8, 11   **D** 4, 7, 5

7. _____

8. Donna bought a cassette for $7.95 and a CD for $11.95. How much change will she receive from a $20 bill?

A $0.01   **B** $0.10   **C** $2.10   **D** Not here

8. _____

9. Which number sentence represents the picture?

A $2 + 4 = 6$ **B** $6 - 2 = 4$
C $2 + 2 = 4$ **D** $3 \times 2 = 6$

9. _____

Name _____

10. Which is an even number?

    A 1   **B** 3   **C** 5   **D** Not here

10. _____

11. Which is a prime number?

    A 15   **B** 16   **C** 17   **D** 18

11. _____

12. Ilya brought 20 sandwiches to the class picnic. He brought 6 more hamburgers than chicken sandwiches. How many hamburgers did he bring?

    A 13 hamburgers   **B** 26 hamburgers
    C 14 hamburgers   **D** 9 hamburgers

12. _____

13. Estimate to decide if the product of 8 and 91 is less than, more than, or equal to 720.

    A Less than   **B** More than   **C** Equal to

13. _____

In 14–18, find the product.

14. $3 \times 4 \times 8$

    A 24   **B** 32   **C** 86   **D** 96

14. _____

15. 4×359

    A 1,436   **B** 1,206   **C** 1,236   **D** 1,338

15. _____

16. $6 \times \$9.28$

    A $5.45   **B** $64.50   **C** $55.68   **D** Not here

16. _____

17. 38×10

    A 3,800   **B** 380   **C** 38,000   **D** 38

17. _____

18.
$$\begin{array}{r} 726 \\ \times\ \ 35 \\ \hline \end{array}$$

    A 25,310   **B** 25,410   **C** 25,180   **D** 5,668

18. _____

19.
$$\begin{array}{r} 2{,}136 \\ \times\ \ \ \ 29 \\ \hline \end{array}$$

    A 19,224   **B** 23,496   **C** 61,944   **D** Not here

19. _____

Name _____

20. Jill is first in line. Lola is between Jill and Eve. Nan is standing behind Eve. Who is second in line?

   A Jill   **B** Lola   **C** Nan   **D** Eve

20. _____

21. Find $45 \div 7$.

   A 5   **B** 6   **C** 7 R4   **D** Not here

21. _____

22. Find $458 \div 5$.

   A 91 R3   **B** 90 R3   **C** 71 R3   **D** Not here

22. _____

23. Laura has a 14-inch long sub sandwich. How many servings can she cut that are each 5 inches long?

   A 4 servings   **B** 3 servings
   C 2 servings   **D** Not here

23. _____

24. Holly spent $25 at the mall. She had 2 ten-dollar bills and 4 one-dollar bills left in her wallet. How much money did she have in her wallet when she went to the mall?

   A $1   **B** $39   **C** $21   **D** $49

24. _____

25. Find the perimeter of the rectangle.

   A 20 cm   **B** 20 square cm
   C 18 cm   **D** 18 square cm

4cm

5cm

25. _____

26. Find the area of the rectangle.

   A 12 square in.   **B** 12 in.
   C 14 square in.   **D** 14 in.

3 in.

4 in.

26. _____

27. Give $\frac{11}{5}$ as a mixed number.

   A. $1\frac{5}{6}$ **B** $2\frac{5}{6}$ **C** $2\frac{1}{5}$ **D** Not here

27. _____

28. Choose the correct comparison.

   A $\frac{2}{5} > \frac{1}{10}$ **B** $\frac{7}{8} < \frac{3}{4}$ **C** $\frac{1}{2} < \frac{1}{4}$ **D** $\frac{2}{3} > \frac{7}{9}$

28. _____

29. Find $\frac{2}{3} + \frac{1}{6}$.

   A $\frac{3}{9}$ **B** $\frac{2}{6}$ **C** $\frac{5}{6}$ **D** $\frac{1}{3}$

29. _____

30. Find $\frac{9}{10} - \frac{3}{5}$.

30. _____

    A $\frac{3}{5}$ **B** $\frac{3}{10}$ **C** $\frac{6}{5}$ **D** Not here

31. Suppose you have 45 coins, all dimes and pennies, that total $2.52. How many dimes do you have?

31. _____

    A 21 dimes   **B** 22 dimes   **C** 23 dimes   **D** Not here

32. Order the decimals from least to greatest: 0.7, 0.35, 1.3.

32. _____

    A 0.7, 1.3, 0.35   **B** 0.35, 0.7, 1.3
    C 0.35, 1.3, 0.7   **D** 0.7, 0.35, 1.3

33. Find 16.4 + 2.93.

33. _____

    A 35.7   **B** 45.7   **C** 18.33   **D** 19.33

34. Find 11.02 − 8.31.

34. _____

    A 3.71   **B** 3.31   **C** 2.71   **D** Not here

35. The Anderson family made a 348-kilometer trip. How many meters did they travel?

35. _____

    A 34.8 meters   **B** 3,480 meters
    C 34,800 meters   **D** 348,000 meters

36. Ben's glass holds 250 milliliters of liquid. Helen's glass holds 0.325 liters. Whose glass holds more?

36. _____

    A Ben's glass   **B** Helen's glass

37. Find 640 ÷ 80.

37. _____

    A 8   **B** 80   **C** 800   **D** 8,000

38. Find 125 ÷ 60.

38. _____

    A. 20 R5   **B** 200 R5   **C** 2 R5   **D** Not here

39. Al, Monica, and Brett are deciding in what order to line up for lunch. How many ways can they line up?

39. _____

    A 1 way   **B** 2 ways   **C** 4 ways   **D** 6 ways

Table of Contents for Answer Forms

Using Answer Forms

The answer forms in the *Assessment Sourcebook* can be used by students to answer test questions. There are two types of answer forms included in the sourcebook, Answer Form for Multiple-Choice Tests and Answer Form for Student-Produced Answers. Although both are formatted for machine scoring, they are easy to score by hand. The form for multiple-choice answers can be used for items with as many as four answer choices. The form for student-produced answers allows students to record numerical answers up to four digits, or up to three digits with decimal points and division bars. Using both these forms gives students practice in recording answers in the machine-scorable format that they will encounter when they take standardized tests.

Answer Form for Multiple-Choice Tests

Students use this form to record answers for multiple-choice tests with as many as 60 items. Have students fill in the correct information in the first three items at the top of the form before they begin the test. Make sure they know what the name of the test is. After tests are scored, you or the student can record the score in the fourth blank.

Be sure students understand that the numbers on the form next to the letter choices correspond to the numbers of the test items on the test. The letters in the circles correspond to the answer choices on the test. When fewer than four letter choices appear for a given test item, students should ignore the extra choices on the answer form. Explain that students are to mark each answer by filling in the lettered circle that corresponds to the answer they choose. They should use a number 2 pencil.

Explain to students that once they have completed the last item of the test, they should leave the rest of the item choices on the form blank.

Before students begin the test, you might want to guide them through the process of completing the form. Have students record the answer to a practice item in the row labeled Practice at the top of the form. Use this Practice item to make sure students understand how to mark their answers.

Caution students to:
- mark the answer in the correct row for each test item;
- fill in only one circle for each test item;
- fill in the answer circle completely.

Answer Form for Student-Produced Answers

This form is for recording numerical answers to problems that students calculate. The format is used for machine-score tests. Many standardized tests such as the SATs use this type of answer form.

Because students write their answers in the spaces at the top of each answer block, this form is also easily hand-scored.

The form can be used for answers expressed as decimals and fractions, as well as for whole numbers. However, it can only accommodate answers with four or fewer digits.

Have students fill in the correct information in the first three items at the top of the form before they begin the test. Make sure they know what the name of the test is. After tests are scored, you or the student can record the score in the fourth blank.

Make sure students understand that the number beside each answer block corresponds to the number of a test item. Then explain how to use the form, referring to the sample answer blocks on the next page. There are two steps to recording each answer as they calculate.

Example 1: Whole Numbers
Suppose the answer is 114.

Step 1: Write the answer in the empty row of marked spaces at the top of the appropriate answer block, one digit to a space. The digit farthest right in the answer goes in the farthest right space, and so on. Write 4 in the rightmost space, 1 in the second space from the right, and 1 in the third. For whole numbers, the space farthest left is the thousands place and the space farthest right is the ones place.

Step 2: Fill in the oval that corresponds to each digit in the column below it. Fill in oval 4 in the righthand column, oval 1 in the second column from the right, and oval 1 in the third column.

Explain that because the answer in Example 1 has only three digits, the leftmost space and the column below it are not marked.

Make sure students understand how to use the form to record answers in fractions and decimals.

Example 2: Decimals
Suppose the answer is 2.34.

Step 1: Write the digits of the answer in the empty spaces, as before, but also write the decimal point in the correct space. Stress to students that a decimal point uses one space. For 2.34, write 2 in the first space, a decimal point in the second space, 3 in the third space, and 4 in the last space as shown.

Step 2: Fill in the oval that corresponds to each digit, as before. For the decimal point, fill in the oval with the decimal point in the column under the space in which the decimal point appears.

Example 3: Fractions
Suppose the answer is $\frac{2}{13}$.

Step 1: Write the digits and the division bar in order in the empty spaces, allowing a full space for the division bar.

Step 2: Fill in the oval that corresponds to the division bar and to each digit.

Explain to students that once they have completed the last item of the test, they should leave the rest of the form blank.

Remind students to:
- write the answer in the correct answer block for each test item;
- carry out both steps 1 and 2 in recording their answers;
- fill in ovals for the decimal point and division bars where appropriate;
- fill in the ovals completely;
- make sure filled-in ovals correspond to the answer they have written above.

Answer Form for Multiple-Choice Tests

Student _____   Date _____

Name of Test _____   Score _____

Practice. Ⓐ Ⓑ Ⓒ Ⓓ

1. Ⓐ Ⓑ Ⓒ Ⓓ   21. Ⓐ Ⓑ Ⓒ Ⓓ   41. Ⓐ Ⓑ Ⓒ Ⓓ
2. Ⓐ Ⓑ Ⓒ Ⓓ   22. Ⓐ Ⓑ Ⓒ Ⓓ   42. Ⓐ Ⓑ Ⓒ Ⓓ
3. Ⓐ Ⓑ Ⓒ Ⓓ   23. Ⓐ Ⓑ Ⓒ Ⓓ   43. Ⓐ Ⓑ Ⓒ Ⓓ
4. Ⓐ Ⓑ Ⓒ Ⓓ   24. Ⓐ Ⓑ Ⓒ Ⓓ   44. Ⓐ Ⓑ Ⓒ Ⓓ
5. Ⓐ Ⓑ Ⓒ Ⓓ   25. Ⓐ Ⓑ Ⓒ Ⓓ   45. Ⓐ Ⓑ Ⓒ Ⓓ

6. Ⓐ Ⓑ Ⓒ Ⓓ   26. Ⓐ Ⓑ Ⓒ Ⓓ   46. Ⓐ Ⓑ Ⓒ Ⓓ
7. Ⓐ Ⓑ Ⓒ Ⓓ   27. Ⓐ Ⓑ Ⓒ Ⓓ   47. Ⓐ Ⓑ Ⓒ Ⓓ
8. Ⓐ Ⓑ Ⓒ Ⓓ   28. Ⓐ Ⓑ Ⓒ Ⓓ   48. Ⓐ Ⓑ Ⓒ Ⓓ
9. Ⓐ Ⓑ Ⓒ Ⓓ   29. Ⓐ Ⓑ Ⓒ Ⓓ   49. Ⓐ Ⓑ Ⓒ Ⓓ
10. Ⓐ Ⓑ Ⓒ Ⓓ   30. Ⓐ Ⓑ Ⓒ Ⓓ   50. Ⓐ Ⓑ Ⓒ Ⓓ

11. Ⓐ Ⓑ Ⓒ Ⓓ   31. Ⓐ Ⓑ Ⓒ Ⓓ   51. Ⓐ Ⓑ Ⓒ Ⓓ
12. Ⓐ Ⓑ Ⓒ Ⓓ   32. Ⓐ Ⓑ Ⓒ Ⓓ   52. Ⓐ Ⓑ Ⓒ Ⓓ
13. Ⓐ Ⓑ Ⓒ Ⓓ   33. Ⓐ Ⓑ Ⓒ Ⓓ   53. Ⓐ Ⓑ Ⓒ Ⓓ
14. Ⓐ Ⓑ Ⓒ Ⓓ   34. Ⓐ Ⓑ Ⓒ Ⓓ   54. Ⓐ Ⓑ Ⓒ Ⓓ
15. Ⓐ Ⓑ Ⓒ Ⓓ   35. Ⓐ Ⓑ Ⓒ Ⓓ   55. Ⓐ Ⓑ Ⓒ Ⓓ

16. Ⓐ Ⓑ Ⓒ Ⓓ   36. Ⓐ Ⓑ Ⓒ Ⓓ   56. Ⓐ Ⓑ Ⓒ Ⓓ
17. Ⓐ Ⓑ Ⓒ Ⓓ   37. Ⓐ Ⓑ Ⓒ Ⓓ   57. Ⓐ Ⓑ Ⓒ Ⓓ
18. Ⓐ Ⓑ Ⓒ Ⓓ   38. Ⓐ Ⓑ Ⓒ Ⓓ   58. Ⓐ Ⓑ Ⓒ Ⓓ
19. Ⓐ Ⓑ Ⓒ Ⓓ   39. Ⓐ Ⓑ Ⓒ Ⓓ   59. Ⓐ Ⓑ Ⓒ Ⓓ
20. Ⓐ Ⓑ Ⓒ Ⓓ   40. Ⓐ Ⓑ Ⓒ Ⓓ   60. Ⓐ Ⓑ Ⓒ Ⓓ

Answer Form for Student-Produced Answers

Student _____   Date _____

Name of Test _____   Score _____

Table of Contents for Answers

Answers

Name _____

Date _____ Score _____

Chapter 1 Test
Form
A

Vocabulary: In 1–3, match each with its meaning.

1. variable
   a. a group of data that appear often on a line plot

2. cluster
   b. numbers that show the units on a graph

3. scale
   c. a letter that stands for a number or a range of numbers

1. ___**c**___

2. ___**a**___

3. ___**b**___

In 4–6, use the bar graph.

4. Which color was chosen most often?

   ___**Blue**___

5. How many more people chose yellow than red?

   ___**2 more**___

6. Add a bar to show that 4 persons chose purple as their favorite color.

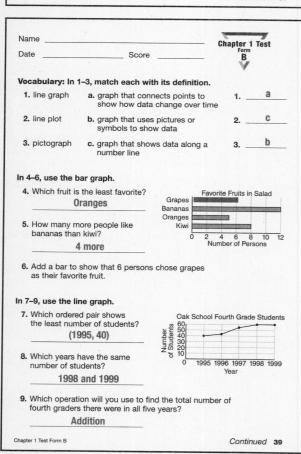

Favorite Colors

Purple / Red / Blue / Yellow — Number of Persons 0–12

In 7–9, use the line graph.

7. What ordered pair shows the height of the plant for Day 6?

   ___**(6, 8)**___

8. What was the plant's height on Day 3?

   ___**4 in.**___

9. Which operation will you use to find how much the plant grew from Day 2 to Day 9?

   ___**Subtraction**___

Plant Growth — Height (in.) vs Day

Chapter 1 Test Form A

Continued 37

Name _____

In 10–12, use the line plot.

10. How many students scored 90 points?

   ___**4 students**___

11. What is the most common score?

   ___**95 points**___

12. Two students scored 105. Add their scores to the line plot.

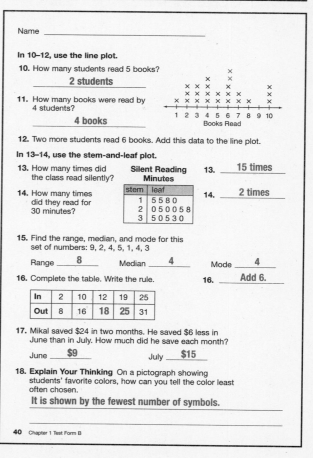

Game Scores (points) 80 85 90 95 100 105

In 13–14, use the stem-and-leaf plot.

13. How many birthdays are on the 20th day?

14. How many birthdays are shown in the plot?

Birthdays	
stem	leaf
0	1 2 5 8 9
1	2 6 9 9 7
2	0 9 0 3 6 7 8 3

13. ___**2 birthdays**___

14. ___**18 birthdays**___

15. Find the range, median, and mode for the set of numbers. Use this set of numbers. 2 9 7 1 3 2 8

   Range ___**8**___   Median ___**3**___   Mode ___**2**___

16. Complete the table. Write the rule.

   ___**Subtract 3.**___

In	18	16	14	12	10
Out	15	13	**11**	**9**	7

17. Su earned $18 in two weeks. She earned $4 more this week than last week. How much did Su earn each week?

   Last week ___**$7**___   This week ___**$11**___

18. **Explain Your Thinking** On a bar graph showing students' favorite sports, explain how you can tell the sport most often chosen.

   ___**It is shown by the longest bar.**___

38 Chapter 1 Test Form A

Name _____

Date _____ Score _____

Chapter 1 Test
Form
B

Vocabulary: In 1–3, match each with its definition.

1. line graph
   a. graph that connects points to show how data change over time

2. line plot
   b. graph that uses pictures or symbols to show data

3. pictograph
   c. graph that shows data along a number line

1. ___**a**___

2. ___**c**___

3. ___**b**___

In 4–6, use the bar graph.

4. Which fruit is the least favorite?

   ___**Oranges**___

5. How many more people like bananas than kiwi?

   ___**4 more**___

6. Add a bar to show that 6 persons chose grapes as their favorite fruit.

Favorite Fruits in Salad

Grapes / Bananas / Oranges / Kiwi — Number of Persons 0–12

In 7–9, use the line graph.

7. Which ordered pair shows the least number of students?

   ___**(1995, 40)**___

8. Which years have the same number of students?

   ___**1998 and 1999**___

9. Which operation will you use to find the total number of fourth graders there were in all five years?

   ___**Addition**___

Oak School Fourth Grade Students — Number of Students vs Year 1995–1999

Chapter 1 Test Form B

Continued 39

Name _____

In 10–12, use the line plot.

10. How many students read 5 books?

   ___**2 students**___

11. How many books were read by 4 students?

   ___**4 books**___

12. Two more students read 6 books. Add this data to the line plot.

Books Read 1 2 3 4 5 6 7 8 9 10

In 13–14, use the stem-and-leaf plot.

13. How many times did the class read silently?

14. How many times did they read for 30 minutes?

Silent Reading Minutes	
stem	leaf
1	5 5 8 0
2	0 5 0 0 5 8
3	5 0 5 3 0

13. ___**15 times**___

14. ___**2 times**___

15. Find the range, median, and mode for this set of numbers: 9, 2, 4, 5, 1, 4, 3

   Range ___**8**___   Median ___**4**___   Mode ___**4**___

16. Complete the table. Write the rule.

16. ___**Add 6.**___

In	2	10	12	19	25
Out	8	16	**18**	**25**	31

17. Mikal saved $24 in two months. He saved $6 less in June than in July. How much did he save each month?

   June ___**$9**___   July ___**$15**___

18. **Explain Your Thinking** On a pictograph showing students' favorite colors, how can you tell the color least often chosen.

   ___**It is shown by the fewest number of symbols.**___

40 Chapter 1 Test Form B

Chapter 2 Test — Form A

Name _____

Date _____ Score _____

Vocabulary: In 1–3, match each with its example.

1. expanded form   **a.** the length of time between 3:30 A.M. and 6:00 A.M.   1. ___b___

2. digits   **b.** 1,000 + 500 + 30 + 9   2. ___c___

3. elapsed time   **c.** 0, 1, 2, 3, 4, 5, 6, 7, 8, 9   3. ___a___

In 4–7, write the value of the underlined digit.

4. 5,7<u>8</u>3   4. ___80___

5. 40,<u>7</u>19   5. ___700___

6. <u>2</u>26,855   6. ___200,000___

7. <u>6</u>,119,088   7. ___6,000,000___

8. Write the word name for 402,000. ___Four hundred two thousand___

9. Write fifty million, six hundred thirty-eight in standard form.   9. ___50,000,638___

In 10–11, complete the table. Write how many ones, tens and hundreds are in each number.

	Number	Hundreds	Tens	Ones
10.	500	5	50	500
11.	3,200	32	320	3,200

In 12–14, compare. Write >, <, or =.

12. 8,601 ■ 7,899   13. 33,812 ■ 33,182   14. 5,455 ■ 54,555

    ___>___   ___>___   ___<___

15. How many different outfits can Jere make if she has red and blue skirts and yellow, green, and white sweaters? Make an organized list to show the outfits.
    ___RY, RG, RW, BY, BG, BW; 6 outfits___

Chapter 2 Test Form A   *Continued*   **55**

Name _____

In 16–17, order the numbers from least to greatest.

16. 36,551   63,155   36,515   ___36,515; 36,551; 63,155___

17. 701,107   707,101   701,701   ___701,107; 701,701; 707,101___

18. Round 5,601 to the nearest thousand.   18. ___6,000___

19. Round 3,482 to the nearest thousand.   19. ___3,000___

In 20–21, write each time two different ways.

20.

21. `6:12`

Possible answers:

20. ___3:40___ / ___20 min before 4___

21. ___12 min after 6___ / ___48 min before 7___

22. Does a store close at 9:00 A.M. or 9:00 P.M.?   22. ___9:00 P.M.___

In 23–25, compare. Write >, <, or =.

23. 8 weeks ■ 3 months   23. ___<___

24. 200 minutes ■ 2 hours   24. ___>___

25. 18 months ■ 2 years   25. ___<___

In 26–28, write each elapsed time.

26. 5:15 P.M. to 5:15 A.M.   26. ___12 hours___

27. 2:00 P.M. to 4:00 P.M.   27. ___2 hours___

28. 1:45 P.M. to 2:15 P.M.   28. ___30 minutes___

29. Which month is the seventh month of the year?   29. ___July___

30. How many months have 31 days?   30. ___7 months___

31. **Explain Your Thinking** Write a 3-digit and a 4-digit number that round to the same number when rounded to the nearest hundred. Explain.
___Any number between 950 and 999, and 1,001 and 1,049 will round to 1,000 when rounded to the nearest hundred.___

56   Chapter 2 Test Form A

Chapter 2 Test — Form B

Name _____

Date _____ Score _____

Vocabulary: In 1–3, match each with its example.

1. standard form   **a.** a year with 366 days   1. ___b___

2. ordinal number   **b.** 35,992,106   2. ___c___

3. leap year   **c.** fourth   3. ___a___

In 4–7, give the value of the underlined digit.

4. 6,<u>8</u>45   4. ___800___

5. 25,86<u>7</u>   5. ___7___

6. 622,7<u>5</u>4,013   6. ___50,000___

7. 324,<u>5</u>60,993   7. ___4,000,000___

8. Write the word name for 7,036. ___Seven thousand thirty-six___

9. Write forty-three million, two hundred thousand seven in standard form.   9. ___43,200,007___

In 10–11, complete the table. Write how many ones, tens, and hundreds are in each number.

	Number	Hundreds	Tens	Ones
10.	500	5	50	500
11.	6,000	60	600	6,000

In 12–14, compare. Write >, <, or =.

12. 8,992 ■ 8,299   13. 4,056 ■ 4,065   14. 55,319 ■ 55,391

    ___>___   ___<___   ___<___

15. How many different outfits can Bob make if he has blue, green, and tan trousers and white and yellow sweaters? Make an organized list to show the outfits.
    ___BW, BY, GW, GY, TW, TY; 6 outfits___

Chapter 2 Test Form B   *Continued*   **57**

Name _____

In 16–17, order the numbers from least to greatest.

16. 48,771   48,177   47,871   ___47,871; 48,177; 48,771___

17. 352,244   253,442   243,552   ___243,552; 253,442; 352,244___

18. Round 4,561 to the nearest thousand.   18. ___5,000___

19. Round 6,025 to the nearest thousand.   19. ___6,000___

In 20–21, write each time two different ways.

20.

21. `2:51`

Possible answers:

20. ___6:10___ / ___10 min after 6___

21. ___51 min after 2___ / ___9 min before 3___

22. Are your classes over at 3:30 A.M. or 3:30 P.M.?   22. ___3:30 P.M.___

In 23–25, compare. Write >, <, or =.

23. 12 days ■ 2 weeks   23. ___<___

24. 2 hours ■ 250 minutes   24. ___<___

25. 2 years ■ 16 months   25. ___>___

In 26–28, write each elapsed time.

26. 2:30 P.M. to 5:30 P.M.   26. ___3 hours___

27. 3:15 A.M. to 3:15 P.M.   27. ___12 hours___

28. 3:15 P.M. to 4:45 P.M.   28. ___1 hour 30 min___

29. Which month is the first month of the year?   29. ___January___

30. How many months have fewer than 31 days?   30. ___5 months___

31. **Explain Your Thinking** Write a 4-digit and a 5-digit number that round to the same number when rounded to the nearest hundred. Explain.
___Any number between 9,950 and 9,999, and 10,001 and 10,049 will round to 10,000 when rounded to the nearest hundred.___

58   Chapter 2 Test Form B

Answers for Chapter Tests Forms A and B   **271**

Form A (top left)

Name _____

Date _____ Score _____

Vocabulary: In 1–3, match each word with its meaning.

1. difference   a. a way to estimate by first looking at the leading digits   1. ___b___

2. estimate   b. number obtained by subtracting   2. ___c___

3. front-end estimation   c. to find a number close to an exact amount   3. ___a___

In 4, complete each number sentence.

4. $7 + 2 = 9$

$70 + 20 = n$ $70 + 20 = 90$

$700 + 200 = 900$

$7,000 + 2,000 = n$ $7,000 + 2,000 = 9,000$

In 5–7, find each sum or difference. Use mental math.

5. $540 + 200$ 6. $360 + 630$ 7. $780 - 420$

    740   990   360

In 8–10, estimate each sum or difference. Round to the nearest hundred.

8. $768 - 284$ 9. $933 - 645$ 10. $529 + 255$

    500   300   800

11. Jay ran a 100-yard dash in 14 seconds. Is the time an exact amount or an estimate?   11. __Exact amount__

In 12–15, find each sum. Estimate to check.

12. $723 + 538$ 12. __1,261__

13. $\begin{array}{r} 4,825 \\ +\ \ 987 \\ \hline 5,812 \end{array}$ 14. $\begin{array}{r} 756 \\ 2,483 \\ +4,309 \\ \hline 7,548 \end{array}$ 15. $\begin{array}{r} 6,987 \\ 7,435 \\ +\ \ 123 \\ \hline 14,545 \end{array}$

16. Find $643 - 291$.   16. __352__

Form A (top right)

Name _____

In 17–19, subtract. Add or estimate to check.

17. $\begin{array}{r} 829 \\ -473 \\ \hline 356 \end{array}$ 18. $\begin{array}{r} 4,071 \\ -2,895 \\ \hline 1,176 \end{array}$ 19. $\begin{array}{r} 6,001 \\ -5,878 \\ \hline 123 \end{array}$

20. Leo earned $290 mowing lawns and $340 pulling weeds. He spent $125. How much did he have left?   20. __$505__

In 21–23, find the sum or difference.

21. $\begin{array}{r} 8,620 \\ -4,000 \\ \hline 4,620 \end{array}$ 22. $\begin{array}{r} 1,468 \\ +3,929 \\ \hline 5,397 \end{array}$ 23. $\begin{array}{r} 3,200 \\ +4,704 \\ \hline 7,904 \end{array}$

In 24–25, compare. Write <, >, or =.

24. $164 ● $16.40   24. ___>___

25. $7.49 ● $14.49   25. ___<___

In 26–28, add or subtract. Estimate to check.

26. $\begin{array}{r} \$24.65 \\ +\ 35.98 \\ \hline \$60.63 \end{array}$ 27. $\begin{array}{r} \$30.69 \\ +\ 29.77 \\ \hline \$60.46 \end{array}$ 28. $\begin{array}{r} \$57.00 \\ -\ 29.88 \\ \hline \$27.12 \end{array}$

29. Ana gives the cashier $5.00 for three items costing $1.50 each. How much change will she receive?   29. __50¢__

In 30–31, find the value for each n.

30. $18 + n = 40$ 30. __22__

31. $n + 400 = 700$ 31. __300__

32. Tiger had $10. Then he saved $4 each week. How much money did he have after 5 weeks?   32. __$30__

33. **Explain Your Thinking** Explain how Agatha could use mental math to find $700 - 196$.
   Possible answer: Add 4 to each number and subtract to get 504.

Form B (bottom left)

Name _____

Date _____ Score _____

Vocabulary: In 1–3, match each with its meaning.

1. addends   a. a number obtained by adding   1. ___b___

2. sum   b. numbers that are added together to make a sum   2. ___a___

3. decimal point   c. a symbol that separates dollar and cent amounts   3. ___c___

In 4, complete each number sentence.

4. $4 + 3 = 7$

$40 + n = 70$ $40 + 30 = 70$

$400 + 300 = 700$

$4,000 + n = 7,000$ $4,000 + 3,000 = 7,000$

In 5–7, find each sum or difference. Use mental math.

5. $430 + 200$ 6. $560 - 310$ 7. $670 - 450$

    630   250   220

In 8–10, estimate each sum or difference. Round to the nearest hundred.

8. $568 + 291$ 9. $255 + 640$ 10. $928 - 799$

    900   900   100

11. David set a school record in pancake eating. Is the record an exact amount or an estimate?   11. __Exact amount__

In 12–15, find each sum. Estimate to check.

12. $856 + 109$ 12. __965__

13. $\begin{array}{r} 2,964 \\ +\ \ 857 \\ \hline 3,821 \end{array}$ 14. $\begin{array}{r} 627 \\ 4,521 \\ +1,234 \\ \hline 6,382 \end{array}$ 15. $\begin{array}{r} 8,296 \\ 928 \\ +9,563 \\ \hline 18,787 \end{array}$

16. Find $679 - 231$.   16. __448__

Form B (bottom right)

Name _____

In 17–19, subtract. Add or estimate to check.

17. $\begin{array}{r} 1,964 \\ -\ \ 577 \\ \hline 1,387 \end{array}$ 18. $\begin{array}{r} 6,207 \\ -4,521 \\ \hline 1,686 \end{array}$ 19. $\begin{array}{r} 8,006 \\ -4,927 \\ \hline 3,079 \end{array}$

20. Toi earned $160 cleaning and $450 walking dogs. She spent $145. How much does she have left?   20. __$465__

In 21–23, find the sum or difference.

21. $\begin{array}{r} 1,500 \\ +3,260 \\ \hline 4,760 \end{array}$ 22. $\begin{array}{r} 5,970 \\ -3,000 \\ \hline 2,970 \end{array}$ 23. $\begin{array}{r} 8,236 \\ -4,389 \\ \hline 3,847 \end{array}$

In 24–25, compare. Write <, >, or =.

24. $17.76 ● $175.60   24. ___<___

25. $19.17 ● $16.20   25. ___>___

In 26–28, add or subtract. Estimate to check.

26. $\begin{array}{r} \$27.66 \\ +\ 94.29 \\ \hline \$121.95 \end{array}$ 27. $\begin{array}{r} \$56.78 \\ +\ \ 8.05 \\ \hline \$64.83 \end{array}$ 28. $\begin{array}{r} \$59.00 \\ -\ 39.37 \\ \hline \$19.63 \end{array}$

29. Derek gives a cashier $10 for three items which cost $1.65 each. How much change will he receive?   29. __$5.05__

In 30–31, find the value for each n.

30. $n + 20 = 45$ 30. __25__

31. $60 = n + 10$ 31. __50__

32. Mariko had $15. Then she saved $5 each week. How much did she have after 4 weeks?   32. __$35__

33. **Explain Your Thinking** Explain how Deidre could use mental math to find $375 + 199$.   **Possible answer: Add 1 to 199 and add. Then subtract 1 from the sum to get 574.**

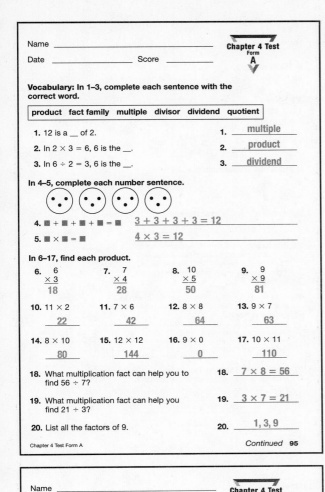

Name _____

Date _____ Score _____

Vocabulary: In 1–3, complete each sentence with the correct word.

product fact family multiple divisor dividend quotient

1. 12 is a ___ of 2.   **1.** _multiple_

2. In 2 × 3 = 6, 6 is the ___.   **2.** _product_

3. In 6 ÷ 2 = 3, 6 is the ___.   **3.** _dividend_

In 4–5, complete each number sentence.

4. ■ + ■ + ■ + ■ = ■   _3 + 3 + 3 + 3 = 12_

5. ■ × ■ = ■   _4 × 3 = 12_

In 6–17, find each product.

6. 6 × 3 = **18**

7. 7 × 4 = **28**

8. 10 × 5 = **50**

9. 9 × 9 = **81**

10. 11 × 2 = **22**

11. 7 × 6 = **42**

12. 8 × 8 = **64**

13. 9 × 7 = **63**

14. 8 × 10 = **80**

15. 12 × 12 = **144**

16. 9 × 0 = **0**

17. 10 × 11 = **110**

18. What multiplication fact can help you to find 56 ÷ 7?   **18.** _7 × 8 = 56_

19. What multiplication fact can help you find 21 ÷ 3?   **19.** _3 × 7 = 21_

20. List all the factors of 9.   **20.** _1, 3, 9_

Chapter 4 Test Form A   *Continued* **95**

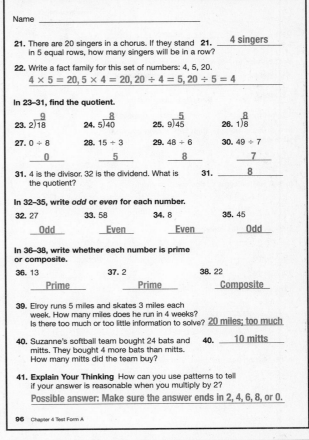

Name _____

21. There are 20 singers in a chorus. If they stand in 5 equal rows, how many singers will be in a row?   **21.** _4 singers_

22. Write a fact family for this set of numbers: 4, 5, 20.
_4 × 5 = 20, 5 × 4 = 20, 20 ÷ 4 = 5, 20 ÷ 5 = 4_

In 23–31, find the quotient.

23. 2)18 = **9**

24. 5)40 = **8**

25. 9)45 = **5**

26. 1)8 = **8**

27. 0 ÷ 8 = **0**

28. 15 ÷ 3 = **5**

29. 48 ÷ 6 = **8**

30. 49 ÷ 7 = **7**

31. 4 is the divisor. 32 is the dividend. What is the quotient?   **31.** _8_

In 32–35, write odd or even for each number.

32. 27 — **Odd**

33. 58 — **Even**

34. 8 — **Even**

35. 45 — **Odd**

In 36–38, write whether each number is prime or composite.

36. 13 — **Prime**

37. 2 — **Prime**

38. 22 — **Composite**

39. Elroy runs 5 miles and skates 3 miles each week. How many miles does he run in 4 weeks? Is there too much or too little information to solve? _20 miles; too much_

40. Suzanne's softball team bought 24 bats and mitts. They bought 4 more bats than mitts. How many mitts did the team buy?   **40.** _10 mitts_

41. **Explain Your Thinking** How can you use patterns to tell if your answer is reasonable when you multiply by 2?
Possible answer: Make sure the answer ends in 2, 4, 6, 8, or 0.

96   Chapter 4 Test Form A

Name _____

Date _____ Score _____

Vocabulary: In 1–3, complete each sentence with the correct word.

factor fact family multiple quotient divisor dividend

1. In 28 ÷ 7 = 4, 7 is the ___.   **1.** _divisor_

2. 24 is a ___ of 4.   **2.** _multiple_

3. In 8 × 2 = 16, 2 is a ___.   **3.** _factor_

In 4–5, complete each number sentence.

4. ■ + ■ + ■ + ■ = ■   _5 + 5 + 5 + 5 = 20_

5. ■ × ■ = ■   _4 × 5 = 20_

In 6–17, find each product.

6. 8 × 4 = **32**

7. 7 × 3 = **21**

8. 11 × 5 = **55**

9. 5 × 9 = **45**

10. 10 × 2 = **20**

11. 7 × 8 = **56**

12. 7 × 7 = **49**

13. 8 × 6 = **48**

14. 7 × 11 = **77**

15. 12 × 10 = **120**

16. 7 × 0 = **0**

17. 11 × 12 = **132**

18. What multiplication fact can help you find 72 ÷ 8?   **18.** _8 × 9 = 72_

19. What multiplication fact can help you find 24 ÷ 4?   **19.** _4 × 6 = 24_

20. List all the factors of 15.   **20.** _1, 3, 5, 15_

Chapter 4 Test Form B   *Continued* **97**

Name _____

21. There are 72 students at a baseball camp. If there will be 9 players on each team, how many teams will there be?   **21.** _8 teams_

22. Write a fact family for this set of numbers: 5, 7, 35.
_5 × 7 = 35, 7 × 5 = 35, 35 ÷ 5 = 7, 35 ÷ 7 = 5_

In 23–30, find each quotient.

23. 2)16 = **8**

24. 5)25 = **5**

25. 9)81 = **9**

26. 9)9 = **1**

27. 0 ÷ 6 = **0**

28. 36 ÷ 4 = **9**

29. 42 ÷ 7 = **6**

30. 54 ÷ 6 = **9**

31. 18 is the dividend. 3 is the divisor. What is the quotient?   **31.** _6_

In 32–35, write odd or even for each number.

32. 67 — **Odd**

33. 38 — **Even**

34. 49 — **Odd**

35. 32 — **Even**

In 36–38, write whether each number is prime or composite.

36. 30 — **Composite**

37. 17 — **Prime**

38. 25 — **Composite**

39. Tania lives 5 blocks from school and 3 blocks from the mall. How many blocks does she travel to and from school in 5 days? Is there too much or too little information to solve? _50 blocks; too much_

40. Art has 18 model cars and ships. He has 8 more cars than ships. How many cars does he have?   **40.** _13 cars_

41. **Explain Your Thinking** How can you use patterns to tell if your answer is reasonable when you multiply by 5?
Possible answer: Make sure the answer ends in 0 or 5.

98   Chapter 4 Test Form B

Answers for Chapter Tests Forms A and B   **273**

Date _____ Score _____

Vocabulary: In 1–3, match each with its meaning.

1. product   a. data arranged in rows and columns   1. ___b___

2. array   b. multiplication answer   2. ___a___

3. factor   c. number being multiplied   3. ___c___

In 4–5, use a multiplication fact to help you find each product.

4. 8×20 4. ___160___

5. 9×70 5. ___630___

In 6–7, use patterns to find each product.

6. $7 \times 3 =$ __21__ $7 \times 30 =$ __210__ $7 \times 300 =$ __2,100__

7. $5 \times 6 =$ __30__ $5 \times 60 =$ __300__ $5 \times 600 =$ __3,000__

In 8–10, estimate each product.

8. 4×91 8. ___360___

9. 48×6 9. ___300___

10. 3×76 10. ___240___

11. Use the array to help you find the product.   11. ___68___

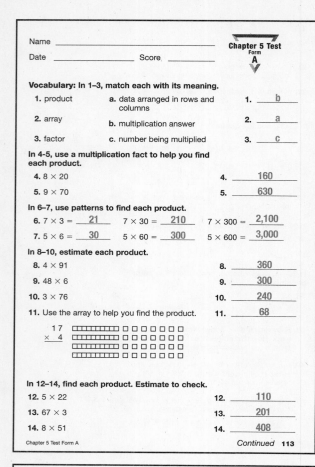

17×4

In 12–14, find each product. Estimate to check.

12. 5×22 12. ___110___

13. 67×3 13. ___201___

14. 8×51 14. ___408___

In 15–20, multiply.

15. 417×9 16. 307×6 15. ___3,753___

16. ___1,842___

17. $8,005 \times 3$ 18. $8,208 \times 3$ 17. ___24,015___

18. ___24,624___

19. $\$3.75 \times 5$ 20. $\$16.41 \times 6$ 19. ___\$18.75___

20. ___\$98.46___

In 21–22, use mental math to multiply.

21. 5×52 21. ___260___

22. 65×3 22. ___195___

23. Write $4 \times 7 \times 5$ in three different ways. Then solve.
$(4 \times 7) \times 5;\ 4 \times (7 \times 5);\ (4 \times 5) \times 7;\ 140$

24. Brenda and three friends went bowling. It cost each person $1.25 to rent shoes and $1.75 to play a game. They each bowled 2 games. How much did it cost the group altogether?   24. ___\$19.00___

25. Alice needs 48 plates. Plates come in packs of 8. Complete the table to find how many packs she needs.   25. ___6 packs___

Number of packs	1	2	3	4	5	6
Number of plates	8	16	24	32	40	48

26. **Explain Your Thinking** Explain how multiplying money amounts is like multiplying whole numbers.
First multiply as though both were whole numbers. Then place the decimal point in the answer.

Date _____ Score _____

Vocabulary: In 1–3, match each with its meaning.

1. multiple   a. data arranged in rows and columns   1. ___b___

2. product   b. product of a given number and a whole number   2. ___c___

3. array   c. multiplication answer   3. ___a___

In 4–5, use a multiplication fact to help find each product.

4. 4×90 4. ___360___

5. 7×300 5. ___2,100___

In 6–7, use patterns to find each product.

6. $9 \times 3 =$ __27__ $9 \times 30 =$ __270__ $9 \times 300 =$ __2,700__

7. $8 \times 5 =$ __40__ $8 \times 50 =$ __400__ $8 \times 500 =$ __4,000__

In 8–10, estimate each product.

8. 6×82 8. ___480___

9. 57×6 9. ___360___

10. 3×48 10. ___150___

11. Use the array to help you find the product.   11. ___42___

14×3

In 12–14, find each product. Estimate to check.

12. 46×4 12. ___184___

13. 8×56 13. ___448___

14. 92×7 14. ___644___

In 15–20, multiply.

15. 328×7 16. 502×7 15. ___2,296___

16. ___3,514___

17. $7,060 \times 9$ 18. $3,405 \times 6$ 17. ___63,540___

18. ___20,430___

19. $\$6.30 \times 7$ 20. $\$14.24 \times 8$ 19. ___\$44.10___

20. ___\$113.92___

In 21–22, use mental math to find each product.

21. 5×73 21. ___365___

22. 49×5 22. ___245___

23. Write $2 \times 9 \times 5$ in three different ways. Then solve.
$(2 \times 9) \times 5;\ 2 \times (9 \times 5);\ (2 \times 5) \times 9;\ 90$

24. Ray orders two medium cheese pizzas for $9.50 each and a large pepperoni pizza at $11.50. He uses a $3 coupon. How much does he need to pay?   24. ___\$27.50___

25. Brianna is planning a class party. She needs 150 napkins for the party. Napkins come in packs of 25. Complete the table to find how many packs of napkins she will need to buy.   25. ___6 packs___

Number of packs	1	2	3	4	5	6
Number of napkins	25	50	75	100	125	150

26. **Explain Your Thinking** Explain why you place a decimal point in your answer when you multiply money amounts?
Since you are multiplying dollars and cents, the decimal point is necessary to separate dollars and cents in the answer.

274   Answers for Chapter Tests Forms A & B

Chapter 6 Test — Form A

Name _____

Date _____ Score _____

Chapter 6 Test Form A

Vocabulary: In 1–3, match each with its meaning.

1. factors — a. the number obtained after multiplying

1. **b**

2. multiple — b. numbers that are multiplied together to obtain a product

2. **c**

3. product — c. the product of a given whole number and any other whole number

3. **a**

In 4–7, use patterns to find each product.

4. $70 \times 8 =$ **560**
   $70 \times 80 =$ **5,600**
   $70 \times 800 =$ **56,000**
   $70 \times 8,000 =$ **560,000**

5. $50 \times 4 =$ **200**
   $50 \times 40 =$ **2,000**
   $50 \times 400 =$ **20,000**
   $50 \times 4,000 =$ **200,000**

6. $40 \times 7 =$ **280**
   $40 \times 70 =$ **2,800**
   $40 \times 700 =$ **28,000**
   $40 \times 7,000 =$ **280,000**

7. $90 \times 5 =$ **450**
   $90 \times 50 =$ **4,500**
   $90 \times 500 =$ **45,000**
   $90 \times 5,000 =$ **450,000**

In 8-14, estimate each product.

8. 84×23 — 8. **1,600**
9. 66×56 — 9. **4,200**
10. 29×78 — 10. **2,400**
11. 53×67 — 11. **3,500**
12. 246×58 — 12. **12,000**
13. 709×88 — 13. **63,000**
14. 395×31 — 14. **12,000**

Chapter 6 Test Form A

Continued 131

Name _____

In 15–24, find each product.

15. $\begin{array}{r} 72 \\ \times\,30 \end{array}$ — 15. **2,160**

16. $\begin{array}{r} 53 \\ \times\,80 \end{array}$ — 16. **4,240**

17. $\begin{array}{r} 41 \\ \times\,28 \end{array}$ — 17. **1,148**

18. $\begin{array}{r} 57 \\ \times\,43 \end{array}$ — 18. **2,451**

19. 95×32 — 19. **3,040**

20. 42×39 — 20. **1,638**

21. $32 \times 1,247$ — 21. **39,904**

22. $2,371 \times 16$ — 22. **37,936**

23. $15 \times \$14.95$ — 23. **$224.25**

24. $12 \times \$24.08$ — 24. **$288.96**

In 25, decide if you should overestimate or underestimate. Solve.

25. Marty plans to deposit $4.50 into his bank account each week. Estimate to see if he will have saved $50 to pay for a computer game at the end of 21 weeks.

    Underestimate: $4 \times 20 = 80$; He will have enough money.

In 26, draw a picture to help you solve each problem.

26. Larry is in a bike race. There are 12 bikes in each row. There are 4 rows in front of him and 8 rows behind him. How many racers are there in all?

    26. **156 racers**

27. **Explain Your Thinking** Describe the steps you would follow to find the product of 1,258 and 47.

    Possible answer: Multiply 1,258 by 7 ones. Then multiply 1,258 by 4 tens. Add the products to get 59,126.

132 Chapter 6 Test Form A

Chapter 6 Test — Form B

Name _____

Date _____ Score _____

Chapter 6 Test Form B

Vocabulary: In 1–3, match each with its meaning.

1. multiple — a. numbers that are multiplied together to obtain a product

1. **b**

2. product — b. the product of a given whole number and any other whole number

2. **c**

3. factors — c. the answer in multiplication

3. **a**

In 4–7, use patterns to find each product.

4. $80 \times 6 =$ **480**
   $80 \times 60 =$ **4,800**
   $80 \times 600 =$ **48,000**
   $80 \times 6,000 =$ **480,000**

5. $60 \times 5 =$ **300**
   $60 \times 50 =$ **3,000**
   $60 \times 500 =$ **30,000**
   $60 \times 5,000 =$ **300,000**

6. $90 \times 8 =$ **720**
   $90 \times 80 =$ **7,200**
   $90 \times 800 =$ **72,000**
   $90 \times 8,000 =$ **720,000**

7. $30 \times 9 =$ **270**
   $30 \times 90 =$ **2,700**
   $30 \times 900 =$ **27,000**
   $30 \times 9,000 =$ **270,000**

In 8–14, estimate each product.

8. 56×22 — 8. **1,200**
9. 49×63 — 9. **3,000**
10. 73×58 — 10. **4,200**
11. 34×94 — 11. **2,700**
12. 376×78 — 12. **32,000**
13. 298×66 — 13. **21,000**
14. 345×28 — 14. **9,000**

Chapter 6 Test Form B

Continued 133

Name _____

In 15–24, find each product.

15. $\begin{array}{r} 64 \\ \times\,20 \end{array}$ — 15. **1,280**

16. $\begin{array}{r} 85 \\ \times\,50 \end{array}$ — 16. **4,250**

17. $\begin{array}{r} 32 \\ \times\,53 \end{array}$ — 17. **1,696**

18. $\begin{array}{r} 65 \\ \times\,34 \end{array}$ — 18. **2,210**

19. 46×85 — 19. **3,910**

20. 56×36 — 20. **2,016**

21. $1,328 \times 32$ — 21. **42,496**

22. $2,485 \times 19$ — 22. **47,215**

23. $\$20.95 \times 12$ — 23. **$251.40**

24. $\$15.05 \times 19$ — 24. **$285.95**

In 25, decide if you should overestimate or underestimate. Solve.

25. Billy Bob needs to buy 5 notebooks. Each notebook costs $1.75. Estimate to see how much money he needs to give to the clerk.

    Overestimate: $5 \times 2 = 10$. He needs about $10.

In 26, draw a picture to help you solve the problem.

26. Gina is in a charity fun run. She is in the seventh row. Altogether there are 15 rows with 14 runners in each row. How many runners are in the rows behind her?

    26. **112 runners**

27. **Explain Your Thinking** Describe the steps you would follow to find the product of 3,425 and 46.

    Possible answer: Multiply 3,425 by 6 ones. Then multiply 3,425 by 4 tens. Add the products to get 157,550.

134 Chapter 6 Test Form B

Answers for Chapter Tests Forms A and B **275**

Chapter 7 Test
Form A ▼

Vocabulary: In 1–4, complete each sentence with one of the words listed.

1. A number is __divisible__ by another number if there is no remainder.

2. Whole numbers that are divisible by 2 are __even__.

3. Average is another word for __mean__.

4. The numbers 3, 17, and 45 are __odd__.

Word List
odd
even
mean
divisible

In 5–10, use patterns to find each quotient.

5. 400 ÷ 8   6. 540 ÷ 9   7. 360 ÷ 4
   50   60   90

8. 240 ÷ 3   9. 420 ÷ 6   10. 180 ÷ 9
   80   70   20

In 11–13, estimate each quotient.

11. 351 ÷ 9   12. 430 ÷ 5   13. 294 ÷ 4
    30–40   80–90   70–80

In 14–25, divide.

14. 6)37   15. 9)49   14. ___6 R1___
                            15. ___5 R4___
16. 23 ÷ 5   17. 59 ÷ 8   16. ___4 R3___
                            17. ___7 R3___
18. 3)37   19. 87 ÷ 6   18. ___12 R1___
                            19. ___14 R3___

---

20. 4)536   21. 739 ÷ 5   20. ___134___
                             21. ___147 R4___
22. 3)92   23. 619 ÷ 6   22. ___30 R2___
                             23. ___103 R1___
24. 4)$5.12   25. $6.09 ÷ 3 24. ___$1.28___
                             25. ___$2.03___

26. Toby made 320 ounces of soup. How many 9-ounce bowls can he fill?   26. ___35 bowls___

In 27–28, find the mean of each set of numbers.

27. 7, 6, 9, 4, 7, 3   27. ___6___

28. 87, 76, 86, 88, 83   28. ___84___

In 29–30, test if each number is divisible by 2, 3, or 5. If it is, then give the quotient.

29. 273   Divisible by 3, 91

30. 578   Divisible by 2, 289

31. Jerry had some apple slices. He ate 5 slices. He threw away 5 slices because they were bruised. He has 3 slices left. How many slices did Jerry start with?   31. ___13 slices___

32. **Explain Your Thinking** How many cars are needed to carry 36 people if 5 people can ride in one car? Explain how you know.
Possible answer: 36 ÷ 5 = 7 R1; so 7 cars can carry 35 people. But we need another car to carry the single person. So we need 8 cars in all.

Chapter 7 Test
Form B ▼

Vocabulary: In 1–4, complete each sentence with one of the words listed.

1. Another word for mean is __average__.

2. A number is __divisible__ by another number if there is no remainder.

3. Whole numbers *not* divisible by 2 are __odd__.

4. The numbers 4, 22, and 36 are __even__.

Word List
odd
even
average
divisible

In 5–10, use patterns to find each quotient.

5. 360 ÷ 6   6. 320 ÷ 8   7. 280 ÷ 4
   60   40   70

8. 200 ÷ 5   9. 630 ÷ 7   10. 450 ÷ 9
   40   90   50

In 11–13, estimate each quotient.

11. 251 ÷ 8   12. 359 ÷ 6   13. 429 ÷ 7
    30–40   50–60   60–70

In 14–25, divide.

14. 6)43   15. 6)57   14. ___7 R1___
                           15. ___9 R3___
16. 35 ÷ 8   17. 29 ÷ 7   16. ___4 R3___
                           17. ___4 R1___
18. 2)47   19. 58 ÷ 4   18. ___23 R1___
                           19. ___14 R2___

---

20. 5)675   21. 845 ÷ 3   20. ___135___
                             21. ___281 R2___
22. 5)54   23. 731 ÷ 7   22. ___10 R4___
                             23. ___104 R3___
24. 3)$4.53   25. $8.61 ÷ 7 24. ___$1.51___
                             25. ___$1.23___

26. Monica has 26 batteries. She plans to store them in bags that hold 8 batteries each. How many bags will Monica need to hold all the batteries?   26. ___4 bags___

In 27–28, find the mean of each set of numbers.

27. 8, 7, 9, 10, 6, 8   27. ___8___

28. 58, 57, 60, 65   28. ___60___

In 29–30, test if each number is divisible by 2, 3, or 5. If it is, then give the quotient.

29. 485   Divisible by 5, 97

30. 753   Divisible by 3, 251

31. Tonya gave 18 pieces of dried fruit to Tasha and put three pieces into a plastic bag. She has 5 pieces left. How many pieces did Tonya start with?   31. ___26 pieces___

32. **Explain Your Thinking** Carl bought 128 inches of ribbon. How many 9-inch strips can he cut? Explain how you know.
Possible answer: 128 ÷ 9 = 14 R2; so 14 strips of ribbon can be cut, with 2 inches of the ribbon left over.

Chapter 8 Test — Form A

Name _____

Date _____ Score _____

Vocabulary: In 1–2, match each with its meaning.

1. congruent   a. a straight path that goes on forever in both directions

2. line   b. having the same size and shape

1. ___b___

2. ___a___

In 3–4, name the solid that each object looks like.

3.   4.

3. ___Cone___

4. ___Sphere___

In 5–6, write the name of each polygon.

5.   6.

5. ___Hexagon___

6. ___Triangle___

In 7–8, the lengths of the sides of a triangle are given. Name each triangle as scalene, isosceles, or equilateral.

7. 4 cm, 7 cm, 4 cm

8. 5 cm, 8 cm, 3 cm

7. ___Isosceles___

8. ___Scalene___

In 9–10, name each triangle as right, acute, or obtuse.

9.   10.

9. ___Acute___

10. ___Right___

In 11–12, tell whether each picture shows a slide, flip, or turn.

11.   12.

11. ___Flip___

12. ___Turn___

Chapter 8 Test Form A

Continued 171

Name _____

13. Is the figure congruent, similar, or neither?

14. Are the lines parallel, intersecting, or perpendicular?

13. ___Similar___

14. ___Parallel___

In 15–16, write the name of each quadrilateral.

15.   16.

15. ___Parallelogram___

16. ___Square___

In 17–18, tell how many lines of symmetry each figure has.

17.   18.

17. ___1 line___

18. ___2 lines___

19. Norman stands behind Dennis. Dennis stands behind Rudy. Norman stands in front of Brad. Who is first in the line?

19. ___Rudy___

In 20–21, a rectangle has length 5 cm and width 6 cm.

20. Find the perimeter of the rectangle.

21. Find the area of the rectangle.

20. ___22 cm___

21. ___30 square cm___

22. A rectangular prism is 4 inches long, 3 inches wide, and 3 inches high. Find its volume.

22. ___36 cubic inches___

23. **Explain Your Thinking** The perimeter of a square measures 40 centimeters. Explain how you can find the length of each side. Then give the length.

Divide the perimeter by 4 since a square has 4 equal sides; 10 cm

172   Chapter 8 Test Form A

Chapter 8 Test — Form B

Name _____

Date _____ Score _____

Vocabulary: In 1–2, match each with its meaning.

1. polygon   a. a closed plane figure made of line segments

2. perimeter   b. the distance around a figure

1. ___a___

2. ___b___

In 3–4, name the solid each object looks like.

3.   4.

3. ___Pyramid___

4. ___Cylinder___

In 5–6, write the name of each polygon.

5.   6.

5. ___Octagon___

6. ___Quadrilateral___

In 7–8, the lengths of the sides of a triangle are given. Name each triangle as scalene, isosceles, or equilateral.

7. 2 cm, 2 cm, 2 cm

8. 5 cm, 8 cm, 5 cm

7. ___Equilateral___

8. ___Isosceles___

In 9–10, name each triangle as right, acute, or obtuse.

9.   10.

9. ___Right___

10. ___Obtuse___

In 11–12, tell whether each picture shows a slide, flip, or turn.

11.   12.

11. ___Turn___

12. ___Slide___

Chapter 8 Test Form B

Continued 173

Name _____

13. Is the figure congruent, similar, or neither?

14. Are the lines parallel, intersecting, or perpendicular?

13. ___Congruent, Similar___

14. ___Intersecting___

In 15–16, write the name of each quadrilateral.

15.   16.

15. ___Rectangle___

16. ___Square___

In 17–18, tell how many lines of symmetry each figure has.

17.   18.

17. ___1 line___

18. ___2 lines___

19. Jody is standing in a line before Marla and behind Pearl. Naomi is in front of Pearl. Who is last in the line?

19. ___Marla___

In 20–21, a rectangle has length 4 in. and width 3 in.

20. Find the perimeter of the rectangle.

21. Find the area of the rectangle.

20. ___14 in.___

21. ___12 square in.___

22. A rectangular prism is 5 cm long, 3 cm wide, and 2 cm high. Find its volume.

22. ___30 cubic cm___

23. **Explain Your Thinking** The perimeter of a rectangle measures 14 inches. Two sides each measure 3 inches. Explain how to find the length of one of the other sides. Then give the length.

Add 3 in. and 3 in. Subtract the sum (6 in.) from 14 in. Divide the difference (8 in.) by 2; 4 in.

174   Chapter 8 Test Form B

Answers for Chapter Tests Forms A and B   **277**

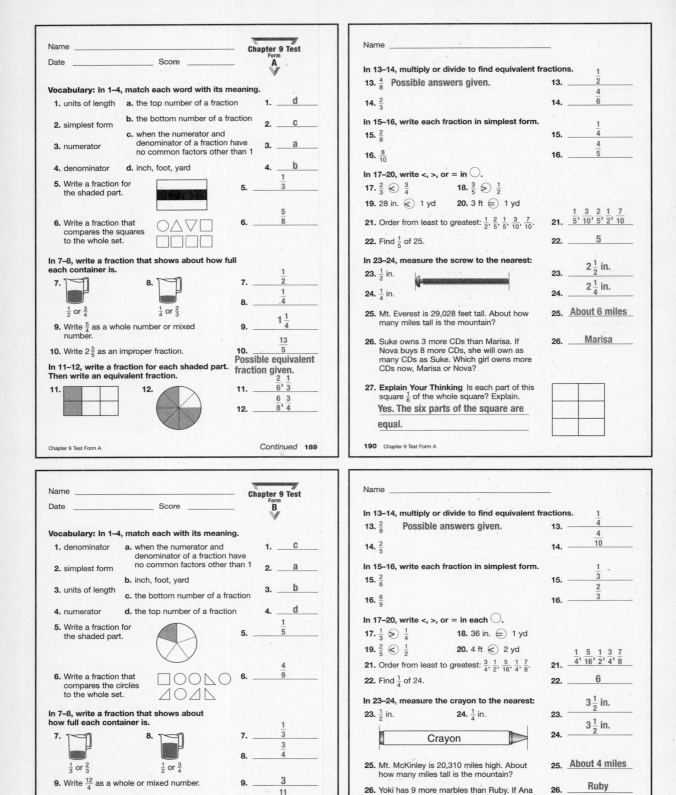

Chapter 10 Test — Form A

Name _____

Date _____ Score _____

In 1–16, find each sum or difference. Simplify.

1. $\frac{1}{5} + \frac{2}{5}$

2. $\frac{1}{8} + \frac{3}{8}$

3. $\frac{2}{3} - \frac{1}{3}$

4. $\frac{11}{12} - \frac{5}{12}$

5. $\frac{1}{6} + \frac{7}{12}$

6. $\frac{7}{10} - \frac{3}{10}$

7. $\frac{5}{8} - \frac{1}{4}$

8. $\frac{1}{15} + \frac{1}{3}$

9. $\frac{5}{7}$
   $- \frac{3}{7}$

10. $\frac{1}{9}$
    $+ \frac{1}{3}$

11. $\frac{14}{15}$
    $- \frac{2}{3}$

12. $\frac{2}{3}$
    $+ \frac{1}{6}$

13. $\frac{3}{4}$
    $- \frac{1}{2}$

14. $\frac{5}{6}$
    $- \frac{1}{3}$

15. $\frac{9}{10}$
    $- \frac{3}{5}$

16. $\frac{1}{8}$
    $+ \frac{3}{4}$

17. Find the value of n for $n + \frac{2}{5} = \frac{4}{5}$.

1. $\frac{3}{5}$

2. $\frac{4}{8} = \frac{1}{2}$

3. $\frac{1}{3}$

4. $\frac{6}{12} = \frac{1}{2}$

5. $\frac{9}{12} = \frac{3}{4}$

6. $\frac{4}{10} = \frac{2}{5}$

7. $\frac{3}{8}$

8. $\frac{6}{15} = \frac{2}{5}$

9. $\frac{2}{7}$

10. $\frac{4}{9}$

11. $\frac{4}{15}$

12. $\frac{5}{6}$

13. $\frac{1}{4}$

14. $\frac{3}{6} = \frac{1}{2}$

15. $\frac{3}{10}$

16. $\frac{7}{8}$

17. $n = \frac{2}{5}$

Chapter 10 Test Form A   Continued 211

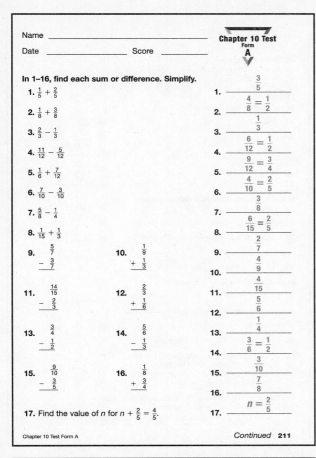

Name _____

In 18–19, write the operation you would use. Then solve.

18. Paolo ate $\frac{1}{8}$ of a pizza and Chandra ate $\frac{1}{4}$. How much of the pizza did they eat in all?

19. Lashonda has $\frac{3}{4}$ yard of fabric. She uses $\frac{3}{8}$ yard to make dolls. How much fabric is left?

In 20–24, choose the better estimate.

20. A box of pens: 8 oz or 8 lb

21. A box of books: 16 oz or 16 lb

22. A car: 2 lb or 2 T

23. A kitchen sink filled with water: 10 pt or 10 gal

24. A soda bottle: 16 c or 16 fl oz

In 25–28, complete.

25. 2 qt = ▨ pt

26. 36 ft = ▨ yd

27. 2 T = ▨ lb

28. 2 lb = ▨ oz

29. How many granola bars could you get for $5?

Granola Bars	2	4	6	8	10
Cost	$1	$2	$3	$4	$5

30. Find n.

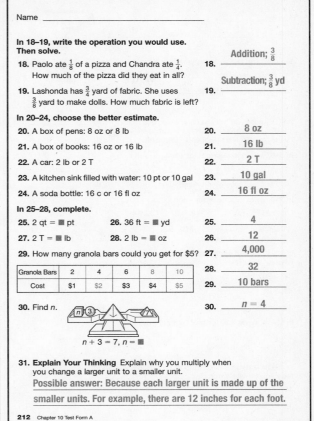

$n + 3 = 7, n =$ ▨

31. **Explain Your Thinking** Explain why you multiply when you change a larger unit to a smaller unit.

Possible answer: Because each larger unit is made up of the smaller units. For example, there are 12 inches for each foot.

18. Addition; $\frac{3}{8}$

19. Subtraction; $\frac{3}{8}$ yd

20. 8 oz

21. 16 lb

22. 2 T

23. 10 gal

24. 16 fl oz

25. 4

26. 12

27. 4,000

28. 32

29. 10 bars

30. $n = 4$

212   Chapter 10 Test Form A

Chapter 10 Test — Form B

Name _____

Date _____ Score _____

In 1–16, find each sum or difference. Simplify.

1. $\frac{2}{7} + \frac{4}{7}$

2. $\frac{1}{6} + \frac{1}{6}$

3. $\frac{8}{9} - \frac{2}{9}$

4. $\frac{9}{10} - \frac{3}{10}$

5. $\frac{1}{4} + \frac{5}{12}$

6. $\frac{4}{5} - \frac{1}{5}$

7. $\frac{2}{3} - \frac{1}{9}$

8. $\frac{2}{15} + \frac{1}{3}$

9. $\frac{2}{3}$
   $- \frac{1}{3}$

10. $\frac{1}{10}$
    $+ \frac{1}{2}$

11. $\frac{14}{15}$
    $- \frac{1}{5}$

12. $\frac{1}{4}$
    $+ \frac{5}{8}$

13. $\frac{5}{8}$
    $- \frac{1}{2}$

14. $\frac{3}{4}$
    $- \frac{1}{8}$

15. $\frac{5}{6}$
    $- \frac{1}{3}$

16. $\frac{1}{5}$
    $- \frac{1}{10}$

17. Find the value of n for $n + \frac{1}{7} = \frac{2}{7}$.

1. $\frac{6}{7}$

2. $\frac{2}{6} = \frac{1}{3}$

3. $\frac{6}{9} = \frac{2}{3}$

4. $\frac{6}{10} = \frac{3}{5}$

5. $\frac{8}{12} = \frac{2}{3}$

6. $\frac{3}{5}$

7. $\frac{3}{9} = \frac{1}{3}$

8. $\frac{7}{15}$

9. $\frac{1}{3}$

10. $\frac{6}{10} = \frac{3}{5}$

11. $\frac{11}{15}$

12. $\frac{7}{8}$

13. $\frac{1}{8}$

14. $\frac{5}{8}$

15. $\frac{3}{6} = \frac{1}{2}$

16. $\frac{1}{10}$

17. $n = \frac{1}{7}$

Chapter 10 Test Form B   Continued 213

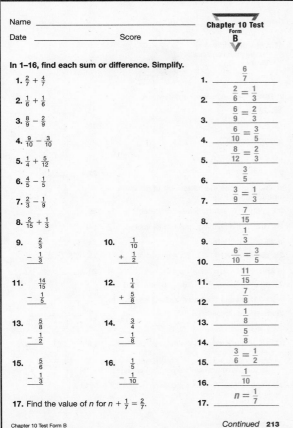

Name _____

In 18–19, write the operation you would use. Then solve.

18. Rene has $\frac{3}{4}$ bushel of apples. He sells $\frac{1}{2}$ bushel. How much does he have left?

19. Joseph rode his bike $\frac{2}{5}$ mile on Saturday and $\frac{3}{10}$ mile on Sunday. How far did he ride in all?

In 20–24, choose the better estimate for weight or capacity.

20. A truck: 4 lb or 4 T

21. A can of fruit: 20 oz or 20 lb

22. Your math book: 2 oz or 2 lb

23. A glass of juice: 6 fl oz or 6 c

24. A bathtub filled with water: 55 pt or 55 gal

In 25–28, complete.

25. 8 qt = ▨ gal

26. 12 ft = ▨ yd

27. 6,000 lb = ▨ T

28. 2 lb = ▨ oz

29. How many tickets could you get for $50?

Tickets	3	6	9	12	15
Cost	$10	$20	$30	$40	$50

30. Find n.

$n + 4 = 9, n =$ ▨

31. **Explain Your Thinking** Explain why you divide when you change a smaller unit to a larger unit.

Possible answer: Because several smaller units make up the larger unit. For example, there are 16 ounces for each pound.

18. Subtraction; $\frac{1}{4}$

19. Add; $\frac{7}{10}$ mile

20. 4 T

21. 20 oz

22. 2 lb

23. 6 fl oz

24. 55 gal

25. 2

26. 4

27. 3

28. 32

29. 15 tickets

30. $n = 5$

214   Chapter 10 Test Form B

Answers for Chapter Tests Forms A and B   **279**

Date _____ Score _____

Vocabulary: In 1–3, write what each word measures.

1. centimeter Length

2. liter Capacity

3. gram Mass

Word List
mass
length
capacity

4. Suppose you have $1.05 in dimes and nickels. You have the same number of dimes as nickels. How many of each do you have?   4. ___ 7 ___

In 5–6, write the decimal for each.

5. $\frac{8}{10}$ 5. ___ 0.8 ___

6. Four and sixty-seven hundredths   6. ___ 4.67 ___

In 7–8, write <, >, or = for each ◯.

7. 0.98 $\lessdot$ 1.07   8. 0.87 $\gtrdot$ 0.09

9. Order 0.32, 0.09, 1.04, 3.52, 0.7 from least to greatest.   0.09, 0.32, 0.7, 1.04, 3.52

In 10–12, round each decimal to the nearest whole number.

10. 3.78   10. ___ 4 ___

11. 2.05   11. ___ 2 ___

12. 6.50   12. ___ 7 ___

In 13–14, write the decimal for each fraction.

13. $\frac{4}{5}$ 13. ___ 0.8 ___

14. $\frac{9}{20}$ 14. ___ 0.45 ___

In 15–16, estimate each sum or difference. Round to the nearest whole number.

15. 6.23 + 3.78   15. ___ 10 ___

16. 27.86 − 13.05   16. ___ 15 ___

Chapter 11 Test Form A   *Continued* **229**

---

17. Write the addition or subtraction sentence for the grid. $0.77 - 0.30 = 0.47$

In 18–22, find each sum or difference.

18. 0.48 + 0.23   18. ___ 0.71 ___

19. 4.73 + 1.26   19. ___ 5.99 ___

20. 0.87 − 0.24   20. ___ 0.63 ___

21. 9.63 − 5.37   21. ___ 4.26 ___

22. 7.34 − 2.28   22. ___ 5.06 ___

In 23–24, choose the better unit of measure for each object.

23. Length of an eraser: centimeter or meter   23. ___ Centimeter ___

24. Length of highway: meter or kilometer   24. ___ Kilometer ___

In 25–26, complete.

25. 400 cm = ■ m   26. 3 m = ■ cm   25. ___ 4 ___

In 27–28, write <, >, or = for each ◯.   26. ___ 300 ___

27. 50 cm $\lessdot$ 5 m   28. 3 m $\doteq$ 300 cm

In 29–30, choose the better estimate for each.

29. Nickel (a 5-cent coin): 5 g or 5 kg   29. ___ 5 g ___

30. Ice-cube tray: 380 mL or 380 L   30. ___ 380 mL ___

31. A soup's temperature was 10.3°C before it was heated. After being heated, its temperature was 84.7°C. What was the temperature change?   31. ___ 74.4°C ___

32. **Explain Your Thinking** Explain how to write a decimal in hundredths that is equal to 0.6.   **Possible answer:**
Annex a zero to 0.6 in the hundredths place: 0.6 = 0.60.

230 Chapter 11 Test Form A

Date _____ Score _____

Vocabulary: In 1–3, write what each word measures.

1. meter Length

2. milliliter Capacity

3. kilogram Mass

Word List
mass
length
capacity

4. Suppose you have $1.10 in dimes and nickels. You have two more dimes than nickels. How many dimes do you have?   4. ___ 8 dimes ___

In 5–6, write the decimal for each.

5. $\frac{7}{10}$ 5. ___ 0.7 ___

6. Five and forty-eight hundredths   6. ___ 5.48 ___

In 7–8, write <, >, or = in each ◯.

7. 1.04 $\gtrdot$ 0.97   8. 1.23 $\gtrdot$ 1.08

9. Order 1.07, 0.67, 0.90, 0.5, 2.73 from least to greatest.   0.5, 0.67, 0.90, 1.07, 2.73

In 10–12, round each decimal to the nearest whole number.

10. 4.36   10. ___ 4 ___

11. 6.87   11. ___ 7 ___

12. 2.50   12. ___ 3 ___

In 13–14, write the decimal for each fraction.

13. $\frac{3}{10}$ 13. ___ 0.3 ___

14. $\frac{9}{25}$ 14. ___ 0.36 ___

In 15–16, estimate each sum or difference. Round to the nearest whole number

15. 3.45 + 9.64   15. ___ 13 ___

16. 36.24 − 21.50   16. ___ 14 ___

Chapter 11 Test Form B   *Continued* **231**

---

17. Write the addition or subtraction sentence for the grid. $0.36 + 0.29 = 0.65$

In 18–22, find each sum or difference.

18. 0.27 + 0.71   18. ___ 0.98 ___

19. 5.43 + 3.29   19. ___ 8.72 ___

20. 0.78 − 0.36   20. ___ 0.42 ___

21. 8.71 − 3.48   21. ___ 5.23 ___

22. 9.62 − 3.29   22. ___ 6.33 ___

In 23–24, choose the better unit of measure for each object.

23. Width of a leaf: centimeter or meter   23. ___ Centimeter ___

24. Height of a building: meter or kilometer   24. ___ Meter ___

In 25–26, complete.

25. 600 cm = ■ m   26. 4 m = ■ cm   25. ___ 6 ___

In 27–28, write <, >, or = in each ◯.   26. ___ 400 ___

27. 40 cm $\lessdot$ 4 m   28. 6,000 cm $\gtrdot$ 6 m

In 29–30, choose the better estimate for each.

29. Sack of potatoes: 5 g or 5 kg   29. ___ 5 kg ___

30. Can of soda pop: 470 mL or 470 L   30. ___ 470 mL ___

31. A pudding's temperature before it was put into the refrigerator was 80.7°C. Its temperature was 15.2°C when it was served. What was the temperature change?   31. ___ 65.5°C ___

32. **Explain Your Thinking** Explain how to write a decimal in tenths that is equal to 0.70.
In 0.70, delete the zero from the hundredths place: 0.70 = 0.7.

232 Chapter 11 Test Form B

Form A (top left)

Name _____

Date _____ Score _____

Vocabulary: In 1–4, match each with its meaning.

1. unlikely   a. the chance that an event will happen

2. probability

   b. result of an action or event

3. impossible   c. probably will not happen

4. outcome   d. definitely will not happen

1. _____ c
2. _____ a
3. _____ d
4. _____ b

In 5–7, find each quotient. Use mental math.

5. 180 ÷ 90

6. 360 ÷ 60

7. 210 ÷ 70

5. _____ 2
6. _____ 6
7. _____ 3

In 8–10, estimate each quotient.

8. 225 ÷ 72

9. 468 ÷ 93

10. 197 ÷ 48

8. _____ About 3
9. _____ About 5
10. _____ About 4

11. Complete: 276 ÷ 90 ● 275 ÷ 90. Use <, >, or =.

11. _____ >

12. Complete: 640 ÷ 8 ● 6,400 ÷ 80. Use <, >, or =.

12. _____ =

In 13–18, divide and check.

13. 368 ÷ 40

14. 429 ÷ 70

15. 60)492

16. 132 ÷ 62

17. 83)507

18. 94)756

13. _____ 9 R8
14. _____ 6 R9
15. _____ 8 R12
16. _____ 2 R8
17. _____ 6 R9
18. _____ 8 R4

Chapter 12 Test Form A   *Continued* **245**

Form A (top right)

Name _____

In 19–20, write whether the event is impossible, unlikely, equally likely as unlikely, likely, or certain.

19. The sun will rise tomorrow morning.

19. _____ Certain

20. It will snow in Washington, D.C., during January.

20. _____ Likely

In 21, write whether the game is fair or unfair. If it is unfair, explain why.

21. A box contains these letters: A, B, C, D, E, F. Kevin gets a point if he draws a vowel. Steve gets a point if he draws a consonant.

Unfair; Steve is more likely to draw a consonant.

22. A counter has a 1 on one side and a 4 on the other side. Another counter has a 3 on one side and a 7 on the other side. List all possible outcomes of flipping both counters.

22. _____ 1, 3; 1, 7; 4, 3; 4, 7

23. What is the probability of rolling an even number on a number cube labeled 1–6? Write your answer as a fraction.

23. _____ $\frac{3}{6}$ or $\frac{1}{2}$

24. In a survey of 25 students, 5 students say they prefer to play basketball rather than baseball. Based on this survey, how many students out of 100 would you expect to play basketball?

24. _____ 20 students

25. José has a model car, a model plane, a model tank, and a model boat. How many ways can he arrange them on a shelf?

25. _____ 24 ways

26. **Explain Your Thinking** Without finding the exact answer, tell whether 548 ÷ 90 will be greater than or less than 6. Explain.

Possible answer:

Estimate: 540 ÷ 90 = 6. The dividend of the exact problem is greater than the dividend of the estimate, and the divisors are the same. So, the exact answer is greater than the estimate.

246   Chapter 12 Test Form A

Form B (bottom left)

Name _____

Date _____ Score _____

Vocabulary: In 1–4, match each with its meaning.

1. certain   a. the chance that an event will happen

2. outcome   b. probably will happen

3. probability   c. result of an action or event

4. likely   d. definitely will happen

1. _____ d
2. _____ c
3. _____ a
4. _____ b

In 5–7, find each quotient. Use mental math.

5. 540 ÷ 60

6. 480 ÷ 80

7. 240 ÷ 80

5. _____ 9
6. _____ 6
7. _____ 3

In 8–10, estimate each quotient.

8. 628 ÷ 92

9. 253 ÷ 41

10. 463 ÷ 47

8. _____ About 7
9. _____ About 6
10. _____ About 9

11. Complete: 480 ÷ 6 ● 4,800 ÷ 60. Use <, >, or =.

11. _____ =

12. Complete: 812 ÷ 90 ● 815 ÷ 90. Use <, >, or =.

12. _____ <

In 13–18, divide and check.

13. 368 ÷ 90

14. 186 ÷ 20

15. 70)423

16. 391 ÷ 76

17. 38)235

18. 59)296

13. _____ 4 R8
14. _____ 9 R6
15. _____ 6 R3
16. _____ 5 R11
17. _____ 6 R7
18. _____ 5 R1

Chapter 12 Test Form B   *Continued* **247**

Form B (bottom right)

Name _____

In 19–20, write whether the event is impossible, unlikely, equally likely as unlikely, likely, or certain.

19. The Atlantic Ocean will dry up this year.

19. _____ Impossible

20. Summer will be hot in New York City.

20. _____ Likely

In 21, write whether the game is fair or unfair. If it is unfair, explain why.

21. A box contains these letters: A, E, I, O, U. Ernesto gets a point is he draws a vowel. Isabel gets a point if she draws a consonant.

Unfair; Ernesto is the only one who can get points.

22. A game tile has an A on one side and a B on the other side. A second tile has a C on one side and a D on the other. List all possible outcomes of flipping both counters.

22. _____ AC, AD, BC, BD

23. What is the probability of rolling a 4 on a number cube labeled 1–6? Write your answer as a fraction.

23. _____ $\frac{1}{6}$

24. In a survey of 30 students, 15 students say they prefer country music to rock music. Based on this survey, how many students out of 300 would you expect to prefer country music?

24. _____ 150 students

25. Mercedes has a cooking book, a novel, a soccer book, and a dictionary. How many ways can she put the books on a shelf?

25. _____ 24 ways

26. **Explain Your Thinking** Without finding the exact answer, tell whether 419 ÷ 60 will be greater than or less than 7.

Possible answer:

Estimate: 420 ÷ 60 = 7. The dividend of the exact problem is less than the dividend of the estimate, and the divisors are the same. So, the exact answer is less than the estimate.

248   Chapter 12 Test Form B

Answers for Chapter Tests Forms A and B   **281**

Answers

Inventory Test

1. D	19. C
2. D	20. A
3. B	21. C
4. C	22. D
5. A	23. B
6. B	24. C
7. A	25. B
8. D	26. B
9. C	27. B
10. D	28. B
11. A	29. C
12. A	30. A
13. D	31. D
14. B	32. C
15. D	33. B
16. A	34. A
17. A	35. B
18. C	36. A

Chapter 1

Quiz, Section A

1. b
2. a
3. c
4. 12 students
5. 6 students
6. Week 4
7. Addition
8. In week 3, the zoo had 300 visitors.
9. 5 students

Quiz, Section B

1. b
2. a
3.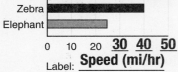
Top Speed of Certain Animals
Label: **Speed (mi/hr)**

4.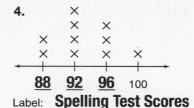

88 92 96 100

Label: **Spelling Test Scores**

5. 14, 6, 5
6. Add 4 or $n + 4$.

In	4	5	7	10	15
Out	8	9	11	14	19

7. Kenny, 7 shots; Elena, 5 shots

Chapter 1 Test
Form C

1. C	14. D
2. D	15. C
3. C	16. B
4. D	17. B
5. B	18. C
6. D	19. C
7. B	20. B
8. B	21. B
9. A	22. B
10. D	23. A
11. B	24. C
12. D	25. A
13. A	26. A

Chapter 1 Test
Form D

See the back of Chapter 1 Test Form D for answers.

Chapter 1 Test
Form E

1. 10 students
2. 6 students
3.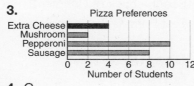
Pizza Preferences
Number of Students
4. G
5. C
6. 40 minutes

7. Friday
8. Addition
9. 4 students
10. $2
11.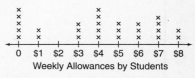
Weekly Allowances by Students

12. B
13. C
14. 18, 28; Add 3.
15. D
16. Possible answer: Rearrange the numbers in order from least to greatest. Find the middle number of the set.

Chapter 1 Test
Form F

1. 30 pizzas
2. B
3. C
4. D
5. A
6. (6, 18)
7. $12.00
8. B
9. 17
10. 38
11. Subtract 3 or $n - 3$
12. 6 chapters
13.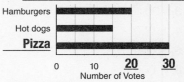
Title: **Favorite School Lunches Served**
Number of Votes

14. Hot dogs
15.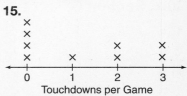
Touchdowns per Game

16. 1 touchdown

Chapter 2
Quiz, Section A

1. c
2. b
3. a
4. 80,000
5. 900
6. 20
7. Eight thousand, five hundred
8. Seven million, thirty-six

	Number	Hundreds	Tens	Ones
9.	400	4	40	400
10.	2,700	27	270	2,700

11. 40,210
12. 2,400,056
13. RB, RY, RG, BY, BG, YG; 6 ways

Quiz, Section B

1. b
2. c
3. a
4. <
5. >
6. <
7. 13,568
8. 401,104; 401,401; 404,101
9. 652; 4,652; 5,642; 6,542
10. 841, 814, 481, 418, 184, 148
11. 800
12. 700
13. 400
14. 5,000
15. 9,000
16. 2,000

Quiz, Section C

1. c
2. a
3. b

4. Possible answers: 2:25 and 25 minutes after 2
5. Possible answers: 50 minutes after 8 and 10 minutes before 9
6. 8:00 A.M.
7. <
8. >
9. 12 hours
10. 3 hours
11. 45 minutes
12. 1 hour 15 minutes
13. March
14. 31 days

Chapter 2 Test Form C

1. C		19. C
2. B		20. C
3. D		21. B
4. C		22. B
5. D		23. A
6. B		24. D
7. D		25. B
8. C		26. C
9. B		27. D
10. C		28. C
11. D		29. A
12. B		30. B
13. A		31. A
14. D		32. B
15. C		33. A
16. C		34. C
17. B		35. D
18. B		

Chapter 2 Test Form D

See the back of Chapter 2 Test Form D for answers.

Chapter 2 Test Form E

1. 600
2. 600,000,000

3. Thirty thousand, forty-three
4. 61,000,579

	Number	Hundreds	Tens	Ones
5.	600	6	60	600
6.	3,700	37	370	3,700

7. <
8. >
9. RB, RN, GB, GN, YB, YN; 6 combinations
10. C
11. B
12. 700
13. 6,000
14. Possible answers: 10:45 and 15 minutes before 11
15. Possible answers: 9 minutes after 8 and 51 minutes before 9
16. B
17. A
18. 8 hours
19. 5 hours 30 minutes
20. 12 months
21. Leap year
22. B
23. Possible answer: Count the hours: 10:45 to 12:45 is 2 hours; count the minutes: 12:45 to 1:25 is 40 minutes; 2 hours 40 minutes

Chapter 2 Test Form F

1. 37
2. 36
3. C
4. A
5. 1 hour 15 minutes
6. 18 minutes
7. D
8. D
9. 23
10. 35
11. 64,108

12. 3,040,561
13. 80,000
14. 5,000,000
15. 2,300
16. 230
17. 566,980
18. 34,998
19. 500
20. 6:00 P.M.
21. 4:00 P.M.
22. D
23. AK, RI, NY, TX
24. AK, TX, NY, RI
25. Hundred

Chapter 3
Quiz, Section A

1. c
2. a
3. b
4. 70; 700; 7,000
5. 2; 20; 200
6. 320
7. 620
8. 450
9. 6,000
10. 7,000
11. 6,000
12. Estimate, exact time of trip is not needed.

Quiz, Section B

1. b
2. A
3. 803
4. 1,206
5. 4,521
6. 4,198
7. 14,035
8. 536
9. 350
10. 2,492
11. 239
12. 4,782
13. 15 campers
14. 426
15. 264

16. 1,953
17. 8,245
18. 26,914

Quiz, Section C

1. $38.20
2. $55.55
3. <
4. >
5. $8.77
6. $173.91
7. $21.12
8. $3.76
9. $64.30
10. $75.22
11. $7.25
12. $2.50
13. 60
14. 500
15. 90, 80, 100; Add 20, then subtract 10.

Chapter 3 Test
Form C

1. D	19. D
2. B	20. B
3. C	21. C
4. C	22. D
5. D	23. A
6. A	24. C
7. B	25. D
8. C	26. A
9. A	27. C
10. D	28. C
11. B	29. B
12. A	30. A
13. B	31. C
14. A	32. A
15. C	33. D
16. C	34. A
17. C	35. B
18. B	36. C

Chapter 3 Test
Form D

See the back of Chapter 3 Test Form D for answers.

Chapter 3 Test
Form E

1. C
2. 950
3. 320
4. 500
5. A
6. Estimate; attendance is not known until the fair takes place.
7. 904
8. 3,006
9. 5,038
10. 9,579
11. 517
12. 3,938
13. 4,180
14. 3,445
15. 5,844
16. 7,402
17. C
18. D
19. A
20. >
21. =
22. $62.71
23. $96.20
24. $48.57
25. D
26. 14, 12, 16; Add 4, then subtract 2.
27. Possible answer: Think, what number plus 30 equals 64? Use counters or mental math to solve. Check that 30 plus the value equals 64. $n = 34$

Chapter 3 Test
Form F

1. 740
2. 340
3. 14,110
4. 3,744
5. 234
6. 3,190
7. $110.60

8. $17.28
9. C
10. 574
11. 400
12. 600
13. B
14. A
15. B
16. C
17. B
18. <
19. 12
20. D
21. $7.25
22. 1 quarter; 2 dimes, 1 nickel; 1 dime, 3 nickels; 5 nickels
23. Estimate

Quarterly Test
Chapters 1–3

1. A	17. D
2. C	18. A
3. A	19. C
4. B	20. C
5. C	21. B
6. C	22. A
7. D	23. C
8. C	24. D
9. B	25. C
10. C	26. C
11. D	27. B
12. A	28. D
13. D	29. A
14. B	30. C
15. A	31. B
16. B	32. D

Chapter 4
Quiz, Section A

1. c
2. a
3. b
4. $8 + 8 + 8 = 24$

5. $3 \times 8 = 24$
6. $2 \times 5 = 10$; $2 + 2 + 2 + 2 + 2 = 10$; 10 apples
7. C
8. 16
9. 35
10. 54
11. 27
12. 0
13. 28
14. 80
15. 99
16. 120
17. 21 times

Quiz, Section B

1. d
2. c
3. b
4. a
5. 5
6. 9
7. 5
8. $7 \times 5 = 35$, $5 \times 7 = 35$, $35 \div 7 = 5$, $35 \div 5 = 7$
9. 7
10. 9
11. 0
12. 24
13. 6
14. 7×7
15. 4 rows

Quiz, Section C

1. Prime
2. Even
3. Odd
4. Composite
5. 6
6. 9
7. 9
8. 7
9. 9
10. 8
11. Odd

12. Even
13. Odd
14. 1, 2, 3, 4, 6, 12
15. Composite
16. Prime
17. Composite
18. $16.00; too much
19. 6 photos

Chapter 4 Test
Form C

1. A	22. D
2. B	23. C
3. D	24. C
4. C	25. C
5. B	26. D
6. A	27. B
7. C	28. A
8. C	29. B
9. D	30. D
10. D	31. C
11. B	32. A
12. B	33. B
13. A	34. A
14. C	35. D
15. A	36. D
16. B	37. C
17. C	38. B
18. B	39. B
19. B	40. A
20. D	41. C
21. A	

Chapter 4 Test
Form D

See the back of Chapter 4 Test Form D for answers.

Chapter 4 Test
Form E

1. $4 + 4 + 4 = 12$
2. $3 \times 4 = 12$
3. B
4. 27

5. 32

6. 54

7. 56

8. 64

9. 0

10. 16

11. 45

12. 63

13. 60

14. 108

15. 88

16. D

17. C

18. 7 girls

19. $3 \times 7 = 21$, $7 \times 3 = 21$, $21 \div 3 = 7$, $21 \div 7 = 3$

20. 1, 2, 7, 14

21. 5

22. 8

23. 5

24. 0

25. 8

26. 5

27. 6

28. 4

29. A

30. A

31. D

32. Too little

33. 7 cartons

34. 10, 12, 14, 16, 18; Possible explanation: Even numbers have 0, 2, 4, 6, or 8 in the ones place.

Chapter 4 Test
Form F

1. 7,543

2. 40

3. 63

4. 10

5. 24

6. 27

7. 56

8. 121

9. 40

10. 9

11. 0

12. 1

13. 9

14. 8

15. 6

16. 8

17. 3

18. D

19. $7 \times 9 = 63$, $9 \times 7 = 63$, $63 \div 7 = 9$, $63 \div 9 = 7$

20. B

21. (4, 1)

22. A

23. C

24. Prime

25. C

26. 80

27. 8 tapes; too much

28. 9 pounds

29. Odd

30. 952 yards

31. 241, 239, 237, 235

Chapter 5
Quiz, Section A

1. b

2. a

3. 240

4. 560

5. 270

6. 40; 400; 4,000

7. 28; 280; 2,800

8. 240

9. 450

10. 4,200

11. 540

12. 56

13. 57

Quiz, Section B

1. 136

2. 370

3. 144

4. 348

5. 108

6. 128

7. 371

8. 729

9. 1,535

10. 2,912

11. 2,427

12. 4,338

13. 35,000

14. 24,048

15. 7,404

16. 36,136

Quiz, Section C

1. $5.80

2. $150.50

3. $299.95

4. 168

5. 459

6. 474

7. 266

8. 180

9. 432

10. 198

11. $(4 \times 7) \times 5$; $4 \times (7 \times 5)$; $(4 \times 5) \times 7$

12. $(2 \times 8) \times 6$; $2 \times (8 \times 6)$; $(2 \times 6) \times 8$

13. $8.00

14. 6 rolls

Number of rolls:

1 2 3 4 5 6

Number of nickels:

40 80 120 160 200 240

Chapter 5 Test
Form C

1. B

2. C

3. B

4. A

5. C

6. C

7. B

8. A

9. A

10. D

11. D

12. C

13. A

14. C

15. A	26. C
16. A	27. C
17. A	28. A
18. B	29. B
19. D	30. A
20. C	31. B
21. B	32. C
22. A	33. C
23. C	34. A
24. A	35. A
25. B	

Chapter 5 Test
Form D

See the back of Chapter 5 Test Form D for answers.

Chapter 5 Test
Form E

1. 280
2. 18; 180; 1,800
3. 40; 400; 4,000
4. C
5. A
6. 57
7. 35
8. 588
9. 952
10. 3,612
11. A
12. D
13. $29.10
14. $80.76
15. 576
16. 215
17. $(8 \times 7) \times 6$; $8 \times (7 \times 6)$; $(8 \times 6) \times 7$; 336
18. $3.35
19. 12 bushels
20. 8 tokens
   Number of tokens:
   1 2 3 4 5 6 7 8
   Number of pitches:
   15 30 45 60 75 90 105 120

21. 7 drops
   Drops of blue:
   1 2 3 4 5 6 7
   Drops of yellow:
   3 6 9 12 15 18 21
22. Since 39 is almost 40, multiply 40×8 to get 320. Then subtract 8 from 320. $320 - 8 = 312$

Chapter 5 Test
Form F

1. 350
2. 210
3. 32; 320; 3,200
4. 54
5. B
6. A
7. D
8. 168 hours
9. D
10. Less than
11. Less than
12. Greater than
13. Multiply 2 and 5 first.
14. A
15. C
16. B
17. 37,984
18. 476,901
19. C
20. D
21. $72.00
   Number of tickets:
   2 4 6 8 10 12
   Cost:
   $12 $24 $36 $48 $60 $72

Chapter 6
Quiz, Section A

1. c
2. a
3. b
4. 120; 1,200; 12,000; 120,000

5. 400; 4,000; 40,000; 400,000
6. 900
7. 1,500
8. 4,800
9. 2,700
10. 1,890
11. 5,950
12. 828
13. 1,215
14. 893
15. 836

Quiz, Section B

1. 306
2. 360
3. 748
4. 1,716
5. 1,624
6. 1,836
7. 9,000
8. 28,000
9. 24,000
10. 12,000
11. 14,000
12. 63,206
13. 93,375
14. 19,860
15. 228,375
16. 184,787
17. 61,834
18. 3,420 trees

Quiz, Section C

1. $125.40
2. $1,599.00
3. $596.53
4. $872.55
5. $131.25
6. $372.40
7. $430.75
8. $1,349.64
9. Overestimate: Possible answer: $20 \times 300 = 6,000$; About 6,000 miles; To be

sure, he should rotate the tires.

10. 70 plants

11. 16 posts

Chapter 6 Test
Form C

1. B	**17.** B
2. A	**18.** B
3. D	**19.** A
4. B	**20.** C
5. A	**21.** A
6. C	**22.** C
7. D	**23.** B
8. B	**24.** D
9. D	**25.** A
10. B	**26.** A
11. B	**27.** A
12. A	**28.** A
13. C	**29.** D
14. C	**30.** A
15. C	**31.** B
16. D	

Chapter 6 Test
Form D

See the back of Chapter 6 Test Form D for answers.

Chapter 6 Test
Form E

1. 120; 1,200; 12,000; 120,000

2. 240; 2,400; 24,000; 240,000

3. C

4. B

5. 10,000

6. 16,000

7. 4,410

8. 1,440

9. D

10. A

11. B

12. D

13. A

14. C

15. D

16. $54.24

17. $134.97

18. Underestimate

19. Sixth row

20. Possible answer: Round each factor. Round 283 to the nearest hundred, which is 300. Round 54 to the nearest ten, which is 50. Then multiply the rounded factors: $300 \times 50 = 15,000$.

Chapter 6 Test
Form F

1. 400; 4,000, 40,000; 400,000

2. 140; 1,400; 14,000; 140,000

3. 3,500

4. B

5. 2,660

6. C

7. D

8. A

9. $370.68

10. 1,547

11. 113

12. 29,010

13. 800,000

14. A

15. 9:00 P.M.

16. A

17. Underestimate, so that you don't run out of gas.

18. 100 singers

19. 14 miles

Quarterly Test
Chapters 1–6

1. B	**4.** A
2. B	**5.** C
3. B	**6.** D

7. B	**22.** C
8. D	**23.** D
9. C	**24.** C
10. A	**25.** B
11. D	**26.** B
12. C	**27.** D
13. B	**28.** A
14. D	**29.** C
15. B	**30.** B
16. C	**31.** B
17. B	**32.** B
18. C	**33.** A
19. C	**34.** C
20. B	**35.** D
21. A	**36.** A

Chapter 7
Quiz, Section A

1. 8, 80, 800

2. 6, 60, 600

3. 50

4. 70

5. 40

6. 700

7. 20

8. 90

9. 400

10. 800

11. 40–50

12. 20–30

13. 50–60

14. 70–80

15. 20–30

16. 80–90

17. 9 R1

18. 6 R3

19. 7

20. 6 R2

21. 5 R3

22. 4 R5

Chapter 7
Quiz, Section B

1.
```
    1 3 R 3
4 ) 5 5
  - 4
    1 5
  - 1 2
      3
```

2.
```
    1 3 R 1
7 ) 9 2
  - 7
    2 2
  - 2 1
      1
```

3.
```
    1 7
2 ) 3 4
  - 2
    1 4
  - 1 4
      0
```

4. 16
5. 16 R4
6. 23 R2
7. 146
8. 184
9. 146 R3
10. 58 R3
11. 63 R1
12. 147 R1
13. 106
14. 180
15. 70 R3
16. 7 pins
17. 13 cars

Quiz, Section C

1. odd
2. average
3. even
4.
```
      $ 0 . 5 4
6 ) $ 3 . 2 4
  - 3 0
      2 4
    - 2 4
        0
```

5.
```
      $ 1 . 3 8
7 ) $ 9 . 6 6
  - 7
    2 6
  - 2 1
      5 6
    - 5 6
        0
```

6.
```
        $ 1 . 2 9
6 ) $ 7 . 7 4
  - 6
    1 7
  - 1 2
      5 4
    - 5 4
        0
```

7. $1.56
8. $0.51
9. 9
10. 75
11. Divisible by 5; 71
12. $28

Form C

1. D	**20.** C
2. A	**21.** A
3. C	**22.** B
4. A	**23.** B
5. C	**24.** B
6. B	**25.** C
7. D	**26.** B
8. A	**27.** A
9. C	**28.** D
10. A	**29.** A
11. B	**30.** C
12. C	**31.** C
13. A	**32.** A
14. D	**33.** D
15. D	**34.** D
16. A	**35.** B
17. B	**36.** B
18. C	**37.** C
19. C	**38.** C

Chapter 7 Test Form D

See the back of Chapter 7 Test Form D for answers.

Chapter 7 Test Form E

1. 80
2. 70
3. 60
4. D
5. A
6. B
7. D
8. 6 R3
9. 5 R2
10. 7 R5
11. 15 R3
12. 18 R4
13. 16 R1
14. 123
15. 131 R2
16. 82
17. 95 R1
18. 101 R3
19. 108 R5
20. $1.52
21. $3.04
22. A
23. B
24. Divisible by 5; 65
25. Divisible by 3; 193
26. 25 jars
27. Add the heights: 48 + 39 + 45 = 132. Then divide by the number of boys: 132 ÷ 3 = 44. The mean height is 44 inches.

Chapter 7 Test Form F

1. 40
2. 8 R4
3. 3 R5

4. 14 R3

5. 12 R2

6. 142 R2

7. 113 R1

8. 97 R1

9. 44 R1

10. 10 R6

11. 103 R3

12. $0.89

13. $1.72

14. B

15. D

16. C

17. 30–40

18. 70–80

19. By 3: 245; By 5: 147

20. A

21. A

22. C

23. 7 boxes

24. D

25. $1.06

Chapter 8
Quiz, Section A

1. Sphere

2. Cube

3. Triangle

4. Octagon

5. Isosceles

6. Equilateral

7. Right

8. Acute

9. Slide

10. Flip

11. Similar

12. Congruent, similar

Quiz, Section B

1. line

2. diagonal

3. line segment

4. Intersecting

5. Perpendicular

6. Rectangle

7. Square

8. 3 lines

9. 2 lines

10. Alano

11. Arnelle

Quiz, Section C

1. True

2. False

3. True

4. False

5. 16 inches

6. 12 inches

7. 20 square inches

8. 36 square inches

9. 6 square centimeters

10. 12 square centimeters

11. 12 cubic centimeters

12. 60 cubic inches

Chapter 8 Test
Form C

1. C

2. D

3. D

4. D

5. C

6. B

7. B

8. A

9. C

10. C

11. A

12. B

13. C

14. B

15. C

16. B

17. A

18. D

19. A

20. B

21. B

22. D

23. C

24. C

25. A

26. D

27. B

28. A

29. B

30. D

31. B

Chapter 8 Test
Form D

See the back of Chapter 8 Test Form D for answers.

Chapter 8 Test
Form E

1. B

2. C

3. A

4. C

5. Equilateral

6. Right

7. Flip

8. Similar

9. A

10. Rectangle

11. B

12. D

13. 28 inches

14. 28 square centimeters

15. 24 cubic centimeters

16. 64 cubic inches

17. First find the different perimeters you can make using the wood strip; then multiply to find the area of each. The square, with an area of 36 square inches (6 by 6), is the greatest area you can frame.

Chapter 8 Test
Form F

1. 3,200

2. 252

3. 4,437

4. 5 R3

5. 164 R1

6. 50 R4

7. D

8. D

9. B

10. Obtuse

11. C

12. Congruent, similar

13. Perpendicular

14. 1 line

15. D

16. 36 feet

17. 15 square inches
18. 24 cubic centimeters
19. Parker
20. 7 cartons

Chapter 9
Quiz, Section A

1. c
2. e
3. a
4. b
5. d
6. $\frac{1}{3}$
7. $\frac{1}{2}$
8. $\frac{1}{4}$
9. $\frac{2}{5}$
10. $\frac{1}{3}$
11. $\frac{1}{2}$
12. $2\frac{1}{3}$
13. $\frac{5}{3}$

Quiz, Section B

1. simplest form
2. equivalent fractions
3. Possible equivalent fraction given. $\frac{2}{4}$, $\frac{1}{2}$
4. Possible equivalent fraction given. $\frac{2}{8}$, $\frac{1}{4}$
5. Possible answer given. $\frac{8}{10}$
6. Possible answer given. $\frac{5}{6}$
7. $\frac{1}{3}$
8. $\frac{2}{5}$
9. <
10. >
11. $\frac{1}{10}$, $\frac{1}{5}$, $\frac{3}{10}$, $\frac{2}{5}$, $\frac{4}{5}$
12. $\frac{3}{16}$, $\frac{3}{8}$, $\frac{1}{2}$, $\frac{5}{8}$, $\frac{3}{4}$
13. 7 shirts

Quiz, Section C

1. 2 in.
2. 4 ft
3. >

4. <
5. =
6. >
7. $3\frac{1}{2}$ in.
8. $3\frac{1}{4}$ in.
9. 3 in.
10. $2\frac{3}{4}$ in.
11. About 2 miles
12. About 3 miles
13. Brooke

Chapter 9 Test Form C

1. C	20. A
2. D	21. B
3. A	22. A
4. C	23. A
5. A	24. D
6. B	25. D
7. C	26. D
8. B	27. B
9. D	28. C
10. B	29. A
11. B	30. B
12. B	31. A
13. A	32. D
14. A	33. B
15. C	34. D
16. B	35. B
17. C	36. B
18. B	37. C
19. A	

Chapter 9 Test Form D

See the back of Chapter 9 Test Form D for answers.

Chapter 9 Test Form E

1. B
2. C
3. B
4. $\frac{1}{3}$

5. $2\frac{1}{6}$
6. $\frac{5}{2}$
7. B
8. Possible answer given. $\frac{4}{5}$
9. Possible answer given. $\frac{4}{6}$
10. C
11. D
12. <
13. >
14. >
15. <
16. C
17. $\frac{1}{4}$, $\frac{5}{16}$, $\frac{3}{8}$, $\frac{1}{2}$, $\frac{9}{16}$
18. $4\frac{1}{2}$ inches
19. About 10 miles
20. cat
21. Equivalent fractions, such as $\frac{4}{8}$ and $\frac{1}{2}$, are equal because they name the same amount. You can draw a picture to verify they are equal, or you can multiply or divide.

Chapter 9 Test Form F

1. 4,815
2. 6,175
3. 547
4. 2,149
5. 1,312
6. 588
7. 7 R3
8. 105 R2
9. 12
10. C
11. A
12. $\frac{1}{3}$
13. $3\frac{3}{4}$
14. $\frac{12}{5}$
15. C
16. A
17. D
18. $\frac{2}{3}$

19. $\frac{1}{5}$

20. <

21. <

22. <

23. <

24. $\frac{1}{6}, \frac{1}{3}, \frac{1}{2}, \frac{2}{3}, \frac{5}{6}$

25. $2\frac{1}{2}$ inches

26. About 6 miles

27. Melvin

28. 8 square feet

Quarterly Test
Chapters 1–9

1. C
2. A
3. A
4. A
5. B
6. A
7. C
8. D
9. B
10. C
11. A
12. B
13. B
14. D
15. D
16. B
17. C
18. A
19. C
20. D
21. D
22. C
23. B
24. C
25. B
26. C
27. A
28. A
29. B
30. C
31. B
32. B
33. A
34. C
35. B
36. B
37. B

Chapter 10
Quiz, Section A

1. $\frac{2}{4} = \frac{1}{2}$
2. $\frac{3}{5}$
3. $\frac{8}{10} = \frac{4}{5}$
4. $\frac{3}{3} = 1$
5. $n = \frac{2}{5}$
6. $n = \frac{1}{3}$
7. $n = \frac{2}{5}$

8. $\frac{3}{8}$
9. $\frac{7}{14} = \frac{1}{2}$
10. $\frac{3}{6} = \frac{1}{2}$
11. $\frac{5}{6}$
12. $\frac{5}{8}$
13. $\frac{5}{10} = \frac{1}{2}$
14. $\frac{5}{9}$
15. $\frac{4}{18} = \frac{2}{9}$

Quiz, Section B

1. $\frac{2}{9}$
2. $\frac{2}{4} = \frac{1}{2}$
3. $\frac{2}{5}$
4. $\frac{4}{12} = \frac{1}{3}$
5. $\frac{7}{10}$
6. $\frac{6}{15} = \frac{2}{5}$
7. $\frac{3}{8}$
8. $\frac{9}{14}$
9. $\frac{2}{12} = \frac{1}{6}$
10. $\frac{2}{4} = \frac{1}{2}$
11. $\frac{6}{8} = \frac{3}{4}$
12. $\frac{5}{9}$
13. $\frac{2}{10} = \frac{1}{5}$
14. Subtraction; $\frac{1}{6}$ cup
15. Addition; $\frac{3}{4}$ cup

Quiz, Section C

1. 95 lb
2. 8 oz
3. 20 lb
4. 2 lb
5. 6 oz
6. 1 c
7. 2 qt
8. 4 gal
9. 16 fl oz
10. 8 fl oz
11. 1
12. 2
13. 24

14. 48
15. 10,000
16. 2
17. 10 tickets
18. $n = 3$

Chapter 10 Test
Form C

1. A
2. C
3. A
4. D
5. C
6. B
7. A
8. D
9. C
10. B
11. D
12. A
13. D
14. B
15. C
16. A
17. C
18. D
19. A
20. B
21. C
22. C
23. B
24. A
25. C
26. B
27. D
28. A
29. C
30. C
31. D
32. B
33. C
34. A
35. B
36. C

Chapter 10 Test
Form D

See the back of Chapter 10 Test Form D for answers.

Chapter 10 Test
Form E

1. $\frac{4}{5}$
2. $\frac{4}{10} = \frac{2}{5}$
3. $\frac{7}{12}$
4. $\frac{5}{10} = \frac{1}{2}$
5. $\frac{3}{8}$
6. $\frac{3}{6} = \frac{1}{2}$
7. $\frac{2}{15}$
8. $\frac{13}{16}$

9. $\frac{7}{8}$

10. $\frac{1}{16}$

11. D

12. C

13. D

14. B

15. 20 lb

16. 12 fl oz

17. B

18. C

19. A

20. 10 peaches

21. Both sides of the scale must be equal, so both sides must be 7. Look for a number that, when added to 5, will be equal to 7. Since 2 added to 5 equals 7, $n = 2$.

Chapter 10 Test Form F

1. $\frac{2}{3}$

2. $\frac{2}{12} = \frac{1}{6}$

3. $\frac{5}{8}$

4. $\frac{3}{6} = \frac{1}{2}$

5. $\frac{8}{15}$

6. $\frac{5}{16}$

7. $\frac{3}{8}$

8. $\frac{7}{9}$

9. 7 R4

10. 102 R1

11. 104 R4

12. $1.56

13. 8 oz

14. 16 lb

15. 5 gal

16. 16 fl oz

17. C

18. D

19. See students' scales.
    $n = 5$

20. D

21. B

22. 15 apples

23. August

24. 4,100 papers

25. 100 papers

Chapter 11
Quiz, Section A

1. Thirty-four hundredths, $\frac{34}{100}$, 0.34

2. 3.3

3. 7.56

4. 0.60

5. 0.9

6. 9

7. <

8. >

9. 0.08, 0.34, 0.7, 1.02, 1.35

10. 0.24, 0.48, 0.5, 1.14, 1.23

11. 2

12. 1

13. 5

14. 0.35

15. 0.16

Quiz, Section B

1. 12

2. 21

3. 10

4. 29

5. $0.20 + 0.67 = 0.87$

6. $0.85 - 0.40 = 0.45$

7. 0.52

8. 0.71

9. 0.53

10. 5.91

11. 6.11

12. 5.68

13. 3.14

14. 6.65 lb

Quiz, Section C

1. Length

2. Mass

3. Length

4. Capacity

5. Meter

6. Centimeter

7. <

8. >

9. =

10. <

11. 370

12. 2.5

13. 3,400

14. 7.8

15. 250 mL

16. 50 L

17. 76°F

Chapter 11 Test Form C

1. D	20. C
2. A	21. D
3. C	22. B
4. D	23. B
5. A	24. B
6. B	25. A
7. C	26. A
8. C	27. D
9. B	28. A
10. A	29. B
11. C	30. B
12. D	31. A
13. C	32. B
14. D	33. C
15. B	34. C
16. C	35. D
17. D	36. A
18. B	37. B
19. C	

Chapter 11 Test Form D

See the back of Chapter 11 Test Form D for answers.

Chapter 11 Test Form E

1. 4.7

2. 7.6
3. 3.58
4. 0.20
5. 0.8
6. >
7. <
8. 0.09, 0.78, 1.03 1.3, 2.01
9. 4
10. 9
11. 0.2
12. 0.16
13. D
14. C
15. 14 dimes
16. 0.83
17. 11.85
18. 4.46
19. 2.35
20. Kilometer
21. Centimeter
22. A
23. C
24. 480
25. 39 kg
26. 2 L
27. C
28. Possible answer: When the decimal points are aligned, the digits in the same place-value positions will line up, making addition in place-value columns easier.

Chapter 11 Test
Form F

1. C
2. B
3. 0.91
4. 13.04
5. 6.24
6. 4.15
7. $\frac{3}{6} = \frac{1}{2}$
8. $\frac{5}{8}$
9. $\frac{5}{9}$
10. $\frac{3}{10}$

11. 6.3
12. 4.35
13. 0.4
14. 8
15. 4
16. 0.9
17. 0.24
18. >
19. 0.07, 0.56, 0.9, 1.03, 1.21
20. 0.07
21. Centimeter
22. Meter
23. 16 L
24. 3 kg
25. A
26. D
27. A
28. 70 kg

Chapter 12
Quiz, Section A

1. 2
2. 4
3. 7
4. 8
5. 7
6. About 9
7. About 6
8. About 8
9. <
10. =
11. 6 R12
12. 8 R16
13. 7 R9
14. 2 R5
15. 4 R1
16. 9 R12
17. 9 R5
18. 6 miles per second

Quiz, Section B

1. b
2. c
3. a
4. Impossible
5. Likely

6. Unfair; The spinner is more likely to land on B.
7. Heads, heads; heads, tails; tails, heads; tails, tails
8. $\frac{1}{6}$
9. 50 students
10. 24 ways

Chapter 12 Test
Form C

1. B
2. A
3. B
4. D
5. C
6. A
7. B
8. D
9. C
10. B
11. C
12. B
13. D
14. C
15. A
16. B
17. D
18. A
19. A
20. B
21. C
22. A
23. A
24. C
25. B
26. D
27. C
28. D
29. A
30. C
31. D
32. A
33. A
34. D
35. D

Chapter 12 Test
Form D

See the back of Chapter 12 Test Form D for answers.

Chapter 12 Test
Form E

1. 3
2. 6
3. 5
4. 3
5. About 7
6. About 5
7. About 9
8. =
9. 6 R9

10. 8 R7
11. 8 R10
12. 5 R7
13. 3 R17
14. 7 R11
15. A
16. C
17. Fair; Both outcomes are equally likely.
18. Red, blue; red, green; white, blue; white, green
19. D
20. C
21. 60 students
22. D
23. The remainder of 23 is greater than the divisor of 21. Since there is another group of 21, the answer should be 6 R2.

Chapter 12 Test
Form F

1. 4
2. 6
3. About 8
4. About 7
5. >
6. 7 R6
7. 8 R9
8. 4 R9
9. 8 R16
10. 8 R9
11. 5 R3
12. 1,710
13. 60
14. C
15. 4 pieces
16. D
17. C
18. Unfair; Dean is more likely to score points.
19. C
20. B
21. 1 L

22. 70 students
23. D

Quarterly Test
Chapters 1–12

1. A	21. D
2. C	22. A
3. C	23. C
4. B	24. D
5. C	25. C
6. D	26. A
7. A	27. C
8. B	28. A
9. D	29. C
10. D	30. B
11. C	31. C
12. A	32. B
13. B	33. D
14. D	34. C
15. A	35. D
16. C	36. B
17. B	37. A
18. B	38. C
19. C	39. D
20. B	

Table of Contents for Management Forms

Using Management Forms

There are several types of management forms included in the *Assessment Sourcebook*. Some forms can be used to record results of student assessment. Others offer at-a-glance information about content objectives. Also included is a Percent Table that provides assistance in scoring formal assessments. Each type of form is described below:

Item Analysis for Individual Assessment: Inventory Test

The inventory test can be used as a baseline assessment at the beginning of the school year. The Item Analysis form for this test can be used to plan activities and assignments that address the strengths and weakness of individual students.

> *"Together, assessment and instruction can build on students' understanding, interest, and experiences."*
>
> *—NCTM Assessment Standards for School Mathematics*

Item Analysis for Individual Assessment: Chapters 1–12

Item Analysis forms for the variety of chapter tests can be used to evaluate student understanding of specific objectives. The forms can also be used to look for patterns in class performance on specific objectives.

These Item Analysis forms also provide suggestions for Review Options for specific objectives. Options from the Student Edition are listed, along with pages from the Practice and Reteaching components.

Item Analysis for Individual Assessment: Quarterly Tests

Quarterly Test Item Analysis can be used to assess student and group performance and plan instruction for the following quarter.

Class Test Record Form

This two-page form may be used for recording chapter test scores and quarterly test scores for the whole class for an entire year.

Item Analysis for Individual Assessment

Grade 4 Inventory Test

Student Name _____   See page 331 for scoring.

Place a ✔ in the column if the student has answered some or all of the questions correctly.

Objectives from Grade 3	Inventory Test		Review Options in Supplements	
	Test Item	✔ if correct	Practice (pages)	Reteaching (pages)
Read a bar graph.	1		P(2)	R(2)
Solve problems by using a guide.	1		P(4)	R(4)
Read and write numbers in the hundreds.	2		P(15)	R(12)
Compare numbers.	3		P(21)	R(17)
Find ending time and the time between events.	4		P(29)	R(24)
Use rounding to estimate sums.	5		P(37)	R(30)
Add 2-digit numbers.	6		P(40)	R(32)
Add 3-digit numbers.	7		P(41)	R33)
Find the sum of more than 2 addends.	8		P(43)	R(35)
Add money amounts.	9		P(50)	R(41)
Subtract 2-digit numbers.	10		P(62)	R(50)
Subtract 3-digit numbers.	11		P(64)	R(52)
Subtract with two regroupings.	12, 13		P(65)	R(53)
Subtract across zeros.	15		P(66)	R(54)
Subtract 4-digit numbers.	13		P(68)	R(55)
Subtract money.	14, 15		P(71)	R(58)
Write multiplication sentences.	16		P(76)	R(61)
Multiply with 5 as a factor.	17		P(80)	R(64)
Multiply with 9 as a factor.	17		P(83)	R(67)
Multiply with 4 as a factor.	18		P(89)	R(71)
Multiply with 6 as a factor.	18		P(90)	R(72)
Multiply with 7 and 8 as factors.	19		P(91)	R(73)
Divide by 5.	20		P(106)	R(84)
Divide by 3 and 4.	21		P(107)	R(85)
Divide by 6 and 7.	22		P(111)	R(88)
Identify lines, line segments, rays, parallel lines, and intersecting lines.	23		P(129)	R(101)
Find and name points on a coordinate grid.	24, 25		P(130)	R(104)
Multiply 2-digit numbers with regrouping.	26		P(139)	R(110)
Multiply money.	27		P(141)	R(112)

continued on next page

Place a ✔ in the column if the student has answered some or all of the questions correctly.

Objectives from Grade 3	Inventory Test		Review Options in Supplements	
	Test Item	✔ if correct	Practice (pages)	Reteaching (pages)
Divide to find quotients and remainders.	28, 29		P(148)	R(118)
Estimate fractional amounts.	30		P(156)	R(124)
Find a fraction of a set.	31		P(158)	R(125)
Solve problems by using logical reasoning.	32		P(168)	R(134)
Name and write hundredths as decimals.	33		P(172)	R(136)
Estimate and compare measurement in meters and kilometers.	34		P(178)	R(141)
Estimate and compare measurement in liters and milliliters.	35		P(183)	R(144)
Estimate and compare measurement in grams and kilograms.	36		P(185)	R(146)

Item Analysis for Individual Assessment: Grade 4, Chapter 1

Chapter 1: Data, Graphs, and Facts Review

Student Name _____

Place a ✔ in the column if the student has answered some or all of the questions correctly. For Test Form D, check all the objectives that are reflected in the student's response.

Review Options in Student Edition
- Section A Review and Practice, page 24
- Section B Review and Practice, page 42
- Chapter 1 Review/Test, page 44
- Chapter 1 Performance Assessment, page 45

Quiz or Test Form	Score	Date

Lesson	Objectives	Quizzes Items	✔	Chapter Test Form A Items	✔	Chapter Test Form B Items	✔	Chapter Test Form C Items	✔	Chapter Test Form D Items	✔	Chapter Test Form E Items	✔	Chapter Test Form F Items	✔	Practice and Reteaching Masters (pages)
Section A																
1-1	Read pictographs and bar graphs.	4, 5		3-5, 18		3-5, 18		1-4				1-2		1, 14		P(1); R(1)
1-2	Read points as ordered pairs on a coordinate grid.	1, 8		7		7		7-8				4-5		6		P(2); R(2)
1-3	Read line graphs.	6-7		8-9		1, 8-9		9-10				6-7		7		P(3); R(3)
1-4	Read line plots.	9		10-11		2, 10-11		13-14				9-10		16		P(4); R(4)
1-5	Read stem-and-leaf plots.	2-3		13-14		13-14		17-18				12-13		9-10		P(5); R(5)
1-6	Solve problems by using a guide.	5		5		5		2, 12				2		7		P(6); R(6)
1-7	Solve problems by choosing an operation.	7		5, 9		5, 9		2, 11-12				2, 8		7-8		P(7); R(7)
Section B																
1-8	Make bar graphs.	3		6		6		5-6				3		13		P(9); R(8)
1-9	Make line plots.	4		12		12		15-16				11		15		P(10); R(9)
1-10	Find range, median, and mode.	1-2, 5		15		15		19-22				12-13, 16		9-10		P(11); R(10)
1-11	Explore algebra by looking for a pattern to find the rule.	6		1, 16		16		23-24				14		11		P(12); R(11)
1-12	Solve problems by using guessing and checking.	7		17		17		25-26				15		12		P(13); R(12)
Prior	Prior objectives													2-5		

Item Analysis for Individual Assessment: Grade 4, Chapter 2

Chapter 2: Place Value and Time

Student Name _____

Place a ✔ in the column if the student has answered some or all of the questions correctly. For Test Form D, check all the objectives that are reflected in the student's response.

Quiz or Test Form	Score	Date

Review Options in Student Edition
- Section A Review and Practice, page 64
- Section B Review and Practice, page 72
- Section C Review and Practice, page 84
- Chapter 2 Review/Test, page 86
- Chapter 2 Performance Assessment, page 87

Lesson	Objectives	Quizzes Items	✔	Chapter Test Form A Items	✔	Chapter Test Form B Items	✔	Chapter Test Form C Items	✔	Chapter Test Form D Items	✔	Chapter Test Form E Items	✔	Chapter Test Form F Items	✔	Review Options in Supplements — Practice and Reteaching Masters (pages)
	Section A															
2-1	Read and write numbers in the thousands.	1, 3-5, 7, 11		1-2, 4-6, 8		4-5, 8		1-5				1, 3		11, 13		P(16); R(13)
2-2	Explore place-value relationships.	9-10		10-11		10-11		6-8				5-6		15-16		P(17); R(14)
2-3	Read and write numbers through the hundred millions.	2, 6, 8, 12		7, 9		6, 7, 9		9-13				2, 4		12, 14		P(18); R(15)
2-4	Solve problems by making an organized list.	13		15		15		14-16				9		7		P(19); R(16)
	Section B															
2-5	Compare numbers to find which is greater.	4-7		12-14		12-14		17-19				7-8		17-18		P(21); R(17)
2-6	Order a group of numbers.	3, 8-10		16-17		16-17		20-21				10-11		23-24		P(22); R(18)
2-7	Explore rounding.	1, 11-16		18-19, 31		18-19, 31		22-24				12-13		19, 25		P(23); R(19)
	Section C															
2-8	Tell time to the minute and identify A.M. and P.M.	1-2, 4-6		20-22		20-22		25-27				14-15		20-21		P(25); R(20)
2-9	Explore estimating time.	7-8		23-25		23-25		28-29				16-17		3-4		P(26); R(21)

Continued on next page.

				Quizzes and Tests from the Assessment Sourcebook										Review Options in Supplements
		Quizzes		Chapter Test Form A		Chapter Test Form B		Chapter Test Form C		Chapter Test Form D		Chapter Test Form E		Chapter Test Form F		Practice and Reteaching Masters (pages)
Lesson	Objectives	Items	✓	Items	✓	Items	✓	Items	✓	Items	✓	Items	✓	Items	✓	
	Section C (continued)															
2-10	Find elapsed time.	3, 9-12		3, 26-28		26-28		30-32				18-19, 23		5-6		P(27); R(22)
2-11	Explore the calendar.	13-14		29-30		2, 3 29-30		33-35				20-22		22		P(28); R(23)
2-12	Solve problems by creating a schedule for making an audio tape.															P(29); R(24)
Prior	Prior objectives													1-2, 8-10		

Chapter 3: Adding and Subtracting Whole Numbers and Money

Student Name _____

Place a ✔ in the column if the student has answered some or all of the questions correctly. For Test Form D, check all the objectives that are reflected in the student's response.

Quiz or Test Form	Score	Date

Review Options in Student Edition
- Section A Review and Practice, page 102
- Section B Review and Practice, page 124
- Section C Review and Practice, page 138
- Chapter 3 Review/Test, page 140
- Chapter 3 Performance Assessment, page 141

Lesson	Objectives	Quizzes Items	✔	Chapter Test Form A Items	✔	Chapter Test Form B Items	✔	Chapter Test Form C Items	✔	Chapter Test Form D Items	✔	Chapter Test Form E Items	✔	Chapter Test Form F Items	✔	Practice and Reteaching Masters (pages)
Section A																
3-1	Explore addition and subtraction patterns.	1-2, 4-5		4		4		1-3				1		17		P(32); R(25)
3-2	Explore adding and subtracting on a thousand chart.	6-8		5-7		5-7		4-7				2-3		1-2		P(33); R(26)
3-3	Estimate sums and differences using rounding.	3, 9-11		8-10		8-10		8-10				4-5		11-12		P(34); R(27)
3-4	Solve problems needing exact answers or estimates.	12		11		11		11-12				6		23		P(35); R(28)
Section B																
3-5	Add 3-digit and 4-digit numbers.	3-5		12-13		12-13		13-14				7-8		3		P(37); R(29)
3-6	Add 3 or 4 addends.	1-2, 6-7		14-15		1, 14-15		15-16				9-10		4		P(38); R(30)
3-7	Subtract 3-digit and 4-digit numbers.	8-10		16-17		16-17		17-18				11-12		5		P(39); R(31)
3-8	Subtract from numbers with zeros.	11-12		18-19		18-19		19-20				13-14		6		P(40); R(32)
3-9	Solve multiple-step problems.	13		20		20		21-22, 32				17		22		P(41); R(33)

Quizzes and Tests from the Assessment Sourcebook — Review Options in Supplements

Continued on next page.

Chapter 3 (continued)

| | | Quizzes and Tests from the Assessment Sourcebook | | | | | | | | | | | | | | Review Options in Supplements |
| | | Quizzes | | Chapter Test Form A | | Chapter Test Form B | | Chapter Test Form C | | Chapter Test Form D | | Chapter Test Form E | | Chapter Test Form F | | Practice and Reteaching Masters (pages) |
Lesson	Objectives	Items	✓	Items	✓	Items	✓	Items	✓	Items	✓	Items	✓	Items	✓	
Section B (continued)																
3-10	Add and subtract numbers mentally.	14-15		33		33		23-24				15-16		9-10		P(42); R(34)
3-11	Choose a calculation method.	16-18		21-23		21-23		25-26				18-19		1-8		P(43); R(35)
Section C																
3-12	Count and compare money.	1-4		3, 24-25		24-25		27-28				20-21		18		P(45); R(36)
3-13	Add and subtract money amounts.	5-10		26-28		26-28		29-30				17, 22-24		7-8		P(46); R(37)
3-14	Explore making change.	11-12		29		29		31-32				17, 25		21-22		P(47); R(38)
3-15	Explore algebra by balancing number sentences.	13-14		30-31		30-31		33-34				27		19		P(48); R(39)
3-16	Solve problems by looking for a pattern.	15		32		32		35-36				26		20		P(49); R(40)
	Prior objectives													13-16, 22		

Item Analysis for Individual Assessment: Grade 4, Chapter 4

Chapter 4: Multiplication and Division Concepts and Facts

Student Name _____

Place a ✔ in the column if the student has answered some or all of the questions correctly. For Test Form D, check all the objectives that are reflected in the student's response.

Quiz or Test Form	Score	Date

Review Options in Student Edition
- Section A Review and Practice, page 164
- Section B Review and Practice, page 174
- Section C Review and Practice, page 190
- Chapter 4 Review/Test, page 192
- Chapter 4 Performance Assessment, page 193

Lesson	Objectives	Quizzes Items	✔	Chapter Test Form A Items	✔	Chapter Test Form B Items	✔	Chapter Test Form C Items	✔	Chapter Test Form D Items	✔	Chapter Test Form E Items	✔	Chapter Test Form F Items	✔	Review Options in Supplements Practice and Reteaching Masters (pages)
Section A																
4-1	Review the meaning of multiplication.	1-6, 17		2, 4-5		3-5		1-4				1-3		18		P(52); R(41)
4-2	Explore patterns in multiplying by 0, 1, 2, 5, and 9.	7-11, 15		1, 8-10, 13, 16, 41		2, 8-10, 40		5-10, 13-14, 19, 21				3-4, 6, 9-12, 14		2-4, 6		P(53); R(42)
4-3	Multiply with 3 or 4 as a factor.	11, 13, 17		6-7		6-7		10-11, 21-22				4-5, 16, 19		5-6, 9		P(54); R(43)
4-4	Multiply with 6, 7, or 8 as a factor.	8-10, 12-14, 17		6-7, 11-14		6-7, 11-14, 16		6, 9, 11-14, 19, 22				5-8, 10, 12-13, 15, 17, 19		2-3, 5, 7		P(55); R(44)
4-5	Explore patterns in multiples of 10, 11, and 12.	14-16		8, 10, 14-15, 17		8, 10, 14-15, 17		15-18				13-15		8-9		P(56); R(45)
4-6	Solve problems by making decisions.															P(57); R(46)
Section B																
4-7	Review the meaning of division.	5-7, 14		18-19		18-19		18-19				17		23		P(59); R(47)
4-8	Explore multiplication and division stories.	2, 8, 15		21-22		21-22		17, 20-22				18-19		19		P(60); R(48)

Quizzes and Tests from the Assessment Sourcebook

Continued on next page.

Lesson	Objectives	Quizzes		Chapter Test Form A		Chapter Test Form B		Chapter Test Form C		Chapter Test Form D		Chapter Test Form E		Chapter Test Form F		Review Options in Supplements: Practice and Reteaching Masters (pages)
		Items	✓	Items	✓	Items	✓	Items	✓	Items	✓	Items	✓	Items	✓	
Section B (continued)																
4-9	Divide with 2, 5, and 9 as divisors.	7, 9-10		3, 21, 23-25		23-25		19, 23-25				18, 21-23		10-12, 16-17		P(61); R(49)
4-10	Divide with 0 and 1.	11-12		26-27		26-27		27-28				24		11		P(62); R(50)
Section C																
4-11	Divide with 3 and 4 as divisors.	5-7		19, 28, 31		28, 31		20, 29-30				19, 25-26		13		P(64); R(51)
4-12	Divide with 6, 7 and 8 as divisors.	8-10		18, 27, 29-30		18, 27, 29, 30		19, 26-27, 31-33				19, 27-28		14-15		P(65); R(52)
4-13	Explore even and odd numbers.	2-3, 11-13		32-35		32-35		34-36				29, 34		29		P(66); R(53)
4-14	Explore factors.	1, 4, 14-17		20, 36-38		20, 36-38		37-39				20, 30-31		24		P(67); R(54)
4-15	Solve problems with too much or too little information.	18		39		39		41				32		27		P(68); R(55)
4-16	Solve problems by comparing strategies.	19		40		40		40				33		28		P(69); R(56)
	Prior objectives													1, 20-22, 25-26, 30-31		

Item Analysis for Individual Assessment: Grade 4, Chapter 5

Chapter 5: Multiplying by 1-Digit Factors

Student Name

Quiz or Test Form	Score	Date

Place a ✔ in the column if the student has answered some or all of the questions correctly. For Test Form D, check all the objectives that are reflected in the student's response.

Review Options in Student Edition

- Section A Review and Practice, page 208
- Section B Review and Practice, page 222
- Section C Review and Practice, page 240
- Chapter 5 Review/Test, page 242
- Chapter 5 Performance Assessment, page 243

Lesson	Objectives	Quizzes Items	✔	Chapter Test Form A Items	✔	Chapter Test Form B Items	✔	Chapter Test Form C Items	✔	Chapter Test Form D Items	✔	Chapter Test Form E Items	✔	Chapter Test Form F Items	✔	Review Options in Supplements: Practice and Reteaching Masters (pages)
	Section A															
5-1	Multiply by multiples of ten.	1, 3-5		1, 4-5		1, 4-5		1-2				1		1		P(72); R(57)
5-2	Explore multiplication patterns.	6-7		6-7		6-7		3-5				2-3		3		P(73); R(58)
5-3	Estimate products.	8-11		8-10		8-10		6-8				4-5		2		P(74); R(59)
5-4	Explore multiplication with arrays.	2, 12-13		2, 11		3, 11		9-10				6		4		P(75); R(60)
	Section B															
5-5	Multiply 2-digit numbers.	1-8		12-14		12-14		11-13				8		5		P(77); R(61)
5-6	Multiply 3-digit numbers.	9-12		15-16		15-16		14-16				9-10		6		P(78); R(62)
5-7	Solve problems by making decisions about cooking.															P(79); R(63)
5-8	Multiply using different methods.	13-16		17-18		17-18		17-19				11-12		10		P(80); R(64)
	Section C															
5-9	Multiply amounts of money.	1-3		19-20, 26		19-20, 26		20-23				13-14		7		P(82); R(65)
5-10	Use mental math to multiply.	4-7		21-22		21-22		24-26				15-16, 22		10-12		P(83); R(66)
5-11	Multiply when you have three factors.	8-12		23		23		27-31				17		13-14		P(84); R(67)

Continued on next page.

Chapter 5 (continued)

Lesson	Objectives	Quizzes		Chapter Test Form A		Chapter Test Form B		Chapter Test Form C		Chapter Test Form D		Chapter Test Form E		Chapter Test Form F		Practice and Reteaching Masters (pages)
		Items	✓	Items	✓	Items	✓	Items	✓	Items	✓	Items	✓	Items	✓	
Section C (continued)																
5-12	Solve multiple-step problems.	13		24		24		32-33				18-19		19-20		P(85); R(68)
5-13	Solve problems by making a table.	14		25		25		34-35				20-21		21		P(86); R(69)
	Prior objectives													8-9, 15-18		

Item Analysis for Individual Assessment: Grade 4, Chapter 6

Chapter 6: Multiplying by 2-Digit Factors

Student Name _____

Place a ✔ in the column if the student has answered some or all of the questions correctly. For Test Form D, check all the objectives that are reflected in the student's response.

Quiz or Test Form	Score	Date

Review Options in Student Edition

- Section A Review and Practice, page 258
- Section B Review and Practice, page 272
- Section C Review and Practice, page 282
- Chapter 6 Review/Test, page 284
- Chapter 6 Performance Assessment, page 285

Lesson	Objectives	Quizzes		Chapter Test Form A		Chapter Test Form B		Chapter Test Form C		Chapter Test Form D		Chapter Test Form E		Chapter Test Form F		Review Options in Supplements: Practice and Reteaching Masters (pages)
		Items	✔	Items	✔	Items	✔	Items	✔	Items	✔	Items	✔	Items	✔	
Section A																
6-1	Explore multiplication patterns	1-5		1-7		1-7		1-3				1-2		1-2		P(89); R(70)
6-2	Estimate products of 2-digit factors.	6-8		8-11		8-11		4-7				3-4		3		P(90); R(71)
6-3	Multiply by multiples of 10.	9-11		15-16		15-16		12-13				7-8		5		P(91); R(72)
6-4	Explore multiplying with 2-digit numbers.	12-15		17-20		17-20		14-18				9-12		6-7		P(92); R(73)
Section B																
6-5	Multiply with 2-digit factors.	1-6, 18		17-20		17-20		14-18				9-12		6-7		P(94); R(74)
6-6	Estimate greater products.	7-11		12-14		12-14		8-11				5-6, 20		4		P(95); R(75)
6-7	Multiply numbers in the thousands.	12-17		21-22, 27		21-22, 27		19-22				13-14		8		P(96); R(76)
6-8	Solve problems by making decisions after analyzing data.															P(97); R(77)
Section C																
6-9	Multiply amounts of money.	1-8		23-24		23-24		23-26				15-17		9		P(99); R(78)
6-10	Solve problems needing overestimates or underestimates.	9		25		25		27-28				18		17		P(100); R(79)

Continued on next page.

310   Item Analysis for Individual Assessment: Chapter 6

Chapter 6 (continued)

<table>
<tr><th rowspan="3">Lesson</th><th rowspan="3">Objectives</th><th colspan="15">Quizzes and Tests from the Assessment Sourcebook</th><th>Review Options in Supplements</th></tr>
<tr><th colspan="2">Quizzes</th><th colspan="2">Chapter Test Form A</th><th colspan="2">Chapter Test Form B</th><th colspan="2">Chapter Test Form C</th><th colspan="2">Chapter Test Form D</th><th colspan="2">Chapter Test Form E</th><th colspan="2">Chapter Test Form F</th><th rowspan="2">Practice and Reteaching Masters (pages)</th></tr>
<tr><th>Items</th><th>✓</th><th>Items</th><th>✓</th><th>Items</th><th>✓</th><th>Items</th><th>✓</th><th>Items</th><th>✓</th><th>Items</th><th>✓</th><th>Items</th><th>✓</th></tr>
<tr><td colspan="17">Section C (continued)</td></tr>
<tr><td>6-11</td><td>Solve problems by drawing a picture.</td><td>10-11</td><td></td><td>26</td><td></td><td>26</td><td></td><td>29-31</td><td></td><td></td><td></td><td>19</td><td></td><td>18</td><td></td><td>P(101); R(80)</td></tr>
<tr><td></td><td>Prior objectives</td><td></td><td></td><td></td><td></td><td></td><td></td><td></td><td></td><td></td><td></td><td></td><td></td><td>10-16, 19</td><td></td><td></td></tr>
</table>

Item Analysis for Individual Assessment: Grade 4, Chapter 7

Chapter 7: Dividing by 1-Digit Divisors

Student Name

Place a ✔ in the column if the student has answered some or all of the questions correctly. For Test Form D, check all the objectives that are reflected in the student's response.

Quiz or Test Form	Score	Date

Review Options in Student Edition

- Section A Review and Practice, page 298
- Section B Review and Practice, page 318
- Section C Review and Practice, page 334
- Chapter 7 Review/Test, page 336
- Chapter 7 Performance Assessment, page 337

Quizzes and Tests from the Assessment Sourcebook — **Review Options in Supplements**

Lesson	Objectives	Quizzes Items	✔	Chapter Test Form A Items	✔	Chapter Test Form B Items	✔	Chapter Test Form C Items	✔	Chapter Test Form D Items	✔	Chapter Test Form E Items	✔	Chapter Test Form F Items	✔	Practice and Reteaching Masters (pages)
Section A																
7-1	Explore division patterns.	1-10		5-10		5-10		1-3				1-3		1		P(104); R(81)
7-2	Use basic facts to estimate quotients.	11-16		11-13		11-13		4-7				4-7		17-18		P(105); R(82)
7-3	Explore division with remainders.	17-22		14-17		14-17		8-11				8-10		2-3		P(106); R(83)
Section B																
7-4	Explore division.	1-3		18-19		18-19		12-15				11-13		4-5		P(108); R(84)
7-5	Divide 2-digit dividends.	4-6		18-19		18-19		12-15				11-13		4-5		P(109); R(85)
7-6	Find 3-digit quotients.	7-9, 12		20-21		20-21		16-18				14-15		6-7		P(110); R(86)
7-7	Find 2- or 3-digit quotients.	10-12		18-21		18-21		16-22				12-17		6-9		P(111); R(87)
7-8	Divide when there are zeros in the quotient	13-15		22-23		22-23		23-25				18-19		10-11		P(112); R(88)
7-9	Solve problems by interpreting remainders.	16-17		26, 32		26, 32		26-28				22-23		23		P(113); R(89)

Continued on next page.

Chapter 7 (continued)

Lesson	Objectives	Quizzes		Chapter Test Form A		Chapter Test Form B		Chapter Test Form C		Chapter Test Form D		Chapter Test Form E		Chapter Test Form F		Review Options in Supplements Practice and Reteaching Masters (pages)
		Items	✓	Items	✓	Items	✓	Items	✓	Items	✓	Items	✓	Items	✓	
Section C																
7-10	Explore division with money.	4-6		24-25		24-25		29-31				20-21		12-13		P(115); R(90)
7-11	Divide money amounts.	7-8		24-25		24-25		29-31				20-21		12-13		P(116); R(91)
7-12	Explore finding the mean.	2, 9-10		3, 27-28		1, 27-28		32-33				27		20		P(117); R(92)
7-13	Explore divisibility.	1, 3, 11		1-2, 4, 29-30		2-4, 29-30		34-35				24-25		19		P(118); R(93)
7-14	Solve problems by working backward.	12		31		31		36-38				26		24		P(119); R(94)
	Prior objectives													14-16, 21-22, 25		

Item Analysis for Individual Assessment: Grade 4, Chapter 8

Chapter 8: Using Geometry

Student Name _____

Quiz or Test Form	Score	Date

Place a ✔ in the column if the student has answered some or all of the questions correctly. For Test Form D, check all the objectives that are reflected in the student's response.

Review Options in Student Edition
- Section A Review and Practice, page 356
- Section B Review and Practice, page 366
- Section C Review and Practice, page 376
- Chapter 8 Review/Test, page 378
- Chapter 8 Performance Assessment, page 379

Lesson	Objectives	Quizzes Items	✔	Chapter Test Form A Items	✔	Chapter Test Form B Items	✔	Chapter Test Form C Items	✔	Chapter Test Form D Items	✔	Chapter Test Form E Items	✔	Chapter Test Form F Items	✔	Review Options in Supplements Practice and Reteaching Masters (pages)
	Section A															
8-1	Explore solids.	1-2		5-6		3-4		1-3				1-2		7		P(122); R(95)
8-2	Explore polygons.	3-4		5-6		1, 5-6		4-6				3-4		8		P(123); R(96)
8-3	Explore triangles.	5-6		7-8		7-8		7-9				5		9		P(124); R(97)
8-4	Classify angles and triangles.	7-8		9-10		9-10		10-11				6		10		P(125); R(98)
8-5	Explore congruent figures and motions.	9-10		1, 11-12		11-12		12-13				7		11		P(126); R(99)
8-6	Explore similar figures.	11-12		13		13		14-15				8		12		P(127); R(100)
	Section B															
8-7	Identify intersecting, parallel, and perpendicular lines.	1,3-5		2, 14		14		16-17				9		13		P(129); R(101)
8-8	Classify quadrilaterals.	6-7		15-16		15-16		18-19				10		15		P(130); R(102)
8-9	Explore line symmetry.	2, 8-9		17-18		17-18		20-21				11		14		P(131); R(103)
8-10	Solve problems by using objects.	10-11		19		19		22-23				12		19		P(132); R(104)
	Section C															
8-11	Explore perimeter.	3, 5-6		20, 23		2, 20, 23		24-25				13		16		P(134); R(105)

Quizzes and Tests from the Assessment Sourcebook

Continued on next page.

Lesson	Objectives	Quizzes		Chapter Test Form A		Chapter Test Form B		Chapter Test Form C		Chapter Test Form D		Chapter Test Form E		Chapter Test Form F		Review Options in Supplements Practice and Reteaching Masters (pages)
		Items	✓	Items	✓	Items	✓	Items	✓	Items	✓	Items	✓	Items	✓	
	Section C (continued)															
8-12	Explore and find the area of rectangles.	1-2, 4 7-10		21		21		26-28				14, 17		17		P(135); R(106)
8-13	Explore volume.	2, 4, 11-12		22		22		29-30				15-16		18		P(136); R(107)
8-14	Solve problems by making decisions about perimeter and area of rectangles.							31				17				P(137); R(108)
	Prior objectives													1-6, 20		

Item Analysis for Individual Assessment: Grade 4, Chapter 9

Chapter 9: Fractions and Customary Measurement

Student Name _____

Place a ✔ in the column if the student has answered some or all of the questions correctly. For Test Form D, check all the objectives that are reflected in the student's response.

Quiz or Test Form	Score	Date

Review Options in Student Edition
- Section A Review and Practice, page 396
- Section B Review and Practice, page 412
- Section C Review and Practice, page 422
- Chapter 9 Review/Test, page 424
- Chapter 9 Performance Assessment, page 425

Lesson	Objectives	Quizzes Items	✔	Chapter Test Form A Items	✔	Chapter Test Form B Items	✔	Chapter Test Form C Items	✔	Chapter Test Form D Items	✔	Chapter Test Form E Items	✔	Chapter Test Form F Items	✔	Practice and Reteaching Masters (pages)
	Section A															
9-1	Explore fractions.	2, 6-7		5, 27		5, 27		1-2				1-2		10		P(140); R(109)
9-2	Name and write fractions of a set or region.	1, 5, 8-9		3-4, 6		1, 4, 6		3-4				3		11		P(141); R(110)
9-3	Estimate fractional amounts.	10-11		7-8		7-8		5-6				4		12		P(142); R(111)
9-4	Explore mixed numbers and improper fractions.	3-4, 12-13		9-10		9-10		7-11				5-6		13-14		P(143); R(112)
9-5	Solve problems by making decisions about what to do with your free time.															P(144); R(113)
	Section B															
9-6	Explore equivalent fractions.	2, 3-4		11-12		11-12		12-13				7		16		P(146); R(114)
9-7	Name and write equivalent fractions.	5-6		13-14		13-14		14-16				8-9, 21		17		P(147); R(115)
9-8	Write fractions in simplest form.	1, 7-8		2, 15-16		2, 15-16		17-20				10-11		18-19		P(148); R(116)
9-9	Compare and order fractions.	9-12		17-18, 21		17-18, 21		21-24				12-13, 17		20-21, 24		P(149); R(117)
9-10	Explore fractions of a set.	13		22		22		25-27				16		9		P(150); R(118)

Quizzes and Tests from the Assessment Sourcebook

Review Options in Supplements

Continued on next page.

Lesson	Objectives	Quizzes Items	✔	Chapter Test Form A Items	✔	Chapter Test Form B Items	✔	Chapter Test Form C Items	✔	Chapter Test Form D Items	✔	Chapter Test Form E Items	✔	Chapter Test Form F Items	✔	Practice and Reteaching Masters (pages)
	Section C (continued)															
9-11	Explore customary units of length.	1-6		1, 19-20		3, 19-20		28-31				14-15		22-23		P(152); R(119)
9-12	Explore measuring fractional parts of an inch.	7-10		23-24		23-24		32-33				18		25		P(153); R(120)
9-13	Explore feet, yards, and miles.	11-12		25		25		34-35				19		26		P(154); R(121)
9-14	Solve problems by using logical reasoning.	13		26		26		36-37				20		27		P(155); R(122)
	Prior objectives													1-8, 15, 28		

Quizzes and Tests from the Assessment Sourcebook

Review Options in Supplements

Item Analysis for Individual Assessment: Grade 4, Chapter 10

Chapter 10: Fraction Operations and Customary Measurement

Student Name _____

Place a ✔ in the column if the student has answered some or all of the questions correctly. For Test Form D, check all the objectives that are reflected in the student's response.

Quiz or Test Form	Score	Date

Review Options in Student Edition

- Section A Review and Practice, page 442
- Section B Review and Practice, page 454
- Section C Review and Practice, page 466
- Chapter 10 Review/Test, page 468
- Chapter 10 Performance Assessment, page 469

Lesson	Objectives	Quizzes Items	✓	Chapter Test Form A Items	✓	Chapter Test Form B Items	✓	Chapter Test Form C Items	✓	Chapter Test Form D Items	✓	Chapter Test Form E Items	✓	Chapter Test Form F Items	✓	Practice and Reteaching Masters (pages)
Section A																
10-1	Explore adding fractions with like denominators.	1-7		1-2, 17		1-2, 17		1, 17-18				1, 11-12		1		P(158); R(123)
10-2	Explore adding fractions with unlike denominators.	8-15		5, 8, 10, 12, 16		5, 8, 10, 12, 16		5-6, 10, 12, 14-15				5-6, 8-9		3, 6, 8		P(159); R(124)
10-3	Add fractions with like and unlike denominators.	1-15		1-2, 5, 8, 10, 12, 16		1-2, 5, 8, 10, 12, 16		1-2, 5-6, 10, 12, 14-15				1, 5-6, 8-9, 11-12		1, 3, 6, 8		P(160); R(125)
10-4	Solve problems by making decisions for planning a community mural.															P(161); R(126)
Section B																
10-5	Explore subtracting fractions.	1-13		3-4, 6-7, 9, 11, 13-15		3-4, 6-7, 9, 11, 13-15		3-4, 7-9, 11, 13, 16				2-4, 7, 10		2, 4, 5, 7		P(163); R(127)
10-6	Subtract fractions.	1-13		3-4, 6-7, 9, 11, 13-15		3-4, 6-7, 9, 11, 13-15		3-4, 7-9, 11, 13, 16				2-4, 7, 10		2, 4, 5, 7		P(164); R(128)
10-7	Solve problems by choosing an operation.	14-15		18-19		18-19		19-22				13-14		21		P(165); R(129)

(Quizzes and Tests from the Assessment Sourcebook)

(Review Options in Supplements)

Continued on next page.

318 Item Analysis for Individual Assessment: Chapter 10

Chapter 10 (continued)

Lesson	Objectives	Quizzes Items	✓	Chapter Test Form A Items	✓	Chapter Test Form B Items	✓	Chapter Test Form C Items	✓	Chapter Test Form D Items	✓	Chapter Test Form E Items	✓	Chapter Test Form F Items	✓	Practice and Reteaching Masters (pages) ✓
Section C																
10-8	Explore weight.	1-5		20-22		20-22		23-25				15		13-14		P(167); R(130)
10-9	Explore capacity.	6-10		23-24		23-24		26-28				16		15-16		P(168); R(131)
10-10	Change units of length, units of weight, and units of capacity.	11-16		25-28, 31		25-28, 31		29-32				17-19		17-18		P(169); R(132)
10-11	Solve problems by drawing a picture and making a table.	17		29		29		33-34				20		22		P(170); R(133)
10-12	Explore algebra by using a balance scale.	18		30		30		35-36				21		19		P(171); R(134)
	Prior objectives													9-12, 20, 23-25		

Item Analysis for Individual Assessment: Grade 4, Chapter 11

Chapter 11: Decimals and Metric Measurement

Student Name _____

Place a ✔ in the column if the student has answered some or all of the questions correctly. For Test Form D, check all the objectives that are reflected in the student's response.

Quiz or Test Form	Score	Date

Review Options in Student Edition
- Section A Review and Practice, page 490
- Section B Review and Practice, page 502
- Section C Review and Practice, page 518
- Chapter 11 Review/Test, page 520
- Chapter 11 Performance Assessment, page 521

Lesson	Objectives	Quizzes Items	✔	Chapter Test Form A Items	✔	Chapter Test Form B Items	✔	Chapter Test Form C Items	✔	Chapter Test Form D Items	✔	Chapter Test Form E Items	✔	Chapter Test Form F Items	✔	Practice and Reteaching Masters (pages)	✔
Section A																	
11-1	Read and write decimals using tenths and hundredths.	1-3		5-6		5-6		1-2				1-3		11-12		P(174); R(135)	
11-2	Explore decimal place-value relationships.	4-5		32		32		3-4				4-5		13		P(175); R(136)	
11-3	Solve problems by using objects/ making an organized list.	6		4		4		13-14				15		27		P(176); R(137)	
11-4	Compare and order decimals.	7-10		7-9		7-9		5-7				6-8		18-19		P(177); R(138)	
11-5	Round decimals to the nearest whole number.	11-13		10-12		10-12		8-10				9-10		14-15		P(178); R(139)	
11-6	Explore fractions as decimals.	14-15		13-14		13-14		11-12				11-12		16-17		P(179); R(140)	
Section B																	
11-7	Estimate decimal sums and differences.	1-4		15-16		15-16		15-16				13-14		1-2		P(181); R(141)	
11-8	Explore adding and subtracting decimals.	5-9		17-18, 20		17-18, 20		17-20				16		3		P(182); R(142)	
11-9	Add and subtract decimals.	10-14		19, 21-22		19, 21-22		18-19, 21-23				17-19, 28		4-6		P(183); R(143)	

Quizzes and Tests from the Assessment Sourcebook

Review Options in Supplements

Continued on next page.

Lesson	Objectives	Quizzes		Chapter Test Form A		Chapter Test Form B		Chapter Test Form C		Chapter Test Form D		Chapter Test Form E		Chapter Test Form F		Review Options in Supplements — Practice and Reteaching Masters (pages)
		Items	✓	Items	✓	Items	✓	Items	✓	Items	✓	Items	✓	Items	✓	
	Section C															
11-10	Expore centimeters, decimeters, and meters.	1, 5-7, 9		1, 23, 27-28		1, 23, 27-28		24-25				21-22		21		P(185); R(144)
11-11	Use and relate meters and kilometers.	3, 8, 10		24		24		24-25				20, 23		22		P(186); R(145)
11-12	Explore length and decimals.	11-12		25-26		25-26		26-27				24		20		P(187); R(146)
11-13	Explore mass.	2, 13-14		3, 29		3, 29		28-31				25		24		P(188); R(147)
11-14	Explore metric capacity.	4, 15-16		2, 30		2, 30		32-35				26		23		P(189); R(148)
11-15	Read Celsuis and Fahrenheit thermometers.	17		31		31		36-37				27		25		P(190); R(149)
11-16	Solve problems by making decisions about planning a new Olympic event.															P(191); R(150)
	Prior objectives													7-10, 26, 28		

Item Analysis for Individual Assessment: Grade 4, Chapter 12

Chapter 12: Dividing by 2-Digit Divisors and Probability

Student Name

Place a ✔ in the column if the student has answered some or all of the questions correctly. For Test Form D, check all the objectives that are reflected in the student's response.

Quiz or Test Form	Score	Date

Review Options in Student Edition
- Section A Review and Practice, page 538
- Section B Review and Practice, page 552
- Chapter 12 Review/Test, page 554
- Chapter 12 Performance Assessment, page 555

Lesson	Objectives	Quizzes Items	✔	Chapter Test Form A Items	✔	Chapter Test Form B Items	✔	Chapter Test Form C Items	✔	Chapter Test Form D Items	✔	Chapter Test Form E Items	✔	Chapter Test Form F Items	✔	Review Options in Supplements — Practice and Reteaching Masters (pages)
Section A																
12-1	Explore division patterns.	1-5		5-7		5-7		1-5				1-4		1-2		P(194); R(151)
12-2	Estimate quotients with 2-digit divisors.	6-10		8-12, 26		8-12, 26		6-10				5-8		3-5		P(195); R(152)
12-3	Divide by multiples of ten.	11-13		13-15		13-15		11-13				9-10		6-7		P(196); R(153)
12-4	Divide by 2-digit divisors.	14-18		16-18		16-18		14-18				11-14, 23		8-11		P(197); R(154)
12-5	Solve problems by making decisions about videotaping a community fair.															P(198); R(155)
Section B																
12-6	Explore likelihood.	1, 4-5		1, 3, 19-20		1, 4, 19-20		19-21				15-16		17		P(200); R(156)
12-7	Explore fairness.	3, 6		4, 21		2, 21		22-24				17		18		P(201); R(157)
12-8	List possible outcomes of an event.	7		22		22		25-27				18		19		P(202); R(158)
12-9	Explore probability.	2, 8		2, 23		3, 23		28-30				19-20		20		P(203); R(159)
12-10	Explore predictions.	9		24		24		31-32				21		22		P(204); R(160)
12-11	Solve problems by solving a simpler problem.	10		25		25		33-35				22		23		P(205); R(161)

Quizzes and Tests from the Assessment Sourcebook

Item Analysis for Individual Assessment

Grade 4 Quarterly Test, Chapters 1–3

Student Name _____   **See page 331 for scoring.**

Place a ✔ in the column if the student has answered some or all of the questions correctly.

Objectives	Lesson	Test Item	✔ if correct	Practice (pages)	Reteaching (pages)
Read line graphs.	1-3	1–3		P(3)	R(3)
Solve problems by using a guide.	1-6	3		P(6)	R(6)
Solve problems by choosing an operation	1-7	4		P(7)	R(7)
Read line plots.	1-4	5, 6		P(4)	R(4)
Find range, median, and mode.	1-10	6, 8		P(11)	R(10)
Read points as an ordered pairs on a coordinate grid.	1-2	7		P(2)	R(2)
Solve problems by guessing and checking.	1-12	9		P(13)	R(12)
Read and write numbers in the thousands.	2-1	10		P(16)	R(13)
Explore place-value relationships.	2-2	11		P(17)	R(14)
Read and write numbers through the hundred millions.	2-3	12		P(18)	R(15)
Solve problems by making an organized list.	2-4	13		P(19)	R(16)
Compare numbers to find which is greater.	2-5	14		P(21)	R(17)
Explore rounding.	2-7	15		P(23)	R(19)
Tell time to the minute and identify A.M. and P.M.	2-8	16, 17		P(25)	R(20)
Find elapsed time.	2-10	18		P(27)	R(22)
Estimate sums and differences using rounding.	3-3	19, 20		P(34)	R(27)
Add 3-digit and 4-digit numbers.	3-5	21, 22		P(37)	R(29)
Add 3 and 4 addends	3-6	23		P(38)	R(30)
Subtract 3-digit and 4-digit numbers.	3-7	24, 25		P(39)	R(31)
Subtract from numbers with zeros.	3-8	26		P(40)	R(32)
Add and subtract money amounts.	3-13	27, 28		P(46)	R(37)
Solve multiple-step problems.	3-9	29		P(41)	R(33)
Add and subtract numbers mentally	3-10	30, 31		P(42)	R(34)
Solve problems by looking for a pattern.	3-16	32		P(49)	R(40)

Item Analysis for Individual Assessment

Grade 4 Quarterly Test, Chapters 1–6

Student Name _____ See page 331 for scoring.

Place a ✔ in the column if the student has answered some or all of the questions correctly.

Objectives	Lesson	Test Item	✔ if correct	Practice (pages)	Reteaching (pages)
		Quarterly Test Chapters 1–6		Review Options in Supplements	
Read pictographs and bar graphs.	1-1	1, 2		P(1)	R(1)
Solve problems by using a guide.	1-6	2		P(6)	R(6)
Find range, median, and mode.	1-10	3		P(11)	R(10)
Solve problems by using guessing and checking	1-12	4		P(13)	R(12)
Read and write numbers in the thousands.	2-1	5		P(16)	R(13)
Order a group of numbers.	2-6	6		P(22)	R(18)
Find elapsed time.	2-10	7		P(27)	R(22)
Solve problems by making an organized list.	2-4	8		P(19)	R(16)
Add 3 and 4 addends.	3-6	9		P(38)	R(30)
Subtract 3-digit and 4-digit numbers.	3-7	10		P(39)	R(31)
Solve multiple-step problems.	3-9	11		P(41)	R(33)
Count and compare money.	3-12	12		P(45)	R(36)
Solve problems by deciding if an exact answer or an estimate is needed.	3-4	13		P(35)	R(28)
Multiply with 3 or 4 as a factor.	4-3	14, 16, 18		P(54)	R(43)
Multiply with 6, 7, or 8 as a factor.	4-4	15-17,19		P(55)	R(44)
Divide with 0 and 1.	4-10	20, 23		P(62)	R(50)
Divide with 3 and 4 as divisors.	4-11	21, 22		P(64)	R(51)
Divide with 6, 7, and 8 as divisors.	4-12	23-25		P(65)	R(52)
Solve problems with too much or too little information.	4-15	26		P(68)	R(55)
Estimate products.	5-3	27		P(74)	R(59)
Multiply 2-digit numbers.	5-5	28		P(77)	R(61)
Multiply 3-digit numbers.	5-6	29		P(78)	R(62)
Multiply when you have three factors.	5-11	30		P(84)	R(67)
Solve problems by making a table.	5-13	31		P(86)	R(69)
Estimate products of 2-digit factors.	6-2	32		P(90)	R(71)
Multiply with 2-digit factors.	6-5	33, 34		P(94)	R(74)
Multiply amounts of money.	6-9	35		P(99)	R(78)
Solve problems by drawing a picture.	6-11	36		P(101)	R(80)

Item Analysis for Individual Assessment

Grade 4 Quarterly Test, Chapters 1–9

Student Name _____ See page 331 for scoring.

Place a ✔ in the column if the student has answered some or all of the questions correctly.

Objectives	Lesson	Test Item	✔ if correct	Practice (pages)	Reteaching (pages)
		Quarterly Test Chapters 1–9		Review Options in Supplements	
Read stem-and-leaf plots.	1-5	1, 2		P(5)	R(5)
Solve problems by using a guide.	1-6	2		P(6)	R(6)
Solve problems by using guessing and checking.	1-12	3		P(13)	R(12)
Solve problems by making an organized list.	2-4	4		P(19)	R(16)
Compare numbers to find which is greater.	2-5	5		P(21)	R(17)
Find elapsed time.	2-10	6		P(27)	R(22)
Solve multiple-step problems.	3-9	7		P(41)	R(33)
Add 3-digit and 4-digit numbers.	3-5	8		P(37)	R(29)
Subtract 3-digit and 4-digit numbers.	3-7	9		P(39)	R(31)
Add and subtract money amounts.	3-13	10		P(46)	R(37)
Multiply with 3 or 4 as a factor.	4-3	11		P(54)	R(43)
Multiply with 6, 7, or 8 as a factor.	4-4	12		P(55)	R(44)
Divide with 3 and 4 as divisors.	4-11	13		P(64)	R(51)
Divide with 6, 7, and 8 as divisors.	4-12	14		P(65)	R(52)
Multiply 2-digit numbers.	5-5	15		P(77)	R(61)
Multiply 3-digit numbers.	5-6	16		P(78)	R(62)
Multiply amounts of money.	5-9	17		P(82)	R(65)
Multiply when you have three factors.	5-11	18		P(84)	R(67)
Multiply with 2-digit factors.	6-5	19		P(94)	R(74)
Multiply numbers in the thousands.	6-7	20		P(96)	R(76)
Multiply amounts of money.	6-9	21		P(99)	R(78)
Divide 2-digit dividends.	7-5	22		P(109)	R(85)
Find 3-digit quotients.	7-6	23		P(110)	R(86)
Find 2- or 3-digit quotients.	7-7	24		P(111)	R(87)
Solve problems by interpreting remainders.	7-9	25		P(113)	R(89)
Solve problems by working backward.	7-14	26		P(119)	R(94)
Classify angles and triangles.	8-4	27		P(125)	R(98)
Identify intersecting, parallel, and perpendicular lines.	8-7	28		P(129)	R(101)
Explore perimeter.	8-11	29		P(134)	R(105)
Explore and find the area of rectangles.	8-12	30		P(135)	R(106)

Continued on next page.

Place a ✔ in the column if the student has answered some or all of the questions correctly.

Objectives	Lesson	Quarterly Test Chapters 1–9		Review Options in Supplements	
		Test Item	✔ if correct	Practice (pages)	Reteaching (pages)
Name and write fractions of a set or region.	9-2	31, 32		P(141)	R(110)
Explore mixed numbers and improper fractions.	9-4	33		143	R(112)
Name and write equivalent fractions.	9-7	34		147	R(115)
Write fractions in simplest form.	9-8	35		148	R(116)
Compare and order fractions.	9-9	36		149	R(117)
Solve problems by using logical reasoning.	9-14	37		155	R(122)

Item Analysis for Individual Assessment

Grade 4 Quarterly Test, Chapters 1–12

Student Name _____

See page 331 for scoring.

Place a ✔ in the column if the student has answered some or all of the questions correctly.

| Objectives | Lesson | Quarterly Test Chapters 1–12 | | Review Options in Supplements | |
		Test Item	✔ if correct	Practice (pages)	Reteaching (pages)
Read pictographs and bar graphs.	1-1	1, 2		P(1)	R(1)
Solve problems by using a guide.	1-6	2		P(6)	R(6)
Read and write numbers in the thousands.*	2-1	3		P(16)	R(13)
Find elapsed time.	2-10	4		P(27)	R(22)
Add 3 and 4 addends.	3-6	5		P(38)	R(30)
Subtract 3-digit and 4-digit numbers.	3-7	5, 6		P(39)	R(31)
Solve problems by looking for a pattern.	3-16	7		P(49)	R(40)
Solve multiple-step problems.	3-9	8		P(41)	R(33)
Add and subtract money amounts.	3-13	8		P(46)	R(37)
Review the meaning of multiplication.*	4-1	9		P(52)	R(41)
Explore even and odd numbers.	4-13	10		P(66)	R(53)
Explore factors.	4-14	11		P(67)	R(54)
Solve problems by comparing strategies.	4-16	12		P(69)	R(56)
Estimate products.	5-3	13		P(74)	R(59)
Multiply when you have 3 factors.	5-11	14		P(84)	R(67)
Multiply 3-digit numbers.	5-5	15		P(77)	R(61)
Multiply amounts of money.	5-9	16		P(82)	R(65)
Multiply by multiples of 10.	6-3	17		P(91)	R(72)
Multiply with 2-digit factors.	6-5	18		P(94)	R(74)
Multiply numbers in the thousands.	6-7	19		P(96)	R(76)
Solve problems by drawing a picture.	6-11	20		P(101)	R(80)
Explore division with remainders.	7-3	21		P(106)	R(83)
Find 2- or 3-digit quotients.	7-7	22		P(111)	R(87)
Solve problems by interpreting remainders.	7-9	23		P(113)	R(89)
Solve problems by working backward.	7-14	24		P(119)	R(94)
Read pictographs and bar graphs.	1-1	1, 2		P(1)	R(1)
Solve problems by using a guide.	1-6	2		P(6)	R(6)
Explore perimeter.	8-11	25		P(134)	R(105)
Explore and find the area of rectangles.	8-12	26		P(135)	R(106)
Explore mixed numbers and improper fractions.	9-4	27		P(143)	R(112)

Continued on next page.

Quarterly Test Chapters 1–12 (continued)

See page 331 for scoring.

Place a ✔ in the column if the student has answered some or all of the questions correctly.

Objectives	Lesson	Quarterly Test Chapters 1–12		Review Options in Supplements	
		Test Item	✔ if correct	Practice (pages)	Reteaching (pages)
Compare and order fractions	9-9	28		P(149)	R(117)
Add fractions with like and unlike denominators.	10-3	29		P160)	R(124)
Subtract fractions.	10-6	30		P(164)	R(128)
Solve problems by drawing a picture and making a table.	10-11	31		P(170)	R(133)
Compare and order decimals.	11-4	32		P(177)	R(138)
Add and subtract decimals.	11-9	33, 34		P(183)	R(143)
Use and relate meters and kilometers.	11-11	35		P(186)	R(145)
Explore metric capacity.	11-14	36		P(189)	R(148)
Divide by multiples of ten.	12-3	37, 38		P(196)	R(153)
Solve problems by solving a simpler problem.	12-11	39		P(205)	R(161)

Class Test Record Form: Chapters 1–6

Students	Tests							
	Chapter			Quarterly	Chapter			Quarterly
	1	2	3	Ch. 1–3	4	5	6	Ch. 1–6
1.								
2.								
3.								
4.								
5.								
6.								
7.								
8.								
9.								
10.								
11.								
12.								
13.								
14.								
15.								
16.								
17.								
18.								
19.								
20.								
21.								
22.								
23.								
24.								
25.								
26.								
27.								
28.								
29.								
30.								
31.								
32.								
33.								
34.								
35.								

Class Test Record Form: Chapters 7–12

Students	Chapter 7	Chapter 8	Chapter 9	Quarterly Ch. 1–9	Chapter 10	Chapter 11	Chapter 12	Quarterly Ch. 1–12
1.								
2.								
3.								
4.								
5.								
6.								
7.								
8.								
9.								
10.								
11.								
12.								
13.								
14.								
15.								
16.								
17.								
18.								
19.								
20.								
21.								
22.								
23.								
24.								
25.								
26.								
27.								
28.								
29.								
30.								
31.								
32.								
33.								
34.								
35.								

Percent Table for Scoring Tests

This table will help you quickly convert a raw test score to a percent score for any test containing up to 53 items.

Directions for using the table

Example: There are 28 items on a test, and a student correctly answers 22 of them.

1. Find the number of items, 28, along the left side of the table.
2. Place a rule or a strip of paper under the row for 28.
3. Find the column for 22, the number of items correctly answered.
4. Go down the column for 22 until you come to the row for 28. The number 79 is the percent score.

Number Correct (columns) / **Number of Items** (rows)

Items	1	2	3	4	5	6	7	8	9	10	11	12	13	14	15	16	17	18	19	20	21	22	23	24	25	26	27	28	29	30	31	32	33	34	35	36	37	38	39	40	41	42	43	44	45	46	47	48	49	50	51	52	53
1	100																																																				
2	50	100																																																			
3	33	67	100																																																		
4	25	50	75	100																																																	
5	20	40	60	80	100																																																
6	17	33	50	67	83	100																																															
7	14	29	43	57	71	86	100																																														
8	13	25	38	50	63	75	88	100																																													
9	11	22	33	44	56	67	78	89	100																																												
10	10	20	30	40	50	60	70	80	90	100																																											
11	9	18	27	36	45	55	64	73	82	91	100																																										
12	8	17	25	33	42	50	58	67	75	83	92	100																																									
13	8	15	23	31	38	46	54	62	69	77	85	92	100																																								
14	7	14	21	29	36	43	50	57	64	71	79	86	93	100																																							
15	7	13	20	27	33	40	47	53	60	67	73	80	87	93	100																																					
16	6	13	19	25	31	38	44	50	56	63	69	75	81	88	94	100																																				
17	6	12	18	24	29	35	41	47	53	59	65	71	76	82	88	94	100																																		
18	6	11	17	22	28	33	39	44	50	56	61	67	72	78	83	89	94	100																																	
19	5	11	16	21	26	32	37	42	47	53	58	63	68	74	79	84	89	95	100																																
20	5	10	15	20	25	30	35	40	45	50	55	60	65	70	75	80	85	90	95	100																															
21	5	10	14	19	24	29	33	38	43	48	52	57	62	67	71	76	81	86	90	95	100																														
22	5	9	14	18	23	27	32	36	41	45	50	55	59	64	68	73	77	82	86	91	95	100																													
23	4	9	13	17	22	26	30	35	39	43	48	52	57	61	65	70	74	78	83	87	91	96	100																												
24	4	8	13	17	21	25	29	33	38	42	46	50	54	58	63	67	71	75	79	83	88	92	96	100																											
25	4	8	12	16	20	24	28	32	36	40	44	48	52	56	60	64	68	72	76	80	84	88	92	96	100																										
26	4	8	12	15	19	23	27	31	35	38	42	46	50	54	58	62	65	69	73	77	81	85	88	92	96	100																									
27	4	7	11	15	19	22	26	30	33	37	41	44	48	52	56	59	63	67	70	74	78	81	85	89	93	96	100																							
28	4	7	11	14	18	21	25	29	32	36	39	43	46	50	54	57	61	64	68	71	75	79	82	86	89	93	96	100																						
29	3	7	10	14	17	21	24	28	31	34	38	41	45	48	52	55	59	62	66	69	72	76	79	83	86	90	93	97	100																				
30	3	7	10	13	17	20	23	27	30	33	37	40	43	47	50	53	57	60	63	67	70	73	77	80	83	87	90	93	97	100																			
31	3	6	10	13	16	19	23	26	29	32	35	39	42	45	48	52	55	58	61	65	68	71	74	77	81	84	87	90	94	97	100																	
32	3	6	9	13	16	19	22	25	28	31	34	38	41	44	47	50	53	56	59	63	66	69	72	75	78	81	84	88	91	94	97	100																
33	3	6	9	12	15	18	21	24	27	30	33	36	39	42	45	48	52	55	58	61	64	67	70	73	76	79	82	85	88	91	94	97	100															
34	3	6	9	12	15	18	21	24	26	29	32	35	38	41	44	47	50	53	56	59	62	65	68	71	74	76	79	82	85	88	91	94	97	100														
35	3	6	9	11	14	17	20	23	26	29	31	34	37	40	43	46	49	51	54	57	60	63	66	69	71	74	77	80	83	86	89	91	94	97	100													
36	3	6	8	11	14	17	19	22	25	28	31	33	36	39	42	44	47	50	53	56	58	61	64	67	69	72	75	78	81	83	86	89	92	94	97	100												
37	3	5	8	11	14	16	19	22	24	27	30	32	35	38	41	43	46	49	51	54	57	59	62	65	68	70	73	76	78	81	84	86	89	92	95	97	100											
38	3	5	8	11	13	16	18	21	24	26	29	32	34	37	39	42	45	47	50	53	55	58	61	63	66	68	71	74	76	79	82	84	87	89	92	95	97	100										
39	3	5	8	10	13	15	18	21	23	26	28	31	33	36	38	41	44	46	49	51	54	56	59	62	64	67	69	72	74	77	79	82	85	87	90	92	95	97	100									
40	3	5	8	10	13	15	18	20	23	25	28	30	33	35	38	40	43	45	48	50	53	55	58	60	63	65	68	70	73	75	78	80	83	85	88	90	93	95	98	100								
41	2	5	7	10	12	15	17	20	22	24	27	29	32	34	37	39	41	44	46	49	51	54	56	59	61	63	66	68	71	73	76	78	80	83	85	88	90	93	95	98	100							
42	2	5	7	10	12	14	17	19	21	24	26	29	31	33	36	38	40	43	45	48	50	52	55	57	60	62	64	67	69	71	74	76	79	81	83	86	88	90	93	95	98	100						
43	2	5	7	9	12	14	16	19	21	23	26	28	30	33	35	37	40	42	44	47	49	51	53	56	58	60	63	65	67	70	72	74	77	79	81	84	86	88	91	93	95	98	100					
44	2	5	7	9	11	14	16	18	20	23	25	27	30	32	34	36	39	41	43	45	48	50	52	55	57	59	61	64	66	68	70	73	75	77	79	82	84	86	89	91	93	95	98	100				
45	2	4	7	9	11	13	16	18	20	22	24	27	29	31	33	36	38	40	42	44	47	49	51	53	56	58	60	62	64	67	69	71	73	76	78	80	82	84	87	89	91	93	96	98	100			
46	2	4	7	9	11	13	15	17	20	22	24	26	28	30	33	35	37	39	41	43	46	48	50	52	54	57	59	61	63	65	67	70	72	74	76	78	80	83	85	87	89	91	93	96	98	100		
47	2	4	6	9	11	13	15	17	19	21	23	26	28	30	32	34	36	38	40	43	45	47	49	51	53	55	57	60	62	64	66	68	70	72	74	77	79	81	83	85	87	89	91	94	96	98	100	
48	2	4	6	8	10	13	15	17	19	21	23	25	27	29	31	33	35	38	40	42	44	46	48	50	52	54	56	58	60	63	65	67	69	71	73	75	77	79	81	83	85	88	90	92	94	96	98	100
49	2	4	6	8	10	12	14	16	18	20	22	24	27	29	31	33	35	37	39	41	43	45	47	49	51	53	55	57	59	61	63	65	67	69	71	73	76	78	80	82	84	86	88	90	92	94	96	98	100
50	2	4	6	8	10	12	14	16	18	20	22	24	26	28	30	32	34	36	38	40	42	44	46	48	50	52	54	56	58	60	62	64	66	68	70	72	74	76	78	80	82	84	86	88	90	92	94	96	98	100
51	2	4	6	8	10	12	14	16	18	20	22	24	25	27	29	31	33	35	37	39	41	43	45	47	49	51	53	55	57	59	61	63	65	67	69	71	73	75	76	78	80	82	84	86	88	90	92	94	96	98	100
52	2	4	6	8	10	12	13	15	17	19	21	23	25	27	29	31	33	35	37	38	40	42	44	46	48	50	52	54	56	58	60	62	63	65	67	69	71	73	75	77	79	81	83	85	87	88	90	92	94	96	98	100
53	2	4	6	8	9	11	13	15	17	19	21	23	25	26	28	30	32	34	36	38	40	42	43	45	47	49	51	53	55	57	58	60	62	64	66	68	70	72	74	75	77	79	81	83	85	87	89	91	92	94	96	98	100